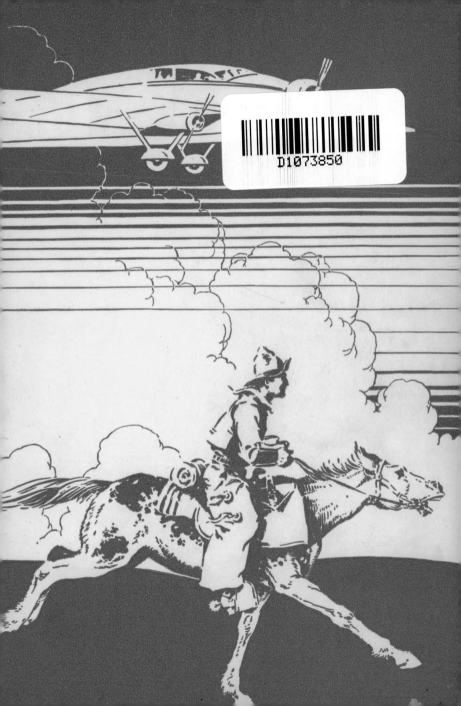

LIFE-READING SERVICE

ELSON-GRAY

BASIC READERS

BOOK SIX

by

WILLIAM H. ELSON
WILLIAM S. GRAY
and
CHRISTINE M. KECK

SCOTT, FORESMAN AND COMPANY
CHICAGO · ATLANTA · DALLAS · NEW YORK

ACKNOWLEDGMENTS

For permission to use copyrighted material, grateful acknowledgment is made to *Forest and Stream* for "Hunting Elephants with a Camera" from "Into the African Blue" by Martin Johnson; to the author for "Woodland Whispers" from "Gossips" in *A Boy's Book of Rhyme* by Clinton Scollard; to D. Appleton & Company for "Tiger, Terror of the Jungle" from "The Tiger Comes" in *Trailing the Tiger* by Mary Hastings Bradley, for "Planting the Tree" by Henry Abbey, for "Young George Washington" from *On the Trail of Washington* by Frederick Trevor Hill, and for "The Way Old Glory Goes" from *Up From Georgia* by Frank L. Stanton; to the author and the *Scientific Monthly* for "Carl Akeley Brings Jungleland to America" from "Carl Akeley and His Work" by Dr. Clyde Fisher; to Macrae Smith Company for "The Family of Bob-White" from *Trails to Woods and Waters* by Clarence Hawkes; to Doubleday, Doran & Company, Inc., for "Bird Nesting in Winter" from *Woodland Tales*, copyright 1921, by Ernest Thompson Seton, for "The Flowers" from *Fairies and Friends* by Rose Fyleman, copyright 1926, and for "Christmas Eve" from *Poems* by Christopher Morley, copyright 1929; to Grace Hastings Sharp for "Starting a Wild-Life Sanctuary" by Dallas Lore Sharp; to Harper & Brothers for "The Cardinal Bird" from *The Laughing Muse* by Arthur Guiterman, for "Tom and His Treasure Chest" from "Tom Chist and the Treasure Box" in *The Book of Pirates* by Howard Pyle, and for "Here Pass Most Wondrous Sights" from "The Aztec Treasure House" by T. A. Janvier; to Helen Gray Cone for "The Dandelions"; to *Nature Magazine* and the author for "Yellow Lilies: The Gold of Rainbow Slough" by R. Bruce Horsfall; to Frederick A. Stokes Company for "Spring Prophecies" from *Sylvan Lyrics and Other Verses* by William Hamilton Hayne; to Harcourt, Brace and Company, Inc., for "The World Is Full of Roads" from "Roads" in *Horses Now and Long Ago* by Lucy Sprague Mitchell, copyright 1926, and for "Abraham Lincoln Grows Up" from *Abe Lincoln Grows Up* by Carl Sandburg, copyright 1928; to the author for "From Indian Trail to Air Mail" by Alice Thompson Paine; to the author for "The Glint of Wings" by Marie Barton, courtesy of *Boy's Life* published by the Boy Scouts of America; to *The Youth's Companion* (now combined with *The American Boy*) for "How Potts Saved the Night Express," by Ray Stannard Baker and for "To Toil and Be Kind" by Mary Carolyn Davies; to the author for "My Book Treasures" from "Sing a Song of Books" by Nancy Byrd Turner; to the author for "True Citizens" by Mary McDowell; to the author and *Child Life* for "Youthful Patriots of Colonial Times" from "Leafing Day" by Janet P. Shaw; to the author for "A Little Song of Life" from *A Wayside Lute* by Lizette Woodworth Reese; to the Century Company for "Marion Andrews, Life Saver" from "The Greater Part" by Mildred Augustine, in *St. Nicholas*, and for "Tim Crogan, The Star Apprentice" from "On Test" by David O. Woodbury in *St. Nicholas*; to the author for "Our Country—America" by Margaret E. Sangster; to the author for "The Spanish Bootblack" and "Mina and Karsten of Norway" by Caroline Mabry; to the author for "The Way of a Polish Lad" by Helen Coale Crew; to the author for "Thomas A. Edison: Light's Golden Jubilee" by Edith A. Heal; to the author for "Walter Damrosch: Music Master of the Air" by Thelma Wilson; to the *Outlook* for "Thanksgiving at Todd's Asylum" by Winthrop Packard; to Charles Scribner's Sons for "The Christmas Truants" by Frank R. Stockton; to the author for "The Bishop's Valentine" by Andrea Hofer Proudfoot.

The Elson-Gray Basic Readers, Book Six is a revision of *The Elson Basic Readers, Book Six*, copyright 1931.

382.7

PREFACE

The authors of the "Basic Readers" have attempted to provide an interesting, purposeful, and comprehensive reading course for the middle grades.

The primary aim of any reading course is to lead pupils to become voluntary and eager readers for both pleasure and information. To achieve this purpose the authors have assembled materials from the world-wide field of children's favorite readings. All of the selections included are of recognized worth in providing pleasure, imparting information, cultivating desirable attitudes, and developing appreciation. Such qualities are essential if the activities of the reading period are to result in enriched experience and permanent reading interests.

While selecting and classifying material for these readers the authors carefully surveyed the field of child literature in order to find selections that appeal strongly to children's interests. The stories and poems chosen have also been evaluated and graded in the light of present-day classroom realities. The material is so organized as to make each of the "Basic Readers" at its appropriate grade level the central core or framework of a larger reading plan. Each unit of *Basic Readers, Book Six* initiates a theme or field of interest which can be followed up and developed through the materials of various readers, library books, reference books, and other sources. Such a plan gives purpose and continuity to all reading materials available in the classroom. This correlation of varied reading-matter is made conveniently effective through

5

the use of a special bibliography in the *Teacher's Guidebook* for *Basic Readers, Book Six.*

A systematic and carefully organized plan of teaching is provided in the "Guidebooks" for use in promoting growth of reading habits and interests from grade to grade. This plan is made concrete and usable through a series of carefully prepared lesson helps for each of the selections in *Basic Readers, Book Six.* This expert guidance helps teachers in making needed preparation for the day's lesson or for larger units of work. Additional exercises in the *Extension-Reading Work-Book* reinforce and extend the training of pupils in correct reading interests and habits. Thus basic reading attitudes and habits are developed through the purposeful use of interesting and significant content.

CONTENTS

7

8 CONTENTS

PART FIVE
BOYS AND GIRLS OF OTHER LANDS

PART SIX
WORKERS AND THEIR WORK

10   CONTENTS

HAVE YOU LEARNED TO READ?

HAVE you ever learned to read? That question probably sounds foolish to you. You are going to read this book, and you surely could not learn your geography or arithmetic lessons if you could not read. In the first grade you found that letters made words, and words made sentences that told a story. "Surely," you think, "I know how to read." But you may be surprised when you are told that many boys and girls, and even grown-up people, do not know how to read. Let us see how this can be true.

First, what do you do when you read? You listen to another person through your eyes and with your mind. The author of a story has been through thrilling adventures; he has seen wonderful sights; he has learned fascinating things through careful study; he has thought out an interesting story. He wants you to see, feel, hear, and wonder just as he has. He uses words to bring you his message. Your eyes are the gateway through which words reach your mind, and your mind must work to understand the message.

Now, in the greatest book ever written, the Bible, we read of people who have eyes, yet cannot see, and ears, yet cannot hear. Many people are like that when they read. They go skipping along through a story without getting half of what the author is trying to tell them. If you asked them to repeat the story, they would omit the best parts. There might be facts that would be valuable to them, but they would pass right over them. They do not *think* as they read.

Perhaps you have been asked to answer some question on a geography or history lesson; you didn't know the answer and felt sure it wasn't in your book. Then you went back to the book and read again. Sure enough, there it was, just as plain as could be! When you read the lesson first, you were not listening to the author; you were not *thinking* about his message. You were not *reading*.

Now, in this book many different authors will talk to you. They will tell you about the world of animals, birds, and trees; they will carry you back hundreds of years to the times of some famous heroes about whom millions of people have read; they will tell you about many other interesting things that are found in the world of books.

Each author has for you a message of his own. How well will you understand what he says to you? *How well have you learned to read?*

At the end of each story you will find a list of questions. When you come to these, say to yourself, "Here are some questions about the author's story. I certainly want to be able to tell what he has told me."

Perhaps you will say, "But I didn't know what some of the words meant." Then your book will answer, "It's your business to find out. There is a glossary in the back of the book, and if you don't find the word there, you have a dictionary. Words are tools that are used to make people understand a message. You have to use them, too, when you want to tell something. The more words you understand, the better you can talk to other people and the more you can learn from them."

Now let us listen to the authors who are waiting to talk to us from the pages of this book. Their stories are only samples from the great world of reading. By reading this book and many others, you will come to know what fascinating and valuable things authors have to tell you.

Part One
The Outdoor World

WOODLAND WHISPERS

CLINTON SCOLLARD

Deep in the woodland you will hear,
If you but lend attentive ear,
A murmurous talk from time to time,
And all the words will run to rhyme.
By light of sun and light of star,
The wind and trees the gossips are;
In whispers to the questioning trees
The wandering wind tells all he sees,
For he can roam and roam and roam
While all the trees must stay at home.

THE BOOK OF NATURE NEVER DISAPPOINTS

A VERY great man once said that the Book of Nature is the only book whose pages never disappoint the reader. What did he mean? Theodore Roosevelt could have told you; he found the world of birds, animals, and flowers so fascinating that even in his busy life he spent many hours studying the wild things of Nature.

Now of course, if you are going to read the Book of Nature, you must understand its language. You can learn its language by reading and observing. Men and women who have spent years studying the out-of-doors have written about the wonderful things they have seen.

Here are some of the strange things they have told us about: Bees were the first paper-makers. A certain kind of flower eats meat. There is a deep-sea fish that carries a lantern. Birds save the lives of all of us by eating insects which would in a few years destroy all plants, from which we get our food.

As you learn more about flowers and birds and animals, you will become interested in preserving them instead of destroying them. Perhaps you can tell some other people about reasons why we should not pick wild flowers or collect birds' eggs.

In this first part of your book you will see the outdoor world through the eyes of some famous students of Nature, and you will learn some things about saving wild life. These stories are only samples, put in this book to help you have eyes that see when you go out of doors, and to let you know what fascinating reading awaits you in books that tell about the world of Nature.

HUNTING ELEPHANTS WITH A CAMERA

Martin Johnson

Perhaps you have thought that the only way to hunt animals is with a gun, but Martin Johnson and his wife, Osa, spent many years hunting them with a camera. In this story he tells you why camera-hunting is far more dangerous and thrilling than hunting to kill. He also tells some most surprising things about elephants.

A CLOSE CALL

My wife, Osa, and I were "camera hunting" in Africa. Boculy, the native whom we had engaged to find elephants for us, came running into camp greatly excited. He was out of breath and raised and lowered his hands exclaiming jerkily in Swahili, his native language: "Big elephants—big elephants—all together—very quiet—come quickly!"

In a few moments we had our gun bearers and camera boys with their heavy loads under way. Shortly after, we came up with the herd. There were seven animals quietly feeding on the edge of the forest. Three were cows, and two were bulls—big fellows. Two "totos," or babies, wandered about in the tall grass.

The elephant herd was ideally placed for still pictures, but we wanted action; so leaving Osa at the camera, I walked forward to stir things up a bit. As I approached, the big bull, sensing danger, goose-stepped forward a few paces. Then he saw me. Instantly his trunk went up and his ears spread. For the space of five seconds we gazed at each other silently. Then his feet stamped angrily, and he snorted

with rage. I knew what was coming and prepared myself as, with a furious grunt, the big tusker lowered his trunk and charged. I turned and ran for my life while Osa cranked away with a will.

It was by the use of such methods that we sometimes obtained our best pictures, but this time I had gone too close, and this old bull seemed particularly revengeful. The other six elephants came tearing after him, and then to my surprise and dismay a dozen more burst out from the woods behind and joined the stampede. The world seemed suddenly filled with elephants, and they were all headed in my direction.

I ran toward the camera, while Osa continued turning the crank. Not that she was enjoying it, but she knew she was getting a wonderful bit of film, and there was nothing she could do for me yet. As I tore up to the camera, she snatched her rifle from her gun boy and fired. The big bull stumbled, nearly knocking over the camera as he crashed by, and fell with a mighty thud. Fortunately for us, the balance of the herd split and passed on.

When it was all over, Osa sat down. And I must confess that my own knees felt a trifle wobbly. It had been a close call, and I would probably not have taken such foolish chances had it not been for my confidence in Osa's marksmanship. She is a better shot than I am and seldom misses her mark even under conditions that would shake the nerves of an experienced hunter. She shoots only when the need is desperate, or when we collect an unusual specimen for the museum; and of course for food when necessary.

ELEPHANT CITIZENS OF THE JUNGLE

I like elephants. They are fine citizens of the jungle. They mind their own business, fight little among themselves, are intelligent in bringing up their young, and have a real sense of loyalty to the tribe. They lead a quiet family life, and never prey on other animals.

Years of work in Africa have given me a close understanding of elephant character. As a rule, I don't think they live much longer than a century. Age and size give them a great dignity. I think the old legend that elephants are blind must come from the fact that they plod along much of the time as though half asleep, paying little attention to other animals. They are so powerful that they are secure from attack and have grown careless through the years.

One day Osa asked Boculy how long elephants live. He

could only say, "Many years." He couldn't count far enough. And of course he did not know. I think one hundred years is a very old age for them.

With most game, the larger the herd the less chance there is of getting a good picture, for they stampede too easily. But with elephants the opposite is true; a single elephant is always on the alert, but a herd is usually more careless.

I once had to shoot a charging elephant to save my life. He was mortally wounded, and I prepared to shoot again to save him from suffering; but before I could raise my gun, two of his companions came on either side of him as if to support him, and he tottered away into the forest. This incident shows how loyal elephants are to members of their tribe. I have seen a mother elephant punish her toto with her trunk, push it into line when it was staggering with weariness, and squirt mud over it when it was crying from the heat. Generally they are very patient with their totos, but when punishment is needed, it is given.

BOCULY, THE ELEPHANT GUIDE

We were fortunate to have employed Boculy for our elephant guide. I believe he knows more about elephants than anyone in the world.

Boculy is a very important person in his own land. Somewhere in the wilds he has a thousand cattle and two hundred fifty camels which some of his wandering tribe tend for him when he is on safari with the white men. He knows all the languages of the plains and the desert, and in some curious way he can get aid from any of these people when we need it. There is a mystery in his wise old face, and his knowledge of wild animals is indeed remarkable. Elephants are his strong point. We call Boculy "little half-brother of the elephants." If he told me I'd find elephants in front of the New York Public Library, I'd believe him, for Boculy knows. He could find "tembo," the elephant, when every other hunter, white or native, would say that no beast could be found. He could see things that are invisible to the rest of us. A bit of mud dropped from a passing hoof was full of meaning to him. He could tell what animal had dropped it. The bending of grass told him the kind of game that had passed, what direction it had taken, and even, at times, how long ago it had left its mark.

Many of the plainer signs can be learned by anyone who spends much time in the wilds. But the slight differences in the ways trodden grass falls to the ground, the different kinds of mud, and other seemingly unimportant traces left by passing jungle folk were full of meaning to Boculy, when to us they were almost invisible. It fascinated me to keep up with him in the field whenever I could, for his knowledge was so amazing and interesting. And the way the old boy had of telling me things made it even more so. He would point out to me the different footprints—the sharp cut of the buffalo's hoof, which kills the grass it touches; the huge, soft print of tembo, the elephant, which simply bruises the blades; the four-leafed clover print of the hyena; the water-lily mark of the leopard. As for "simba," the lion, he leaves little trace of his weight. One rarely finds his footprints. Swiftly and silently he slips through the grass, and it rises again, concealing his passage.

No other African I have ever known approached Boculy

in knowledge and skill. Boculy, with his naked eye, would pick out an animal that I could barely find with field glasses. The "little half-brother of the elephants," like the tembo for whom we named him, would shuffle along muttering to himself. Then when you thought he was half asleep, he would stoop, pick up a bit of mud or a leaf, sniff the trail, and say, "Over by the Old Lady Waterhole you find five bull tembo, four cows, and three totos." And we would. That was the amazing part of it. Boculy was always right.

Once when I had finished a lot of good elephant film, I gave a picture show for Boculy and the boys. With Boculy on a box next to us, we ran off several thousand feet of film. It was a joy to watch his wrinkled old face. He had never seen a movie, and I doubt if he had understood what we had been doing with our camera in all our crazy wanderings through the jungle. All he could say when he saw the pictures—in many of which he appeared—was "Ah-h-h, Ah-h-h!" He was overcome with feeling.

I enjoyed myself greatly that night. At last I was even with Boculy, for my magic of the camera was even more of a mystery to him than his magic knowledge of the jungle and its ways was to me.

CAMERA HUNTING

Hunting with the camera has become more important to the study of wild life than hunting with the rifle. Osa and I seldom shoot except for food or to save ourselves or our workers in times of great danger. Osa usually holds the gun, and it is my faith in her nerve that has made possible most of our best pictures. Twice she has dropped elephants at my feet. Once a lion charged me in the open. I kept cranking because she held the gun. At fifteen feet she fired. It didn't stop him. She fired again, and the lion dropped so close that I could touch his mane with my toe.

I usually become so interested in the pictures I am getting that I don't realize the danger. Osa looks out for that.

Photographing wild life is a very dangerous business for the person who hasn't had wide experience and who does not know just what chances he can take with safety. After spending years in the jungle, one comes to know how a particular animal is likely to act. But we take every care, because there is always some uncertainty as to what wild animals will do.

Camera hunting is a life work that I would not advise for many people. It is thrilling if you like it; but for every thrill there may be days, perhaps weeks, of dull, tiresome preparation. Often after endless labor of tracking animals, planning with care, lugging cameras and other things, and coming right up on the beasts you are looking for, you do not get a good film. Then again, you secure a picture that makes you want to stand out in the middle of the desert and shout the tidings to the world.

Boculy found so many elephants for us that we gradually became accustomed to the big beasts and set our cameras many times for them without fear. On one such occasion, when we were in our blind at night, a long file of elephants came down for water. As they approached our flashlight apparatus, they stopped. For several minutes they hesitated, their trunks waving in the air. Then one elephant left the herd. As he moved away, he would stop every fifteen or twenty feet to wave his trunk. He seemed greatly puzzled

and finally went back to the herd. The elephants held a conference at which there was not a sound. Finally they went to the water by another route. We got no pictures that night.

One old female got the habit of breaking into our vegetable garden. She particularly liked sweet potatoes and was quite orderly about securing them. Every night she would pick over a space about ten square feet, eating everything in that area and going away without damaging anything else.

We found that this old lady was entering the garden at a hole which she had made in the hedge beside a great yellow-wood tree. Here we rigged up our wires and camera with everything so set that the elephant would spring the flash-light herself. We had scarcely gone to bed when we heard a boom. We dashed out only to find that she had disappeared. We were too excited to wait till morning to develop the plates; so we rushed to do this task at once. The pictures were wonderfully clear. What a thrill we camera hunters got from every good picture—a greater thrill than any mere game-hunter can know.

Although we doubted that she would return, we set up the apparatus again the following night. Again we heard the flashlight boom and again we rushed to develop the film.

The third night we heard the crashing of branches on the edge of the forest. There was the old lady contentedly feeding. When she had finished her meal, she strolled slowly down the line of houses where my gun bearers and camera boys slept, quietly ripping off the thatched roofs as she went. In a moment the natives came tumbling out of their huts, greatly frightened. The old tembo disappeared.

One astonishing thing about elephants is the way they can vanish so noiselessly into the forest, in spite of their great size. I have seen them melt out of sight with little or no movement that could be noticed. I say again that I like elephants. The majority of them are kind; they know their place in life and are content to keep it.

Notes and Questions

1. Give at least one reason of your own to explain—
   (a) why taking motion pictures of savage animals is dangerous.
   (b) why motion pictures of animals are valuable.
   Perhaps you can give more than one reason for each.
2. (a) What dangerous thing that Martin Johnson did is told about in the first part of this story?
   (b) Why did he do it?
   (c) What two things saved his life and the lives of the others?

3. For what three reasons did the Johnsons kill animals?

4. Give four facts about elephant character that made Martin Johnson like them.

5. *(a)* About how old do elephants grow?

(b) Why do they seem so careless, and even sleepy?

6. *(a)* To what African tribe did Boculy belong?

(b) What two things are told about Boculy that would lead you to believe that his home was not in the dense, tropical jungle forests?

7. What were the two main things about Boculy that made him so valuable to Martin Johnson?

8. What signs of wild life can you read and understand, such as animal tracks, different bird songs, etc.? Make a list of them.

9. How are elephants valuable to men? You may have learned this in your geography. If not, look up the answer.

10. Find and be ready to read—

(a) a paragraph that shows the intelligence and loyalty of elephants.

(b) a paragraph that tells what a skillful tracker Boculy was.

(c) a paragraph that tells of some of the problems and rewards of camera hunting.

11. In some reference book, look up facts about Boculy's tribe. Be ready to tell where they live, what they do, etc.

Were there words in this story that you did not understand? Don't forget to use the glossary in the back of the book to find the meanings and pronunciations of words.

If you enjoyed this story, you will want to read *Jungle Babies,* by Osa Johnson, *Three Boy Scouts in Africa,* by Douglas, Martin, and Oliver, and "Toomai of the Elephants," Kipling (in *The Jungle Book*).

TIGER, TERROR OF THE JUNGLE

Mary Hastings Bradley

To us in America the tiger is an interesting animal; but to the people of the jungle he is a constant terror, inspiring fear in every living thing. This story tells how one feels when he meets a tiger face to face in the jungles of Asia.

Mary Hastings Bradley, the author of the story, and her husband, Herbert, live in Chicago. They are both great lovers of the out-of-doors, and have made many trips to Africa and Asia to study the animals and the wild tribes who live there.

A DAY OF WAITING

Before dawn we were up, in the blackness of the early tropic hours, buckling on cartridge pouches and seeing to the guns, in order to start the moment the light permitted tracking. Suddenly a native appeared like a ghost out of the darkness by our tents. The tiger had eaten of the dead buffalo with which we had hoped to bait him!

Excitement gripped us. A tiger—our chance at last! "Are you sure that it is a tiger which has eaten?" we wanted to know, remembering the day when we had waited and waited and a giant reptile, not a tiger, had appeared.

The tracker was positive. The buffalo had been eaten as a tiger begins eating—at the tail. The tiger must be somewhere near, ready to return. We must hurry to reach our bush before the light came. Hastily we swallowed some hot coffee and snatched a bite or two of bread while the horses were led up; then we mounted and set out, the tracker running along ahead of us as guide.

The land was ghostly with the first signs of morning, and through the grayness the giant pines rose darkly like columns in some dim underground vault. The guide circled in and out the trees, and our horses followed closely. Then we dismounted and stole through the brush on foot till we were on the edge of the ravine, directly above the dead buffalo. More than halfway down the steep slope was the bush, across which a screen of reeds had been built, and the buffalo was a hundred and fifty feet beyond that, directly in front of the green wall of the jungle.

Down the slope we crept, crouching low, and being as silent-footed as possible in the attempt to deceive the stealthy beast, who might be in any bush before us at the moment. If he saw us, the hunt was probably finished before it was begun. We should spend our weary hours there in vain.

We reached the shelter of the blind and cautiously raised the leaves that covered the tiny holes left for peepholes. There was a long stretch of tall, waving grass sloping down before us with bushes on each side, then the dark blue that we knew to be the dead buffalo, and beyond, the blotting darkness of the jungle.

My husband, Herbert, and I took our positions, each with an eye at a peephole, our guns leaning beside us. The tracker squatted on his heels at our side, patient and motionless. It was growing lighter and lighter; the darkness paled as the brightness gained in the east. There were little morning noises, the familiar sounding crow of the wild cock, the cropping of a family of wild pigs on the grassy slope to the right, the bark of a distant deer.

The sun seemed to shoot up in the sky, and its heat poured out on us as if a door had been opened from a furnace. We stood still there, motionless, staring out intently. There was nothing to do but stand and wait and watch. I kept telling myself that somewhere out in that green into which I was straining my eyes was the great striped beast we had hunted so long, sleeping, or perhaps padding about on stealthy feet, staring through the jungle at us.

Six o'clock. Seven o'clock. Eight o'clock. Nine o'clock. . . . Our friends, the Kings, had got their tiger at a quarter to nine; so I had decided that nine would be our lucky hour, but nine o'clock passed with nothing happening. Then I remembered a story I had heard about a tiger that had been seen at eleven o'clock, and I set eleven as the time at which things would happen.

The minutes passed with unbelievable slowness. The sun

burned hotter and hotter. We would not stir. One of us could have rested while the other watched, but we were too excited for that. Our nerves were tense.

Eleven o'clock. Nothing happened. Then twelve. The sun was high overhead. I felt burning up; the blood throbbed in my temples. I thought of the nights on an African mountain when we had stood on guard against plundering elephants, shivering with cold on the windswept heights, and I wondered why I had ever objected to cold and wind.

From the jungle beyond us came the sound of splashing water. Tigers play in water. Was it the tiger—or was it the herd of wild cattle we had seen the day before? I looked questioningly down at the tracker; he grinned back at me as if he, too, thought it were a tiger.

A little later it seemed to me that I could see the gleam of a striped face for an instant between the green jungle growths. It was gone even as I thought I saw it, and I told myself that it was all a trick of my straining eyes. I was getting so that I could see tigers all over the place.

At two o'clock came a rush of clouds, which gave warning of the storm that was sweeping up toward us. The darkness shut swiftly in about us, the heavens opened overhead, and all the waters in them came crashing down on us. The tracker shivered and slipped softly away up the ravine. We put our guns under our coats to keep them dry, and for the next two hours we stood there in the soaking downpour, wondering if we had really been nice and dry and hot a short time before. Then the rain ceased and the sun came out more faintly; the tall grass about us, bending with rain, began to straighten, while the glistening, beaded drops on it dried. We now took turns sitting down close by the blind, cautiously stretching a cramped arm or leg. There was little hope—just determination left.

THE TIGER COMES

The day was fading fast. Five-thirty. . . . Five-forty. . . . In a few minutes it would be too dark to see to shoot if anything did come. As soon as it was dusk, the tiger might begin to prowl, and do his prowling anywhere about us. We began to glance over our shoulders rather cautiously.

Only fifteen minutes more in which it would be possible to shoot, I thought, glancing at my wrist watch. It was just five forty-five. I was at the blind, peering through the peephole at Herbert's side, and Herbert was directly behind me, sitting down. There was a feeling in the air that the day was done. And then, as I looked out, realizing that every moment was slipping by bearing away forever the chances it might have held—I saw something.

Out of the wall of distant shadows came a gleam of gold and black—vivid as lightning against the green—and the tiger walked out of the jungle!

Never in my life had I seen such a picture. Elephants by moonlight, lions at dawn, gorillas at blazing noon I had seen, but nothing was ever so beautiful and so glorious as that tiger walking out of his jungle. He was everything that was wild and savage, lordly and sinister. For a moment I could imagine I was dreaming. He stood clearly outlined against the background of the forest, and he looked enormous. The great striped roundness of him was like a barrel. Then he moved, and seemed to flow along the ground, nearer and nearer.

He stopped, and looked up at our bush. I could hardly breathe. If he should take alarm! He stared with a threatening look; then, as if satisfied, he turned his head toward the dead buffalo and walked over toward it.

Then I dared let the leaf go back into place while I turned to Herbert behind me. My lips formed, "Tiger here," and over Herbert's face came a look of deepest pity. "Poor girl," he thought, "she has dreamed tigers and she has looked for tigers—and now she thinks she is seeing them!"

Then his face changed. He rose, and I moved to his side as he stepped forward to his place. Noiselessly we lifted the leaves over our peepholes and raised our guns to fill the opening. My eyes raced down the barrel of my rifle in frantic fear lest the tiger be gone.

The tiger was there, to the right of the buffalo, a picture of savage life and death. So he must have stood many times over his kills, cautious, yet bold in his great strength, lording it over all the jungle and inspiring terror in every living thing.

I dared not extend my gun as I wished; I leveled it as best I could, stepping backwards, and aimed at the head for the brain-shot I had been told was the best. "Ready?" I breathed; then, before Herbert's signal came back, the tiger began to move his head from side to side, looking up at us.

I had been told to wait till he began to eat, when I would have a chance for a clear aim, but I dared not wait. I shifted my aim hastily from the brain to a black stripe across the

backbone at the top of the shoulder. I never felt so cold and tense in my life.

"Ready," breathed Herbert. I was to fire at any time now, and he was to follow with his big gun in case mine had missed. He was giving me the shot, but we weren't going to lose that tiger if we could help it.

I fired on the instant, and the roar of his gun followed mine. Then the roar of the tiger drowned them both.

I tore out around the corner of the blind where I could see in the open, and Herbert plunged after me. The tiger was down; we could not see him in the deep grass, but his snarling roars told us he was out there.

"He's down!" we said, and then, "He's gone!" for now we had a clearer outlook and saw that he was gone from beside the buffalo. The snarls were going away.

THE END OF A TERRIBLE KILLER

Now we had been warned not to follow a wounded tiger, but to wait a few hours and then track him. It was good advice, but this was a case not for advice but for action. It was darkening each instant, and there was no time to waste.

So down we went through that long grass, step by step, watching each side for there might be a tigress anywhere. We came to the buffalo and followed the flattened grass trail leading back into the jungle. It was dim in there, but there was light enough to see. The tiger was lying stretched out, about fifty yards from the buffalo. As we came up, he roared with fury, dying as he was. Every night of his life he had fed on some defenseless creature, and now a sudden, sharp blow had struck him down. He had been terrible in life, and he was terrible in death.

With guns ready, we stood watching that last moment of his life, keeping ourselves on guard for the possible tigress. The native tracker had heard the shooting from the top of the ravine where he had come out to wait for us, and now he and his men came stealing in to us, the tracker with his own gun alert, for he, too, feared a tigress. When they were quite sure the tiger was dead, they all took hold of that great barrel of a body and staggered with it into the open. It was all the eight men could do to carry it.

He was a huge beast, big and fat, with a gorgeous skin. One shoulder, the left, was smashed from Herbert's bullet. But my shot had gone to its mark, straight through the black stripe into the backbone. That tiger was a dead tiger the instant he fell, yet such was his dying strength that he had pushed himself fifty yards downhill into the jungle.

Quickly now and loudly we counted the whiskers and tied them with grass to protect them from the natives. For tiger whiskers are the most useful sort of magic—just one of them ground up and slipped into the food of a neighbor is considered a strong enough charm to kill him. From the anxious way in which the natives stayed about the tiger's head we imagined that there were several unpopular neighbors in the village that they wished to work upon.

The size of that tiger gave us a thrill. We had grown so hopeless that we would have been thankful for any tiger, and here was a great killer in the strength of his powers, second, we found out later, to the record for height.

The natives were as excited as we were. A tiger, the overlord of the jungle, the enemy of everything with life, had been killed. Chanting and singing, they carried the tiger, slung to a pole, back to the camp. Night had now fallen, and we carried a light. We could see its reflection shining in the eyes of staring deer. Then, as they caught the scent of their dead enemy—or us—they would snort and fly.

Down before the tents the natives put the tiger; so livelooking was his pose that he seemed alive. There were wild doings of triumph about the natives' fire that night, but there was great peace about ours.

All through the night I kept waking. The moon stood high overhead, its light white as snow upon the still earth. The shadows of the pines were like little pools of ink about the base of each tree. In the clear moonlight the great tiger lay brilliant in gold and black beauty, proud and perfect in his death as when he had stalked over those plains in life to seek his quivering prey.

NOTES AND QUESTIONS

1. Give one reason why you think Martin Johnson would not have called tigers good citizens of the jungle.

2. Find a short sentence on page 25 that best tells how the Bradleys felt at the thought of facing a tiger.

3. On page 26 the author calls the tiger a "stealthy beast." Make a list of four other words or groups of words by which she makes us understand what this animal is like.

4. Here is a list of phrases that the author used to help us see what she saw and feel as she felt. In one column write the phrases that help us see. In another, write those that help us feel.

could hardly breathe	dim underground vault
appeared like a ghost	straining eyes
heat poured	blotting darkness
gleam of gold	green wall of the jungle
blood throbbed	nerves were tense
glistening, beaded drops	wall of shadows
clearly outlined	frantic fear
so cold and tense	reflection shining
like little pools of ink	great peace

5. What short paragraph describes the moment of greatest excitement in the story? Give the page number and the first four words.

6. What did the natives believe about the tiger that shows how deadly they considered him to be?

7. For each word in the first list choose a word or words from the second list that mean the same. Write the pairs together.

(1) sinister, intently, tense, vivid, stealthy, cropping, prowl.

(2) strained, search cautiously, quiet and cautious, eating grass, earnestly, evil, brilliant.

Other jungle stories that you would enjoy are: "The Tiger's Roar" and "Topsy-Turvy Land," Wells (in *The Jungle Man and His Animals*); "Jinny, the Taming of a Bad Monkey," Seton, and "An Exciting Lion Hunt," White (in *Child-Library Readers, Book Six*).

CARL AKELEY BRINGS JUNGLELAND TO AMERICA

Dr. Clyde Fisher

Very few boys and girls, or even men and women, can go to Africa to see and study the wild life there. Carl Akeley had a dream of bringing Jungleland to America so that you and I could see and learn about the life on that great and beautiful continent.

Dr. Clyde Fisher, who wrote this story of Carl Akeley, is a famous student of Nature. He tells us how Akeley's dream came true, and why he was the kind of man that we all like.

AKELEY CHOOSES TO BE A TAXIDERMIST

Into the deepest jungles of the continent that he lovingly called "Brightest Africa," Carl Akeley went five different times, to study its wild animal life and to collect specimens for American museums. Known to the world as a big-game hunter and explorer, Akeley was born on a farm in Orleans County, New York. He says of himself: "By all the rules of the game I should have been a farmer, but for some reason or other I was always more interested in birds and chipmunks than in crops and cattle."

At the age of thirteen, Akeley saw in *The Youth's Companion* an advertisement of a book on taxidermy, that is, a book which explains how to stuff and mount the skins of birds and animals. Though this book cost but a dollar, he could not buy it. Later he was able to borrow a copy from one of the older boys of the neighborhood. That book probably helped Akeley to decide what his work in life was to be. At any rate he became the world's greatest taxidermist; he developed a method of mounting birds and animals which is without doubt one of his greatest services to man.

In order to enlarge his knowledge of taxidermy gained from books, Akeley took a few painting lessons from a lady in a village near his father's farm; for he wanted to paint lifelike backgrounds for his mounted birds and animals. So far as known, Akeley's early attempts of this sort were the first experiments with painted backgrounds for mounted groups.

Upon the advice of a newly-made English friend who was greatly interested in taxidermy, Akeley, at the age of nineteen, decided to go to Rochester, New York, and apply for work at Ward's Natural Science Establishment. At that time Ward's was famous for preparing museum specimens; moreover, it was the headquarters of taxidermy in America.

Akeley hardly slept a wink the night after he had decided to take his friend's advice and go to Ward's. Rising early the next morning he walked three miles to the railway station to catch the train for Rochester. He walked through most of the streets of Rochester, his courage sinking lower and lower, before he finally found the great arch, made of the jaws of a whale, which marked the entrance to the establishment. Here he suddenly became so timid that he had to walk a mile or so back and forth to screw up courage to ring the professor's bell.

As a result of this visit Akeley was offered a position at the small salary of three dollars and fifty cents a week. He found a boarding house where he could get a room and meals for four dollars a week. Thus he began to learn taxidermy.

At that time little was known about the work which Akeley had chosen for himself. To mount a deer skin, for example, was simple. It was first soaked in a "pickle-bath" containing salt and alum to preserve it, and then washed with a poison soap to keep insects from eating it. After the skin was dried, the bones were replaced in the legs, and the body stuffed with straw. Then, to make the body thinner at any point, it was sewed through with a long needle and drawn in.

These results did not satisfy Akeley's dreams, even those of his boyhood. While at Ward's, he made some attempts to improve these rough and clumsy methods of taxidermy, but his methods for the most part were not used, because no one would then pay for better work. Akeley tells us that museums at that time preferred bird skins to bird groups and wired skeletons to animal groups; they cared little for exhibits that would be really interesting to people.

AKELEY DEVELOPS NEW METHODS OF TAXIDERMY

Akeley's great dream was to mount animals in "habitat" groups, that is, in their natural poses and in the proper setting of plant life and landscape, aided by painted backgrounds. Not being able to do this, he began to look elsewhere for work.

William Morton Wheeler, one of his fellow workers at Ward's, had left and was teaching in the high school in Milwaukee. To help Akeley continue his education, Wheeler offered to tutor him if he would come to Milwaukee. Akeley accepted, and got a job at the Milwaukee Museum to pay for food and lodging. Here he stayed for eight years, working at taxidermy in the museum and in a shop of his own.

One of the directors of the Milwaukee Museum had visited Lapland and had brought back the skin of a reindeer, together with a Lapp sledge and harness, all of which he was anxious to have shown in the museum. Akeley arranged these articles into a group which showed a Lapp driving his reindeer over the snow, the first habitat group he ever built. Later he mounted a group of orang-utans in lifelike poses, using some bare branches to give the proper setting.

The reindeer and the orang-utan work encouraged Akeley to suggest similar habitat groups of the fur-bearing animals of Wisconsin. The first of these to be built was the muskrat group, which still stands as good as new.

From Milwaukee, Akeley went to the Field Museum of Natural History in Chicago. In 1896, under the direction of this museum, he made his first expedition to Africa. While studying the wild life in this part of the world, Akeley made up his mind to try the giant task of bringing Africa to America—not the animals alone, but the animals in their natural surroundings.

After returning from Africa, Akeley worked steadily for nine years as chief of the department of taxidermy of the Field Museum, mounting the animals which he had collected and at the same time improving his new method of taxidermy.

To do taxidermy by the Akeley method, one must know the animals in their native surroundings; he must be able to collect his own specimens; he must know animal structure; and he must be a sculptor, for the animal must be modeled in clay. Then he must have enough artistic sense to make his group pleasing as well as accurate.

The first step in the Akeley method of taxidermy is to make a life-size model of the animal to be mounted. In order to be sure that the model is accurate, it is checked by

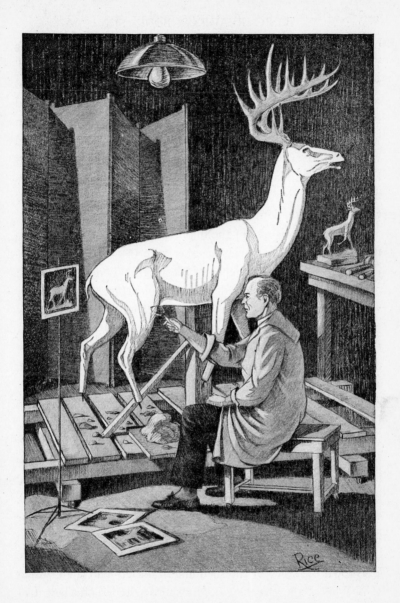

measurements made in the field before the animal was skinned, by photographs of the animal, and by "trying on" the skin itself. The second step is to take a plaster mold of the clay model. This mold is often cast in sections and is used in constructing the manikin, or framework, upon which the skin is mounted. Each section of the mold is lined with glue, over which is laid a sheet of muslin. On top of the muslin are placed several layers of wire cloth and papier-mache, each layer being worked carefully into the crevice of the mold and made moisture-proof by a coat of shellac.

This manikin is one of the important features of the Akeley method. The papier-mache together with the wire cloth makes the framework strong, light, and lasting. When the last coat of shellac is thoroughly dry, the whole thing is put under water to melt the glue so that the sections of the manikin will come out of the mold. The sections are then put together in a clean and perfect likeness of the original clay model. Finally, the skin is drawn over the manikin, to which it is carefully cemented. After various finishing details, the mounted animal is ready to take its place in the habitat group for which it was prepared.

Besides the group of African animals which Akeley prepared for the Field Museum, there is a series of splendid groups of American animals which has attracted the attention and won the admiration of thousands of visitors. These are the seasonal deer groups, made in Akeley's own shop and later placed in the Field Museum. There are four groups, in which the Virginia deer is shown in each season of the year. Here are shown the story of the shedding of antlers and the growing of new ones; the changing of the short-haired reddish coat of summer to the longer-haired gray coat of winter; the story of the young and their growth, as well as the entire round of the seasons in the plant life appearing in the backgrounds. It took Akeley four years to complete these groups, for as he went along he had to work out his method of constructing manikins and of making such background materials as artificial snow, moss, and leaves. These years were the period of greatest development in Akeley's method of taxidermy.

ROOSEVELT AFRICAN HALL

Akeley's second expedition to Africa was made in 1905, when he collected the elephants for "The Fighting Bulls," now perhaps the outstanding group in the Stanley Field Hall of the Field Museum in Chicago.

In 1909 Akeley made his third expedition to Africa, this time for the American Museum of Natural History in New York City. Among other things, he collected the animals for the statuesque group of African elephants to be placed in the African Hall of the American Museum. They now stand where they were mounted, awaiting the completion of Akeley's dream, which was the construction of African Hall, proposed by Akeley as a monument to his great friend, our naturalist president, Theodore Roosevelt. In fact, the cow elephant of the group was collected by Roosevelt and the calf by his son Kermit, when they were hunting with Akeley.

It was on this expedition that Akeley planned more fully his dream of African Hall. On the main floor, the outstanding feature is to be the great elephant group which Akeley called "The Alarm." Since the elephant is the largest land animal now living and is a fine example of wild animal

life in Africa, it is fitting that the elephant should be the outstanding animal in this hall. There will also be a family
group of the black rhino and a similar group of the square-
lipped or white rhino.   At the sides of these will be three
large bronze figures of native lion-spearmen.   These groups
will last forever without the protection of glass cases.   All
have been finished and are ready to be installed in African
Hall as soon as it shall have been built.

Around this central hall there will be forty wonderful
habitat groups of animals, twenty of which will be viewed
from the main floor and twenty from the balcony. In all
these groups the animals will be shown in their natural surroundings of forest, plain, river, or mountain, with backgrounds painted by trained artists from sketches made in the
field. An indoor field-trip through this hall when completed
will be almost as good as touring the African wilds. Since

the great game animals are now decreasing, it will soon be impossible to see in Africa as much of African wild life as is shown in this great hall.

As a part of his third expedition to Africa, Akeley had planned to go into the forests of gorilla country. He was compelled, however, to postpone his study of the gorillas because of a skirmish he had with an old elephant. In this sudden encounter Akeley was left crushed and unconscious, and several months were required for his recovery. It was not until his fourth expedition, in 1921-22, that he entered the country where the gorillas live, a country of marvelous beauty with large open forests and sunny hillsides. At this time he made the first motion pictures ever taken of wild gorillas in their natural surroundings. By his studies he showed that these man-like apes are hardly wild—that they are not at all the ferocious beasts they were formerly considered to be. The gorillas already prepared for the African Hall are the only ones ever mounted by a man who has seen them free in their native surroundings.

On his fifth and last expedition to Africa, on which he embarked January 30, 1926, Akeley planned to collect the material for five of the large groups of African Hall. He was probably making collections for the gorilla group as the last bit of work he did in Africa, for he passed away on the slopes of Mount Mikeno in the heart of the gorilla country. His fearless wife, Mary Jobe Akeley, remained in Africa to direct the completion of his work.

Although Akeley could not live to see his dream of African Hall come true, fortunately he had trained, and trained well, other men who will be able to do the work as he had planned it, and these men will be inspired to a great work as a memorial to their master. African Hall will be a complete record for all time of the animal life, the native customs, and the beautiful scenery of a large continent, a thing of great beauty, as well as accuracy—just as Carl Akeley dreamed it should be.

CARL AKELEY, CONSERVATIONIST

It has been more than thirty years since Carl Akeley first went to Africa. At the time and on later trips he realized that the magnificent game animals of that continent were certain to decrease and even to disappear if something were not done to save them. Akeley always was a conservationist; he collected specimens of wild life only to preserve them in American museums. In that way he accomplished his great task of bringing Africa to America. But Akeley wished, above all, to preserve in Africa the native wild life of that continent. Therefore he secured the establishment of a great National Park in Central Africa, called the Albert National Park, in the Belgian Congo. This preserve was set apart in 1925 by a royal decree of King Albert of Belgium. It provides complete protection for all the wild life within its borders, especially the gorilla, in which Akeley was greatly interested.

Now Akeley's body lies in this beautiful wild-life preserve, surrounded by the great charm and natural beauty of the continent that he loved. No more suitable final resting place could be imagined. Moreover, it is of his own choosing. At the time he captured his biggest gorilla specimen, Akeley said to his friends, the Bradleys, who were with him, "I wish I could be buried here when I die."

In a final review of Carl Akeley's work, one is impressed with the unusual ability of the man. In less than three-score years he accomplished more than most men do in four-score years. He stands out as an explorer, a sculptor, a taxidermist, an inventor, a conservationist; but more than all of these he stands out as a man with the qualities that we all like—namely, straightforwardness, honesty, simplicity, and genuineness.

NOTES AND QUESTIONS

1. In what two important ways did Carl Akeley improve taxidermy?

2. Below are the steps used in mounting animals by Akeley's method, but they are not in correct order. Put them in the right order.

 (a) Making a manikin of wire cloth and papier-mache
 (b) Modeling the animal in clay
 (c) Soaking the mold and the manikin in water
 (d) Making a mold of the clay model
 (e) Measuring the animal before it is skinned
 (f) Cementing the skin on to the manikin

3. (a) In what way did Akeley show that he was an inventor?
 (b) Which part of his method called for ability as an artist?
 (c) Why was it necessary for him to be a sculptor?

4. Name three places where you can find some of Akeley's work.

5. Akeley brought Jungleland to America. What did he do to save Jungleland in Africa?

6. Be ready to read lines that tell the kind of man Akeley was.

Carl Akeley was a great friend of the Bradleys' about whom you read in the tiger story. Mary Hastings Bradley says, "I grew up in love with Africa, for we had a family friendship with Carl Akeley, and his returns from Africa were wonderful times for us."

You will enjoy reading Carl Akeley's book, *In Brightest Africa*, and *J. T. Jr., Biography of a Monkey*, by Delia Akeley.

THE CARDINAL BIRD

ARTHUR GUITERMAN

Where snowdrifts are deepest he frolics along,
A flicker of crimson, a chirrup of song,
My cardinal bird of the frost-powdered wing,
Composing new lyrics to whistle in Spring.

A plump little prelate, the park is his church;
The pulpit he loves is a cliff-sheltered birch;
And there, in his rubicund livery dressed,
Arranging his feathers and ruffling his crest,

He preaches, with most unconventional glee,
A sermon addressed to the squirrels and me,
Commending the wisdom of those that display
The brightest of colors when heavens are gray.

THE FAMILY OF BOB-WHITE

Clarence Hawkes

When you have read this story, you will understand better why so many people love the out-of-doors and the study of wild life. The Book of Nature is full of interesting facts. Clarence Hawkes here tells about the life of Bob-White, or the quail. As you will learn, even a harmless bird like Bob-White lives a life of adventure and danger.

BOB-WHITE IN SPRINGTIME

Bob-White was not a showy bird, although his suit was neat and quite jaunty. His back and shoulders were grayish brown, while his undersides were lighter. The feathers on the top of his head stood up like a small pompadour, and under his throat was a white necktie. Such a dress would not attract the eyes of his enemies—hawks, owls, or men.

Bob-White sat on the top of the gate one spring morning, whistling his merry call, "bob-white, bob, bob-bob-white, bob-white, bob, bob-white." Each time when he stopped whistling he hopped down on the top bar of the gateway and strutted back and forth like a turkey cock. First he would extend one wing to its full sweep, then the other, and finally spreading both wings and his funny short tail he would strut up and down as if to say, "Now if you want to see a fine bird, just look at me."

But Bob-White was whistling for something else besides good spirits this morning. He was whistling for a wife. Presently down across the fields as though in answer to his

calling came a clear "white, white, white." Bob-White heard
it and was pleased. He redoubled his calls of "bob-white,
bob-white," and listened regularly for the musical "white,
white, white" that came in return from a lady quail down in
the thicket.

When this calling and answering had gone on for some
time, Bob-White flew away, and his wings made such a
whirring sound and struck so fast that this fact alone showed
him to be a member of the partridge family. He is the smallest of all the partridges, and is known in parts of the South
as the Virginia partridge.

MRS. BOB-WHITE AND HER BROOD

At first Bob-White could not locate the shy little lady
quail who had been calling to him from the thicket; but he
finally discovered her picking away for dear life at weed-seed,

just as though breakfast was much more to her taste than love-making. For a long time she would take no notice of him, but he strutted up and down so long that she finally looked up. Little by little, Bob-White gained her goodwill, until at last she would let him help her scratch for weed-seeds. They spent a very pleasant forenoon together, and the thing was as good as settled. About ten days later Mr. and Mrs. Bob-White selected a place for their nest. It was under the edge of an old fallen log, well screened from view and sheltered from the rain. Each day for more than two weeks Mrs. Bob-White laid an egg in the nest, until the number was sixteen.

Two or three times during the long three weeks that followed, Mr. Bob-White took his turn upon the eggs for half an hour, while his wife went for a dust bath.

About the twentieth of June Mrs. Bob-White appeared, closely followed by fourteen quail chicks. She was clucking and bristling like the good mother partridge that she was, while each of the tiny chicks was spry as a cricket. After the first tiny little creature had picked his way through the shell, his "peep" had set all the others to work, and in half an hour the whole brood had arrived. Then when they had dried and had a little time in which to gain strength, they were ready for the world.

Forth they all came, the mother clucking and bristling and the chicks scampering this way and that, pecking at almost invisible plant-lice and bugs, feeding themselves within the same hour that they came from the nest. For two or three nights Mrs. Bob-White led them back to the old nest, but after that it was given up, and they never returned to it.

FAMILY MISFORTUNES

One night when they were about a week old, Mrs. Bob-White led them to sleep in a little hollow under an overhanging rock. During the night there was a terrible downpour of rain, and the hollow filled rapidly. Before the young mother could conduct her chicks to higher and drier ground, three were drowned in the puddle.

For the first two weeks Bob-White stayed with his family trying to protect them and giving his wife much good advice about bringing up children; but she finally told him that she could get along quite well without him, and he flew away. After this, there were no disasters in the quail family for nearly two months.

The August moon hung large and bright above the eastern hills. There was the smell of ripening fruit and corn on the summer night air; the cricket and the katydid were singing in the grass. Down from the deep woods came Mr. Raccoon, shuffling along across the pasture like a little bear. Soon a fresh puff of night wind brought him a most exciting scent. He knew it quite well. It was that of a bevy of quail in hiding. The old raccoon knew just how they stood in that circular bunch with their tails all together and their heads looking outward, that they might face in every direction.

He flattened himself to the ground and crept forward almost as still as a cat. Now he was no longer like a clumsy little bear; he was a cautious hunter. Once he heard the bevy stirring in their sleep; then he lay very still and waited until the mother bird's "creets" and the soft "peeps" of the chickens had ceased. He now crept forward again. Nearer and nearer he drew, going more cautiously with each step, until at last he was within springing distance. He then flattened himself out on the ground, strained all his muscles until they were like steel, and with a sudden motion sprang full in the midst of the sleeping bevy.

Click, click, click, went his jaws, snapping like lightning in every direction. There was the sudden whir of many wings and a chorus of squeaks, peeps, and squawks from a dozen birds; and in three seconds' time the bevy was gone with the exception of two wounded birds who fluttered feebly in the grass. But a bite apiece from Mr. Raccoon soon stopped their fluttering.

August and September came and went, and the quail family grew plump upon grain and weed-seed, but the loss of grain to the farmer was more than paid for by the weed-seed they destroyed.

October with its corn in the shock and golden pumpkins and harvested grain and fruit was with us when another hunter came down from the great woods. This hunter did not shuffle as the old raccoon had done; his gait was a steady trot. It was Red-Fox, the wise, and a much more successful hunter than the old raccoon.

He, too, got a scent of quail down in the pasture and followed it eagerly. His step was swift and sure, and his nose was keen. Swiftly like a dark shadow he advanced until he located the sleeping quail under an old brush fence. Then he crept forward foot by foot until he was almost upon them, when with a sudden spring he darted into their midst.

Almost at once there could be heard the sudden whir of many wings and cries of fear and pain mingled with the rapid click, click of the fox's jaws. When the bevy was

gone, and Mr. Fox nosed about under the fence, he found
he also had bagged a pair of quail.

A FAMILY REUNION

No more misfortunes happened to the quail family until the
first day of the hunting season. This day was indeed one of
sorrow to the family of Bob-White. Toward night, a biting
sleet and rainstorm set in and the hunting ceased, but the
quail family had been scattered in every direction. Their
friends at the farmhouse wondered if any had survived; so
old Ben and a small boy went out into the storm to look for
the quail. The old man went ahead with a long swinging
stride, while the small boy trotted after him.

These two had watched over the quail family from the very
first. They had discovered the nest under the old log and
had visited it several times while the eggs were hatching.
They had fished the three water-soaked chicks out of the
puddle after the rainstorm which filled the little hollow where
the brood was sleeping that night with their mother. They
had also happened upon the remains of the old raccoon's
supper, scattered about near that circle of footprints. The
evil doings of Red Fox they had likewise discovered while
repairing the brush fence. They had also seen the quail many
times in neighboring grain fields and had heard their cheery
"more wet" before each rainstorm; so it was no wonder that
their hearts were heavy tonight.

The old man sprang lightly over the barway into the pasture, while the boy crawled between the bars. They went on
for fifteen or twenty rods and then crawled under a clump
of small spruce trees and sat down where the leaves were still

dry. Suddenly from their very midst came a clear shrill whistle, "bob-white, bob-white, bob-bob-white."

"They are right here in the bush, Ben," exclaimed the boy in an eager whisper.

The old man chuckled and laughed softly.

"That was my call," he whispered. "I had my hand over my mouth so you could not tell where the sound came from." Again he repeated the musical call; he and the boy waited and listened. Then, faint and far across the pasture land, like an echo, came the reply, "bob-white, bob-white, bob-bob-white."

"That's a bob-white," whispered Ben. "Now keep perfectly still and you will hear something worth while."

Presently the two watchers under the little spruce heard the well-known whir of short, fast-beating wings, and a second later Bob-White himself plumped down under the cover within two yards of them. He shook the wet from his wings, preened his feathers for a moment, and then swelling out his breast uttered his sweet call-note. The old man and the boy waited, listening as the real Bob-White sounded his roll call.

Again came the low whistle from far away in the pasture land, but this time it was only "white, white, white." Soon the swift whir of beating wings was heard, and a moment later the second quail alighted under the scrub spruce.

"Cureet, curee, cur-r, cur-r-r," cried Bob-White in soft, quail words of welcome. "Peep, pure-e-, e-e, e-e," replied the chicken. The greeting and reply were scarcely over when another quail whirred under the bush, and another, and still another.

"Cureet, cure-e-e, cur-r, cure-e-e," was the greeting of Bob-White to each newcomer as they huddled together and rejoiced in bird language that they had found one another again. After a few minutes they quieted down, and the listeners knew that the quail had formed themselves into the well-known bunch and fallen asleep; so they stole quietly away, leaving the quail dry and comfortable under the spruce. But it was only part of the family, just Bob-White and four of his chicks; the little hen and the other four had gone away in the hunter's game bag.

BOB-WHITE MEETS DISASTER

One morning in midwinter the small boy who had gone to the pasture that night with Old Ben to search for the quail awoke to find the world ice-clad and snow-bound and in the clutch of a terrible freeze. The windows were so clouded with frost that he could not see out until he had melted the frost with his breath. When he had cleared a window, he cried aloud with grief, for there upon the window sill, huddled close to the glass, was the stiff form of his Bob-White. Poor little Bob-White; he had escaped the hawk, the owl, the weasel, the fox, the raccoon, and the hunter, but the great freeze had caught him, so near and yet so far from cover.

Notes and Questions

1. What was the author's main purpose in writing this story: *(a)* to tell about the habits of Bob-White, or *(b)* to make the reader have a kindly and helpful feeling toward Bob-White by showing what a hard time he has keeping alive?

2. This story tells many interesting things about Bob-White, such as his color, how he flies, etc. Make a list of at least six such facts. Label it "Facts About Bob-White." Perhaps you can find more.

3. How does Bob-White help the farmer?

4. *(a)* How do heavy snows make it difficult for birds to keep alive? (You will have to do a little thinking to answer this question.)

   (b) If you live on a farm, what can you do to help Bob-White in winter?

5. To show that Clarence Hawkes was a careful student of Nature, tell two things he learned about Bob-White that could be discovered only by careful watching.

Perhaps you do not know that Clarence Hawkes has been blind for many years. Yet, so deeply does he love Nature and so closely has he studied it, that he has been able to write many stories of the outdoor world.

You would enjoy reading the book, *Trails to Woods and Waters*, by Hawkes. Another good bird story is "Redruff, the Story of the Don Valley Partridge," Seton (in *Wild Animals I Have Known*).

BIRD-NESTING IN WINTER

ERNEST THOMPSON SETON

Ernest Thompson Seton has for a long time been studying birds and animals, and writing about them. He is also an artist of wild life. For a number of years he lived in the backwoods of Canada and on the plains of the West. In this article he gives some very sensible advice about gathering birds' nests.

What good are old bird-nests? These are some of the uses they serve: A deer mouse seeking the safety of a bramble thicket and a warm house, will make his own nest in the deserted home of a cat-bird. A gray squirrel will roof over the open nest of a crow or hawk and so make it a castle in the air for himself. But one of the strangest uses is this: the solitary sandpiper is a bird that cannot build a tree nest for itself and yet loves to give to its eggs the safety of a high place; so it lays in the old nest of a robin, or other tree bird, and there its young are hatched. But this is only in the Far North. There are plenty of old bird-nests left for other uses and for you.

Bird-nesting in summer is wicked, cruel, and against the law. But bird-nesting in winter is good fun and harms no one if we take only the little nests that are built in forked twigs

56

or on rock ledges. For most little birds prefer to make a new nest for themselves each season.

If you get the nest of a goldfinch (floss nest), a phoebe (moss nest), a robin (mud nest), a vireo (good nest), a kingbird (rag nest), an oriole (bag nest), you have six different kinds of beautiful nests that are easily kept for the museum, and you do no harm in taking them.

NOTES AND QUESTIONS

1. Why is it cruel to collect bird nests in summer?

2. What kinds of birds usually make new nests each season?

3. Turn back to page 14, and find something there that shows how extremely foolish it is for people to destroy birds.

4. Make a list of all the materials you know that birds use to make nests. Perhaps you can give some that are not mentioned in this story.

5. Make a list of birds that nest on the ground and another list of those that nest in trees.

6. If you have any birds' nests, bring them to school and study how they are made.

7. If you have ever watched birds building nests, be ready to tell the class what you saw.

Ernest Thompson Seton's books will give you many happy hours of reading, and will tell you many interesting things. *Woodland Tales*, *Lives of the Hunted*, and *Wild Animals I Have Known* have been read by thousands of boys and girls.

STARTING A WILD-LIFE SANCTUARY

Dallas Lore Sharp

Do you recall reading about the great Albert National Park that Carl Akeley helped establish in Africa? If wild animals need protection in that vast, unsettled continent, think how badly they must need it in our land of cities and farms! Many people are today greatly alarmed because the wild life of our country is disappearing so rapidly.

Dallas Lore Sharp, a famous preacher, teacher, and writer, tells how you and I can help save wild life from destruction. He set us a good example during his life by making a seven-acre refuge for birds near his home in Massachusetts.

What is a wild-life sanctuary? What does the making of one require? Such a sanctuary ought to be, if possible, the wildest piece of land within or near the borders of your town. To make a sanctuary of it means simply that the owner will give it over to wildness and to all wild life, posting it with notices to everyone that this piece of land is free from all harm and all alarm to every wild thing.

Thus one can turn his farm into a sanctuary. There would be no more plowing and planting done on a farm that was actually turned over to wildness and all wild things. One can also turn his city house-lot into a sanctuary—by simply adding a bird-bath and seeds and a piece of suet. Of course, there would be trouble in keeping prowling cats away.

Both farm and city house-lots are excellent sanctuaries; but they are not the best kind for several reasons, chief of which is their lack of wildness. Originally, the whole land was wild and was covered with wild life, and with wild Indians besides. The Indians have been removed from us, very largely. With them have gone some of the larger animals, as well as many of the lovely smaller ones, and many plants, while the danger of complete destruction hangs like a dreadful shadow over many more.

So the sanctuary ought naturally to take the wildest, swampiest, roughest and most forsaken piece of waste land anywhere about the town. If there is one wetter, darker, more abandoned piece of country near at hand than any other, choose that for the sanctuary. If it contains hills and a stream, a pond, or a spring, as well as trees and a sunny opening, so much the better. If there happens to be any waste land about the town, then that is the best place for a wild-life sanctuary.

Such land is cheap, and many an owner will be glad to give it outright for sanctuary purposes. If the leaders of the community are led to see that a wild place for wild life is just as necessary as a cultivated park for cultivated things, then the town might make of such waste land a public sanctuary. But if there is a local bird-club or any other organization interested in the nation-wide movement for conservation of wild things, then that is the organization to take over the purchase and upkeep of the sanctuary.

Any amount of land will do, but the more the better, for wild life requires considerable room. It likes a stretch of woods so deep that it cannot see daylight on the distant side. It likes ripe seeds enough by the river for the bobolinks and redwings to flock in, and for the breeze to play in, making

running ripples all summer long. There must be room for the
fox, the skunk, the snake, and then the muskrat swimming
down the silvery surface of the pond. The sanctuary must be
big enough for all these wild things to move about.

The more varied the kinds of land in the sanctuary, the
greater is the variety of wild things that can grow and den
and build there. What a number of strange kinds of wild
life can be found in any bit of water! How many ferns and
lichens will grow on the north walls of a rocky slope! On a
single piece of swamp land as many as eight different wild
orchids may grow, and near at hand perhaps twenty-four kinds
of ferns may be found. The catbird likes a low, briery tangle
for his nest; the brown thrasher likes the higher, hardwood
sproutlands; the crow wants a tall pine; the broad-winged
hawk, a big hard-to-climb white oak. Get an old, wild-apple
tree into the sanctuary for the bluebird, the king-bird, the tree-
swallow, and the chebec. Have a bit of pasture-land for the
vesper sparrow and the meadow-lark; and for the song sparrow put a patch of wild roses in the middle of it.

In this sanctuary, so far as possible, you wish every tree to
dwell, every shrub, flower, fern, and lichen that were here in
the beginning. You want every bird and beast and reptile,
every fish and frog and crab and shellfish, worm and smallest
thing that formerly called the neighborhood his home, to find
a dwelling place here, now and always. This will be a place as
wild and natural as it originally was, into which you can slip
now and then to watch the wild things all about you.

If arbutus never grew here, do not plant it, though it may
grow in the woods not more than twenty miles away. Don't
build cages for wild animals that never belonged here. This

is not a wild-animal zoo. You don't want any stuffed "specimens" or boxes of insects and butterflies, for this is not a museum. It is a wild-life sanctuary for all wild living things which know it as their home.

You must post it with notices against hunters and all kinds of destroyers who break and pick and carry away. If you live in Massachusetts, the state Audubon Society will furnish you at small expense with excellent cloth warnings to tack up about the borders of the sanctuary. In some states the fish and game commissions will take over the land and post and police it for a time. Over the entrance, on the twin pines or upon a big overhanging limb, should be placed a sign reading, PLEASE DO NOT HARM NOR MAKE ALARM.

Within the sanctuary you will open narrow trails running crisscross to every different part and particularly interesting place and thing. And under a cover at the entrance a map of these trails may well be hung, showing not only the way they go and their names, but also the whole size and shape of the land. In addition to this map, it will be a good thing to post a list of the birds known to nest within the sanctuary; another list of the winter birds that visit it, together with those that stay the year around. So with the flowers, the shrubs and trees, the animals, and other wild forms.

Many of us do not get away from our own villages and out of our towns for any kind of vacation. We cannot go far for Nature, but Nature can be brought close to us. A small sanctuary of a few waste acres, or a few rich man's acres, within easy reach of town and village, will soon win the confidence of bird and flower and beast, and before we know it, they will all be living happily within its protecting borders.

The possession of such a place, the sharing of such a place with all wild inhabitants, would be a blessing to our village, and to us. We American people deeply need the freedom and friendliness of the open spaces, and we need to get this touch of nature in our earliest childhood. Nature, along with books and friends, should be a chief source of happiness to everyone.

NOTES AND QUESTIONS

1. In one sentence tell Dallas Sharp's purpose in writing this selection.

2. In this selection Dallas Sharp answers some important questions. Write five questions that he answers. You may begin this way: *(a) What is a wild-life sanctuary?* Be sure your questions tell the main ideas.

3. How would you know from this selection that the author was a close student of nature? You can prove it from what is said on page 60.

4. In this story are the names of a number of different animals, birds, trees, and flowers. Make a list of those that are found near where you live. Make another list of those not named by the author that would live in a sanctuary near your home.

5. Tell of some place near your home that might be made into a sanctuary, or tell of a place where wild life can now be found.

6. The author makes clear why wild life needs our help. Be ready to read lines in which he tells why wild-life sanctuaries are valuable to us.

You would enjoy reading "Wild Geese" and "The Dance of the Alder Swale" in Dallas Lore Sharp's book, *Beyond Pasture Bars*.

THE FLOWERS

ROSE FYLEMAN

The gardener works away for hours
To make the borders gay with flowers.
He plants the bulbs and sows the seeds,
He digs and hoes and rakes and weeds,
And every day has work to do
In winter and in summer too.

But in the Windy Wood I found
The bluebells thick upon the ground,
And in the sloping fields below
Thousands of yellow cowslips grow;
And yet to tend them there is none
Except the wind and rain and sun.

THE DANDELIONS

HELEN GRAY CONE

Upon a showery night and still,
  Without a sound of warning,
A trooper band surprised the hill,
  And held it in the morning.

We were not waked by bugle notes;
  No cheer our dreams invaded;
And yet, at dawn, their yellow coats
  On the green slopes paraded.

We careless folk the deed forgot,
  Till one day, idly walking,
We marked upon the selfsame spot
  A crowd of veterans talking.

They shook their trembling heads and gray
  With pride and noiseless laughter;
When, well-a-day! they blew away,
  And ne'er were heard of after!

YELLOW LILIES: THE GOLD OF RAINBOW SLOUGH

R. Bruce Horsfall

Bruce Horsfall is one of America's greatest artists of birds and animals. If you read *Nature Magazine*, you will find some of his pictures there. He has also painted many backgrounds for mounted animals, such as you read about in the story of Carl Akeley.

A small boy, his shoes tied together with their own strings and slung over one shoulder, trudged along the muddy shore of Rainbow Slough. At each step the black soil oozed up in curly ribbons between his toes, while the hard clay a few inches below made walking slippery. But this was better than the higher slope where the saw grass grew—the grass with notched edges which cut like knives. It had already left several stinging slashes on his ankles and legs below the reach of his rolled-down trousers.

It was hot mid-day in early August. The air shimmered in a misty haze; not a breath of wind stirred the surface of the pond which lay quiet in the steaming heat. The buzz of countless insects and the hum of bees and flies filled the drowsy air. The smell of decaying plants and drying mud, mingled with the odors of growing plants, freshly cut marsh grass, and water lilies, came to the boy's nostrils. But he thoroughly enjoyed every whiff as he recognized the well-known odors of Rainbow Slough.

There was the spicy odor of the pennyroyal, tansy, and other marsh flowers; the sharp sweetness in the odor of the horsemint; and the overpowering perfume of the white pond lilies just beyond his depth out there in the water. However, he was not after white lilies, nor did he pick the lovely marsh mallows as he passed along, well knowing that they would droop and wither before he could get them home. They were so beautiful where they were! Neither did he pick the spikes of cardinal flowers, brilliant against their background of black mud or green grass.

This small boy had but one purpose in mind. He was after gold—yes, yellow gold—the gold of the lotus, and his nose told him while yet a mile away that his favorite lilies were in bloom and awaiting his coming.

He would get them, a big bunch of them—yellow lilies for his mother. He was tired now, yet knew it not. He had come a long, long trail since eight that morning; fully nine miles—seven of them lonely miles beyond the last house.

Anyone might have wondered what so small a boy was doing so far from home, for he was undersized in spite of his twelve years. But he was a self-reliant lad, and he had a purpose. What mattered that it had taken so much time for the journey; there had been so many interesting things to see. At noon he had rested and drunk at a cooling and refreshing spring under an overhanging cliff where he had often been before with his older brothers. The rest of the way was strange to him; yet he had made no mistake when he left the railroad and the hills and struck out across the wide river bottom to the lily pond. He had been there before by boat and the river route; so he knew when he came to the winding slough that he had found the right place.

He took off his clothes, tied them in a bundle, then held shoes and all upon his head and waded in. Halfway across,

a sudden fright overtook him as the water weeds gripped about his legs, but only for a moment. Quickly turning on his back he kicked loose, and thus swimming above the weeds, though without the use of his hands, was soon on the other side. He then took up his march to where the lotus grew.

Soon he stopped to admire the beauty of the garden spider, whose web strung across his path. He gently frightened her so that she started swinging like a pendulum, as these spiders do when disturbed. Then he gently coaxed out of her resting place in a curled-over leaf another garden spider, very skillful in weaving wheel-shaped webs of great beauty. The wonderful webs of these two spiders he was careful not to disturb, stopping only to leave a grasshopper or other insect as a token of good-will.

At the foot of an open muddy slope he saw a round, black mass about the size of a dinner plate moving in the water's edge. Going closer, he discovered a father catfish, or bull-head, in charge of his multitude of babies. The young ones were swimming round and round while the father guarded just outside in the deeper water. The boy thought the old bull-head was the mother, and did not learn until years later that it was the father who takes charge of the eggs and the young.

While he watched, a small rock bass stole up to grab a baby catfish, and was promptly chased away by father bullhead, but at once another bass stole up from the other side, snatched one, and made his safe getaway. Thus these two pirates took turns from one side or the other until the distracted father knew not what to do.

Fascinated, the small boy watched what was going on in the water, sympathizing wholly with the catfish but power-less to help. He knew that the baby multitude had already dwindled to half its original size, and would continue to dwindle until only a thin line remained along the shore in the shallow water. So our young friend went regretfully on his way.

At the lotus bed the boy wandered delighted from flower to flower. Breathing deeply the sweet odor from each lily before plucking it, he marveled that the blossom could draw such a wealth of sweetness from the stickiest and blackest of mud. The young unopened blossoms had the finest fra-grance, and of these he picked a dozen—a fair-sized bouquet. Wrapping a cool lily pad or two about their stems, he tied the whole together with twigs of young willow. Unwillingly he then turned away from the charming spot.

Pausing a few moments later for a last glimpse at father catfish and his babies, the boy thought that the little black wriggling mass had grown smaller, even during the short

time he had spent at the lotus bed. Yet tarry he could
not, for the afternoon was now well spent.

When he arrived at the place where he had crossed the
slough, there arose the problem of how to get the heavy bunch
of lilies over the pond. He needed both hands to hold his
clothes upon his head, and the added burden of lilies would
have sunk his head too low in the water. The lilies must be
towed, yet he could not spare a hand to hold them. What was
he to do? Ah, he had it, a towing rope of braided grass—just
the thing. In a few moments he had a loop of the grass rope
about his arm; the bundle of lilies was attached to the other
end of the rope so that it floated out behind. The little fellow
was a queer-looking object as he slowly but steadily crossed
that wide lily pond. Twice he let his tired legs feel for bottom
before he reached the other side, wading out to shore.

Tied to the bank near by, there was an old flat-bottomed
boat, partly filled with water. On the seat of this boat the
boy rested while his feet were drying. By the time he had
again put on his shoes and stockings, the sun was fast going
down the hills. Already the nighthawks were beginning to
wing their way over the meadows with their hungry babies
in close pursuit; many tree swallows swung back and forth,
taking their evening dips in the waters of the lily pond.

While he was yet a long way from home, dusk settled down;
the little screech owls came out of their holes in the hollow
trees and followed beside him along the railroad track. They
kept him company with their quavering owl talk, reminding
him of his pet owl at home. Indeed, their tremulous call, like
quiet laughter, was such a touch of home to him that he
whoo-whooed and laughed in return.

The way now did not seem nearly so long, and the weight of the lotus blossoms swinging over his back by the rope of grass was almost forgotten. He could laugh though his feet were heavy and his shoulders tired, for his heart was light with the success of what he had done.

About nine that night a tired but happy boy stepped into the gleaming lamplight of his home. No need to ask where he had been, for there was but one place where those lilies grew, and the mother's eyes shone brightly as the tired little nature-lover laid the precious lilies in her lap.

NOTES AND QUESTIONS

1. Why did this boy enjoy his walk even though the way was long and hot?

2. What do you think was the most interesting thing the boy saw? Be ready to tell about it in your own words.

3. Why did the boy leave insects in the spiders' webs?

4. Bruce Horsfall has used words that help us greatly to see, hear, and feel; for example, *soil oozed*, *stinging slashes*. Make a list of eight other words or groups of words that helped you feel and see.

5. Below are twelve words and phrases. For each word find another word or words in the list that mean the same. When you have finished, you will have six pairs, like this: *drowsy—sleepy*.

dwindle	tarry	stay longer
walked steadily	deeply interested	grow smaller
distracted	fascinated	shimmered
trembled	trudged	worried

6. In two paragraphs Bruce Horsfall tells of the sights, sounds, and odors the boy experienced. Be ready to read these paragraphs.

7. Find and be ready to read lines that show how this boy loved and understood Nature.

You would enjoy reading "Cardinal Flowers" and "A Pond Lily's Guests," Patch (in *Holiday Pond*).

PLANTING THE TREE

Henry Abbey

What do we plant when we plant the tree?
We plant the ship, which will cross the sea.
We plant the mast to carry the sails;
We plant the planks to withstand the gales—
The keel, the keelson, and beam, and knee;
We plant the ship when we plant the tree.

What do we plant when we plant the tree?
We plant the houses for you and me.
We plant the rafters, the shingles, the floors;
We plant the studding, the laths, the doors,
The beams and siding, all parts that be;
We plant the house when we plant the tree.

What do we plant when we plant the tree?
A thousand things that we daily see;
We plant the spire that out-towers the crag,
We plant the staff for our country's flag,
We plant the shade, from the hot sun free;
We plant all these when we plant the tree.

SPRING PROPHECIES

PAUL HAMILTON HAYNE

Today the wind has a milder range,
And seems to hint of a secret change;
For the gossipy breezes bring to me
The delicate odor of buds to be
   In the gardens and groves of Spring.

The early grass in a sheltered nook
Unsheathes its blades near the forest brook;
In the first faint green of the elm I see
A gracious token of leaves to be
   In the gardens and groves of Spring.

The peach trees brighten the river's brink
With their dainty blossoms of white and pink,
And over the orchard there comes to me
The subtle fragrance of fruit to be
   In the gardens and groves of Spring.

The rigor of winter has passed away,
While the earth seems yearning to meet her May,
And the voice of a bird in melodious glee
Foretells the sweetness of songs to be
   In the gardens and groves of Spring.

MARCH

William Cullen Bryant

The stormy March is come at last,
  With wind, and cloud, and changing skies;
I hear the rushing of the blast
  That through the snowy valley flies.

Ah, passing few are they who speak,
  Wild, stormy month! in praise of thee;
Yet, though thy winds are loud and bleak,
  Thou art a welcome month to me.

For thou to northern lands again
  The glad and glorious sun dost bring,
And thou has joined the gentle train
  And wear'st the gentle name of Spring.

And, in thy reign of blast and storm,
  Smiles many a long, bright, sunny day,
When the changed winds are soft and warm,
  And heaven puts on the blue of May.

Thou bring'st the hope of those calm skies
  And that soft time of sunny showers
When the wide bloom, on earth that lies,
  Seems of a brighter world than ours.

A BACKWARD LOOK

IN THE selections you have just read, you have been seeing the outdoor world through the eyes of people who love it and can read its language. You have become acquainted with just a few of the thousands of pages of fascinating stories that have been written about the wild things which live on this earth with us human beings.

Think back over these stories and poems. Which was the most exciting? Did that exciting story interest you most of all, or was there some other story that was more interesting to you? What serious fact did you learn about the wild life not only of our country but of the world?

Old Boculy knew his outdoor world probably better than you know arithmetic or spelling or geography, and it is almost certain that he knew it better than you know the wild life that surrounds you. How many animals and how many birds can you name that live in your part of the country? It would be interesting for each of you to make a separate list of the animals, birds, and flowers that may be found near your home. Then compare lists and see how many different kinds have been named by the class.

Have you thought of any ways in which you can help protect the wild life in your part of the country? Have you tried to interest older people in protecting birds and wild flowers?

If you have read an interesting book on preserving outdoor life, your classmates would like to know the title. On page 449 is a list of books on outdoor life. You will gain pleasure and knowledge from reading them.

Part Two
Airways and Roadways

THE WORLD IS FULL OF ROADS
LUCY SPRAGUE MITCHELL

The world is full of roads.
Roads of stone and roads of sand
Stretching barren 'cross the land;
Roads which are covered with needles of pine;
Ice roads and snow roads which glitter and shine;
Roads of dirt and roads of grass,
And roads which climb to the mountain pass;
Roads of iron and roads of steel
Down which thunder the iron wheel;
Roads of water and roads of air—
The roads of the world are everywhere.

"THE MAIL MUST GO THROUGH"

The Mail Must Go Through!" That famous expression stands for the spirit of the men who have carried the United States Mail. No matter what the danger or hardship, nothing must stop the safe delivery of the messages that the people of our land are sending to each other. From the pony-express riders of long ago to the air-mail pilots of today the same spirit of determination has held true.

This faithfulness to duty has been the spirit of all those whose business it is to see that messages are sent or that people and things are carried from one place to another. The radio operator must stay at his key on the sinking vessel, flashing out calls for help. The captain and his crew are the last to leave the ship. The telephone operator stays at the switchboard, warning of the forest fire or the flood that is sweeping down upon the people. The railroad engineer must have a quick mind and a brave heart as he sits at the throttle of his engine.

Men have always wanted to travel speedily and to send messages swiftly from one place to another. They have invented powerful machines and delicate instruments to help them do so. But speed, alone, is not enough. There must be safety. The lives of passengers must be guarded, and the important message must go through. Always there has been this battle between speed and safety. The machines men make are not human. Skillful hands and courageous hearts must guide them.

The stories in this part of your book will tell you about some of the workers who send the messages and carry the people of the world swiftly and safely.

FROM INDIAN TRAIL TO AIR MAIL

Alice T. Paine

When the postman leaves the mail at your door, he is just one of over 350,000 people who are busy every day seeing that the mail is delivered throughout our country. The post office in your town is one of the 50,000 post offices in the United States. Over fifteen billion stamps are used every year. Let us see how this great business of message-carrying has grown since the days when our country was young.

In the early days of our country, the colonists lived in little settlements along the Atlantic coast all the way from Massachusetts to Carolina. They were separated from each other by dense forests and wide rivers. England, the land from which they had come, was far away across the Atlantic Ocean. There were no telephones or telegraphs or ocean cables or trains or highways, and of course there were no radios or airplanes.

Today, if we wish to send a message, we can have it delivered anywhere in the United States within a few hours. If any important event happens, we may know of it within a few minutes. We have sent messages to Byrd at the South Pole, and we have received messages from him over thousands of miles of ice and snow, mountains and seas.

It is hard for us to realize how different things were in the early days. When George Washington died at Mount Vernon, the news did not reach Boston for ten days. When a new president was elected, people did not hear of it for over a month. If you lived then and your father or mother or brother or sister went on a journey, you could not hear from the traveler for many a day.

But the colonists were brave, strong people. In spite of the forests and the rivers, they sent their letters back and forth and kept the news moving from Boston to Albany, from Albany to New York, from New York to Philadelphia, and so on; and from all these places the news traveled slowly but surely across the mountains to the daring pioneers in the Mississippi Valley. Many of our highways and railroads today follow these old paths of the first mail carriers.

At first the colonists sent their letters by couriers, or runners. Often these runners were Indians who knew the forest trails and could run for miles and miles without stopping. The Indian trails were the first paths of the white men, too, and the heavy boots of the settlers slowly deepened the paths that the soft moccasins of the red men had made.

The colonists had no horses at first, but as soon as they got them, the couriers went on horseback wherever they could. Sometimes the snow was too deep for any horse, and then the courier had to wear snowshoes, as he sometimes does today in the far North. We are told that one courier on snowshoes took nine days to go forty miles through snowdrifts from six to fourteen feet deep.

The colonists asked the King of England to help them start a regular mail service, but the king was too far away to care. So they slowly began to help themselves. Massachusetts, Virginia, Pennsylvania, and some of the other colonies gave to certain men the right to carry letters and to be paid for it. These men were supposed to keep the mail carefully locked, to make regular trips between certain places, to be courteous at all times, and to help travelers in any way that they could. Sometimes they took travelers with them, and we know of at least one woman, Madame Knight, who made a journey riding on horseback behind the postman as he made his way through the forests and forded deep rivers.

The places where the courier changed horses were called posts; and there was a line of these posts between Boston and New York and between New York and Philadelphia. In the far South and West, where there were not so many people, there were fewer posts and postmen.

At last the king appointed a Postmaster General for the colonies, and after several men had held the office, it came to the great Benjamin Franklin. Franklin at once set about trying to improve the mail service. He traveled over the colonies, visiting many of the posts, and he tried in every way to make the mails move quickly and safely.

Then came the Revolutionary War. The colonies broke away from the King of England and became the United States of America. Franklin, who had been the king's Postmaster General, now became the Postmaster General of the United States. The first thing he had to do was to see that George Washington could send messages to his soldiers along the battle fronts. The next thing he had to do was to see that letters could be sent back and forth among all the colonies, so that they could all work together as the new United States. He did all this so well, and he improved the mail service in so many ways that he has been called the father of the United States Post Office.

After the couriers on horseback, came the stage coaches. Some of these mail coaches must have been wonderful sights,

for they were painted green, with red wheels. On the doors were the words, "United States Mail Stage," painted in bright yellow, with a spread eagle "of a size and color to suit" over the words. But often their bright colors were covered with mud, and in many places they could not be used at all because of bad roads. Much of the mail was still carried on horseback, especially in the far South and West.

As the years passed, the American people began to follow Daniel Boone and other brave pioneers westward across the mountains. They did not stop until they came to the Pacific Ocean, and wherever they went, the United States Mail went too. Roads were built across the mountains, and fine mail coaches carried letters and travelers as far as the roads went. When the roads ended, the mail went on, sometimes by river boats and sometimes on horseback. Nothing was too difficult for Uncle Sam's mail, and many brave men gave their lives for it. They fought the Indians from the Atlantic Ocean to the Pacific Ocean. They were often hungry and cold and tired, but they carried Uncle Sam's mail.

When the steam engine was invented and the first railroad trains began to run on the steel rails, one of the first things they carried was the United States Mail. Finally, to save time, one of the coaches of the train was used for a post office on wheels, and while the train rushed through the night, mail clerks were busy sorting the mail and locking it up in big bags so that it would be all ready to throw off the train at the different towns along the railroad. In this way, the mail could go faster and more safely than ever before.

Of course it took many years to build railroads everywhere, and where the railroads ended, mail had still to be taken by stage coach and horseback. Perhaps you have read about the Pony Express, which took the mail at the end of the railroad in St. Joseph, Missouri, and carried it westward to Sacramento on the Pacific coast. By using the steam engine and the wonderful ponies and riders of the Pony Express, Uncle Sam could get his mail clear across the continent in nine days. This was quite a change from the time when it took a lonely courier on snowshoes nine days to go forty miles.

Today the railroads go all the way across the continent, and only in the far-off corners of the mountains or in Alaska does mail have to go by snowshoes or dog sleds.

Sometimes not even the bravest or cleverest man on earth can take your letters where you want them to go, because you have not written the address so that anyone can read it, or you have left off part of it. Do you know what Uncle Sam does then?   He sends it to the Dead Letter Office in Washington, D. C., where skillful people try to find out where to send it or to return it to the sender.

Another thing that Uncle Sam does for you is to protect your money in the mails, and this is the way it is done.   If you wish to send money to anyone, you go to the post office and buy a money order for the amount that you wish to send. This money order is a slip of paper that can be sent in a letter, and the person to whom it is sent can take it to the post office in his town and get the money that you sent him.   In this way no money can be lost or stolen.   Before Uncle Sam arranged this way of sending money, there were hundreds of dollars lost every year.

By means of the post office Uncle Sam also helps people to save money.   If you wish to save a little money every week, ask your postmaster about Uncle Sam's way of doing it.   He will be glad to tell you.   In fact, the post office is your closest connection with Uncle Sam in your town.   The United States flag floats over it to show that it belongs not to the town, not to the county, not to the state, but to the whole United States, and the great central post office is in Washington, D. C., the capital of our nation.   So whenever you go into your post office, you are in Uncle Sam's special property.

Uncle Sam is working all the time to improve his mail service.   Besides the railroads, with their fast-moving post offices on wheels, we have today splendid highways, along which mail is carried in motor trucks; but most wonderful of all is Uncle Sam's air mail.   You can buy a cheap little stamp at any post office, and with it you can send your letter flying through the air like a bird from one ocean to the other.   Like

the great steam engines on the railroad tracks, these engines
with wings fly through the darkness, over deserts and mountains, guided here and there by powerful search-lights. Sometimes the brave men who carry the mail fall in some lonely
spot, but their courage does not fail, and Uncle Sam's mail is
not lost if they can help it.

The United States Mail goes to all parts of the world.
Steamboats as big as hotels carry it to foreign lands. New
air-mail routes have been started between the United States
and South America. Perhaps you have read how Lindbergh
flew with the first air mail to the different countries of South
America. Probably you know that men in both Europe and
America are working toward the day when airplanes will carry
the mail regularly and safely across the broad Atlantic.

NOTES AND QUESTIONS

1. List five different ways by which mail has been carried since the early days of our country. Make your list in correct order to show the first way, the second way, etc.

In sentences 2, 3, 4, 5, and 6 tell what words belong in the blanks.

2. The slowest method of carrying mail mentioned in this selection is by *(a)* _____. The swiftest method is by *(b)* _____.

3. _____ is known as the "Father of the United States Post Office."

4. The post office helps people to _____ and to _____ money.

5. The post office is in charge of the _____.

6. Letters that the post office cannot deliver are sent to the _____.

7. What can you do to make sure that a letter will be returned to you if you have made a mistake in the address on the envelope?

8. What were some of the dangers of carrying mail by the Pony Express? What mail-carriers face danger in this age? Be prepared to discuss these questions.

9. If anyone in the class has a stamp collection, have him tell about the different kinds of United States stamps. For example, are all two-cent stamps alike? What are the differences?

10. Here are some other important services offered by the post office. Perhaps some members of the class can tell what they are. If not, look them up, and make a report.

> *(a)* Registered letters *(b)* Insured packages *(c)* Special
> delivery *(d)* Parcel post

You would enjoy reading "The Pony Express Rider," Walker (in *How They Carried the Mail);* "The Spirit of Communication," Paine, and "From a Railway Carriage," Stevenson (both in *Child-Library Readers, Book Six);* "The Telegraph," Wynne (in *For Days and Days).*

WEST WIND: THE YANKEE CLIPPER SHIP

CORNELIA MEIGS

Do you remember how Columbus's ship looked, with its high, blunt bow and stern? For hundreds of years sailing ships had been built in that way, and they were slow, clumsy, and hard to handle. Then came the Yankee clippers—the swiftest and most beautiful sailing ships ever built. They were so beloved by all sailors that they were called "The Darlings of the Sea." This author has made up an interesting story about a clipper ship.

THE SHIPMASTER AND HIS MODEL

From the time when they first went to school to learn their letters, Jonathan Adams and Humphrey Reynolds spent most of their waking hours in each other's company. They looked for birds' nests together in the woods at the edge of the broad Susquehanna River, they paddled along its marshy banks, they played interesting games in that busy, entrancing place, Jonathan's father's shipyard. Or they would stand side by side watching a great ship of war come sailing up the bay with square white sails and darkly outlined rigging, the vessel that was commanded by Captain Reynolds, Humphrey's father. The two boys talked much of what they would do when they were men; they would sit for long hours on the wharf, their legs dangling above the water, discussing the future.

"I am going into the navy like my father," Humphrey would say, "and I intend to sail in the finest and fastest ship of the

From "The Tree of Jade" in Cornelia Meigs's *The Pool of Stars*. By permission of the Macmillan Company.

whole fleet to the very ends of the world and back again. And I will have you for an officer, Jonathan."

"No," Jonathan would return seriously, "I get sick when I go to sea, and I don't like hardtack and salt pork. No, I will stay at home in my father's yards and some· day I will build a ship that is a real ship and not just tubs like these."

They parted when they were seventeen and did not meet again for years; for Humphrey went into the navy as he had planned, and Jonathan, with mallet and chisel in hand and with that sober, earnest air that always clung to him, was already at work in his father's shipyard. In time he became master of the entire business, while Humphrey was scouring the seas, sailing on just those far voyages of which he had so often dreamed.

Jonathan had his dreams also, but he did not speak of them, only toiled away at building the heavy, sturdy vessels that carried America's trade overseas early in the last century. Honest ships they were and reliable, as sure of coming to port as though they had belonged to the age of steam, but oh, how long it took them to make a voyage! When alone in his dingy little office, Jonathan, with the door fastened, would push aside the pile of plans and drawings and would get out the model of a strange vessel, sharp, slender, and graceful, with a hull like a racing yacht. He would set it upon the bench to carve a little here, to alter a curve by a hair's breadth there, or merely to stand staring at it sometimes for hours at a time, staring and thinking.

One day when he was standing, utterly lost in his thoughts, there came a knock at the door, followed quickly by a second one and a third, all during the moment that it took the ship-

master to put out of sight his beloved model. When the door was opened, there strode in a tall sunburned person in blue uniform. It was Captain Humphrey Reynolds, come at last to see his old comrade, bringing a roll of government papers under his arm.

"Congress has decided suddenly to increase the navy," the young officer explained, "and the orders are going out to build twelve ships in haste. One of the contracts is to come to you, if you will take it. They are even in such need that they have not had time to draw up full plans; so the man who builds this ship and the officer who superintends the construction can really have something to say about the design."

He looked his old friend very steadily in the eye and saw a slow smile of deep, unspoken delight dawn upon the ship-builder's face. Jonathan Adams' hard hands did not often tremble, but they shook a little now as he reached up to the shelf above the bench and brought down his model.

"I have been thinking about such a design since I was ten years old," he said, "and the chance to build it has come at last. We will make them a real ship, Humphrey, and the whole world will open its eyes when it sees you sail her."

BUILDING THE SHIP

She grew up quickly on the ways, that ship of theirs, with her bowsprit standing far out over the neighboring street, and with people stopping in the lane to watch Jonathan's whole force of workmen toiling up and down her sides. Old navy officers, some of whom had seen the ships of the Revolutionary War, and who had all fought in the War of Eighteen-Twelve, would inspect her and would shake their heads.

"Look at that sharp bow and narrow hull," one would say; "such a ship will never be seaworthy in the world. Why can't these young fellows stick to the models we have tried out for them?"

"And see the spread of sail this drawing shows," another would comment, pointing fiercely with a stubby forefinger; "why, the whole ridiculous affair will capsize in the first good puff of wind! I'm thankful I don't have to go to sea in her."

But the two comrades closed their ears and sat, often far into the night, in the cramped little office, poring over drawings and comparing designs.

"You have her thought out to the last ring, block, and halyard," Humphrey would say, "and you never even knew if you could build her. What a dreamer you are!"

"It takes dreaming to keep a man at his work," Jonathan

would answer. "How do you think I would have had the patience, all these years, to drive wooden pins into cross-timbers, or to mend the riggings of slow-going coastwise vessels if I had not been thinking of just such a ship as this, and seen her, in my mind's eye, putting to sea under full sail, to smash every sailing record that has been known?"

The day of the launching came, then the stepping of the giant masts, the completing of the rigging, and the bending of the new sails. It began to come to Humphrey's ears that sailors and wharfmen and even some naval officers were all saying that the new ship, the *West Wind*, would never stand a storm.

"They are the kind of men," Humphrey scoffed, "who would be sailing vessels like Noah's Ark, if such people as Jonathan Adams did not have the courage, sometimes, to build something new. No, the *West Wind* is going to teach all the ship-masters something they never knew before, once she clears the harbor for Gibraltar."

It is probably only a short paragraph in your history book that tells you how, a little more than a hundred years ago, the seas swarmed with pirates whose home ports were the North African cities of Algiers, Tripoli, and Tunis. The great nations of Europe and, with them, the young United States, used to buy safety from these lawless Barbary States by sending them gifts and tribute. But when, finally, the ruler of Tripoli sent word to our President that his last gift was not large enough and that more gold must be sent, the answer was a fleet of American warships that bombarded the astonished monarch's seaports.

There were many lively encounters during that little war,

many feats of daring seamanship of which history has lost sight. But for years after the struggle was over, the United States still policed the Mediterranean Sea with such thoroughness that the pirate ships that dared risk leaving port were bold and desperate indeed. It was thither that the *West Wind* was to sail, with important messages for the commodore of the Mediterranean fleet.

OFF TO PIRATE WATERS

At last the ship was ready, a rare and beautiful sight with her slim hull, her rows of guns, and her towering sails of silvery new canvas. She sailed with the early tide, at daybreak of a mid-April morning, a ghostly fairy-like thing, slipping away in the gray light and the mist of dawn. Jonathan stood on the dock to watch her go, staring fixedly after his winged dream, flying at last across the Atlantic.

"There will be tales to tell when she comes back," he said at last, "and I look for her to cut down the sailing time by three, four, five days, perhaps. She is a good ship, and she will not disappoint us."

His stout faith in his ship was matched only by Humphrey's steady confidence. Others might have said that this maiden voyage was a heart-breaking one for Humphrey and his crew. Their living-quarters were narrow, and the labor was heavy; while the handling of the new vessel was, in itself, very difficult to learn. The weather was stormy and the winds fitful, but the *West Wind* did not disappoint the two good friends who had made her. The storms lent her wings so that, at last, anxiety and discontent gave way entirely to pride in the speed that she was making. There was a certain old sailor, however, who scoffed at all claims of the ship's speed, and who even refused to believe the record that she was making from day to day.

"Twenty-three days is the best she will do," he vowed over and over again. "I will stake a year's pay on it that she can't make an hour less."

Yet, on the nineteenth day of their passage, a warm, gusty afternoon of early May, it was he who came himself to the captain, round-eyed with amazement, to report—

"There's land been sighted, sir, and I don't understand it at all. It—it looks like Gibraltar!"

So she came through the gates of the Mediterranean, a gentle breeze behind her, "sails all filled and asleep," as the seamen said, a swift slender hull under a cloud of snowy canvas. She pushed into the straits where had sailed back and forth the daring Phoenician vessels, the Roman galleys, and the high-decked ships of Venice and of Spain, but she was no lesser vessel than any one of them, for she was the first of the Yankee clipper ships!

"But that was only a trial," Humphrey kept saying, "when we were learning to handle her. On the voyage home we'll show you even more plainly what she can do."

SETTING A RECORD FOR THE RETURN VOYAGE

That voyage was now soon to be, for the vessel had been selected to carry back the commodore's messages and reports to Washington from Tripoli. On the day before she was to sail, a message came from the ruler of Tripoli that he was sending his personal agent, an Arab, to make the ship a friendly visit of farewell. Captain Reynolds sighed deeply when he heard this news, for it came from a government which pretended to be very friendly but was secretly treacherous. The stout dusky minister of state came over the side, gorgeous in his jewels and satins, inspected the ship with solemn interest, and expressed not only surprise, but some doubts when told of the time she had made between America and Gibraltar.

"Why, it cannot be done!" he cried. Not even pirate ships, it seemed, could fly on such swift wings. "There are favorable winds and chances for good luck on the eastern passage, but when your prow is turned toward home again, when you are obliged to go southward to get the trade winds which blow for all ships alike, then you will find that this is an ordinary ship, just like all the rest."

"We will equal our record or better it," Humphrey replied obstinately, "although, as I admit, the westward voyage is a longer and a more difficult one. But the *West Wind*, sir, is a ship not like other ships."

The dark visitor shrugged his shoulders, slipped one sleek hand within his satin robe, and laid a handful of gold coins upon the table.

"A gift from my ruler to you," he said.

"But what for?" Humphrey asked.

"A mere token, sent with the message that the ruler of Tripoli begs you to be a little blind, if you should see a vessel of ours in pursuit of some French or British trading vessel. You Americans are so hasty and interfere so often in matters which do not concern you."

"We drive no bargains to be paid for in stolen coin," returned Humphrey hotly. "Have you not learned once what America thinks of piracy?"

"America is far away," the minister answered dryly. "News carries thither slowly, and as slowly comes back again. It is twenty years since your country fought mine; we believe that America is ceasing to watch us. The Atlantic is a broad and windy sea."

"You do not know," the young officer replied slowly, "that there is a wise man in my country, my comrade and dear friend, who has learned how to make the Atlantic a thousand miles less broad. He built this ship with which we have shortened the voyage by four days and will, when we set sail again, lessen it by more than that. Your pirate vessels are swift, but Yankee wits are swifter, and presently your vessels will bring back a tale—for every sea-coast will ring with it— that Jonathan Adams' ship, the *West Wind,* has crossed the ocean in eighteen days."

"Eighteen days," scoffed the other, "that is past any man's belief. Ships move by sails, not wings!"

"Eighteen days," repeated Humphrey sternly. "I promise you that you will hear of our voyage made in just that time. And when other vessels are built to match or to better her, our country will come a great stride nearer to you, a thousand miles nearer to traitors, murderers, and thieves."

Humphrey brought his hand down upon the table with such force that the gold coins went rolling and tumbling to the floor, and the important-looking Arab was forced to go down on his hands and knees to pick them up. When he arose, Humphrey was standing by the door, which he held open.

The Arab departed in a great show of dignity and was rowed ashore. Then Humphrey, with a sigh of relief, turned himself to the preparations for getting under way. He had

vowed a vow within himself that Jonathan Adams should not
be disappointed, and that on the homeward voyage they would
shorten the passage by the five days for which he had hoped.

ALL RECORDS BROKEN AT LAST

In the days that followed, whatever went wrong, whatever
accident, small or great, befell the ship on her race across the
Atlantic, the wind never failed. Lines parted, tackle jammed,
and sails carried away, but still the wind held. The oldest
but ablest seaman, he who had not believed in Gibraltar when
he saw it, fell from a yard and was picked up with a broken
knee. A falling block, dropping from a height to the deck
below, crushed, as it fell, the shoulder of another sailor. But
still the wind held and still the ship cut the South-Atlantic
rollers like an arrow. Seven days, eight days, nine days—they
were halfway across, and excitement had begun to run breath-
lessly high.

At the end of the ninth day, while the *West Wind* was wallowing in a cross sea, it was discovered that the water casks
had broken loose from their lashings; that two of them were
crushed, others injured, and that the greater portion of their
precious water had leaked away.

"Then we have need to make port all the more quickly,"
Captain Reynolds said grimly, and stood by in person while,
to each man including himself, the small allowance of water
for each day was measured out.

The days passed while the men grew weaker and more
sluggish at their work, but still the breeze held and the speed
of the *West Wind* did not falter. They passed no ship from
which they could obtain water; their only hope lay in the

making of port. They turned northward, lost the trade winds, seemed for a terrible moment to be hanging becalmed, but a stiff breeze caught them and bore them still toward home. Captain Reynolds himself looked more worn and haggard than did any of his men. They were like the flitting ghosts of a ship's crew that morning when the lookout's husky call of "Land-ho" announced the low green shore of Maryland. *Eighteen days from Gibraltar and all records broken at last!*

She came into the Susquehanna River for repairs, did the worn but triumphant *West Wind*, and Jonathan Adams came rowing out to board her, his sober face for once all wreathed in smiles.

"By five days you shortened the voyage," he said, "and I had not really hoped for more than four. I always said she was not a tub, but a real ship at last. There will be others like her, and her children's children will dare to spread such sail that they will cross the Atlantic in half your time."

Jonathan Adams' ship the *West Wind* sailed on many voyages and was the model for other vessels of her class, bigger and swifter even than herself—the great race of American clippers that once ruled the seas. They gave our country the highest place in the world's shipping, and they brought her, even as Humphrey had said, a thousand miles nearer to her neighbors across the Atlantic.

NOTES AND QUESTIONS

1. Jonathan's ship was swifter than any other sailing ship. What two things about the ship made it swifter?

2. Many sailors believed that a bad storm would sink the ship. What two things about the ship made them think so?

3. Three things made it possible for Jonathan to build the ship:

(a) Something he had done

(b) Something that had happened

(c) The way a certain person felt toward him

Tell what each of these was.

4. Humphrey was sent by the Government to watch over the building of the ship. What risk did he run in allowing Jonathan to go ahead with this new kind of vessel?

5. Write the names *Jonathan* and *Humphrey* on your paper, and after each name write the words from this list that describe that person. *Adventure-loving, enthusiastic, serious-minded, daring, painstaking, honest, patient, determined, loyal, quiet.*

Some of these words may describe both men.

6. Name in order the bodies of water crossed on the voyage of the *West Wind.* Begin with the Susquehanna River. You may have to use your geography maps for this.

7. *(a)* Tell three accidents that happened on the return voyage.

(b) Which was the most serious accident? Why?

8. Below are the main points of this story, but they are not in the right order. Put them in the correct order.

The visit of the pirate messenger

The first voyage of the *West Wind*

Two boys who loved ships

The return of the *West Wind*

Jonathan and his dreams

The building of the *West Wind*

9. There are a number of words in this story that a sailor could explain better than anyone else. Make a list of ten such words.

You would find the *Picture Book of Ships,* by Gimmage, very interesting, and you would enjoy reading "The Story of the Ship," Husband (in *Child-Library Readers, Book Six*); "The Sextant," Dunn (in *Skyward Ho!,* Mathiews).

THE GLINT OF WINGS

Marie Barton

What makes a good aviator? Is it enough just to learn how to fly and to understand the machinery of airplanes? In this story you will learn what kind of person an aviator should be, and you will read of the strange way in which Clint Warren showed that he had in him the making of a good pilot.

CLINT YEARNS TO FLY

Clattering up the rock-worn trail on his wiry little pony, Clint Warren watched the sun snatching purple shadows from the hills ahead of him. Beyond their greenness rose the gray crags of a lofty mountain range. All the morning he pressed up the fence-line of his father's ranch, stopping to mend a break, to tighten a wire, to dislodge a large boulder that might crash down unexpectedly, or to call to a Mexican herder trotting after the snowy Angora goats.

His noon meal he ate under a twisted juniper tree. "It's good to be home," he told himself for the fiftieth time. Yet his restless brown eyes were lifted to the mountains. "Wish, though, I were up there; the higher the better!" An eagle circled the summit, great-winged and sure of flight. Clint's keen, eager eyes followed it to the upper air, to a mere speck, to nothing.

He sprang to his feet. "Come!" he whispered to his beast. "Let's climb, too!" He swung into the saddle and dug his heels into the pony's flanks. "The fence can wait. The top calls. I've got to go!"

After three hundred yards of climbing, the panting little beast was pulled to a sudden turn. He looked around inquiringly. "Nothing doing. Let's get on back. Dad's counting on me to help with the work on the ranch for a while!" Clint's jaw squared, and soon his determined arm was jerking a fallen fence post into place.

The sun was ready to slide over behind the highest peak when Clint's alert ear caught a far droning sound. Louder it swelled, and louder. His gaze leaped toward the oncoming roar and met the glint of wings that far outshone the eagle's in bigness and might. Proudly the great man-bird curved through the ridge of the West Range, swooped then to a steady whir as though to graze the boy's upturned head, and drove into the lower horizon, straight and swift and beautiful.

It was the nearest Clint had ever been to an airplane. He thrilled at the sight, the sound, and the power of it. His fingers tingled to get hold of the throbbing motor. Wings! That's what he wanted. Yes, wings! He, too, would fly with the sureness of an eagle, with the daring of a mail pilot!

"Dad," he said that evening as he waited to get his father's attention, "I've decided, now I have finished high school, that I'm going to be a mail pilot. An air school's what I want—not a regular college."

"Are you sure?"

The boy nodded.

"Very well, Son. You may never be a Lindbergh. But character is what counts—in flying, in ranching, or what not."

Joyfully Clint jumped to his feet. "Oh, Dad! When can I start?"

"That's the question," replied his father. "I haven't the money to help you, but I'll pay you wages just as I do the other hands on the ranch. Then it will be your job to save money for your training in aviation."

WORKING AND SAVING ON THE RANCH

Clint's summer went by on wings, wings shining with hope, wings heavy with waiting, great droning wings beckoning to him. From before sunup till past sundown he and his father would cram the hours with work. Then after supper the two would drop down on the creaky old plank steps of the ranch house, talking a little sometimes, often simply resting there, each one quietly thinking his own thoughts.

For Clint, the bright spot now in ranch life was the regular zooming of the air-mail over the mountains. How he watched for that glint of wings! "Some day," he would promise himself, "I, too, shall fly!"

Twice during the summer the people of the mountainside met for an all-day picnic and barbecue. On these occasions Clint talked freely with the younger people. Here he learned that all the boys wanted to fly, or thought they did. But Clint *knew* he wanted to fly, knew it more deeply every day.

Of course he could not earn enough money to go into training this fall. But perhaps the next fall. Or surely the year after. So he worked and saved. He subscribed for a magazine on aviation, and he read up on aircraft until he knew every detail of how an airplane is constructed and operated.

On the first of November Mr. Warren started off to town in the morning on business.

"Look out for the goats, Clint, if a rain should blow up," was his farewell warning to his son. "You know they can't stand a wet norther. I shall be gone for a day or two. If the sky isn't clear in the morning, the herders know that they are not to take the goats out till the sun shines, even if they have to wait until noon. All you've got to see to is that they're penned at night. Good-by."

Not until Clint had seen all the goats in their pens that night did he rest from his duties. After he had eaten his supper in the ranch house, he took up the newspaper which had come that morning, and drew his chair into the scant light of the kerosene lamp.

At the first headline his eyes started; his pulse quickened. "AIRPLANE MEET AT CENTERVILLE, NOVEMBER THIRD, AT TEN A. M.," he read. "WORLD FLYER COMING IN INTEREST OF NEW AVIATION SCHOOL. SCHOLARSHIP TO BE AWARDED FROM THIS DISTRICT."

Clint's heart beat faster as he read the words.

"Application for scholarship must be made in person."

The hand that held the newspaper shook with excitement. So Clint read the notice to himself again. And again.

"Applicants must be over eighteen—" And he would be eighteen tomorrow! There would be an alertness test—an endurance test; character would score high. The world pilot would cast the deciding vote.

"And I stand a chance!" the boy exclaimed to himself as he went off to his own room. His strong-muscled body, wearied with the day's work, soon relaxed in sleep. Wings! Wings! The air seemed to vibrate with the whir of wings. Great eagle wings! Even greater man-wings!

The next day Clint went gaily about his ranch duties. The sun beat down hot—too hot—as he made his way to the lower goat camp.

CLINT STAYS ON THE JOB

An hour or two later the heated air began to quiver suddenly. Clint glanced quickly toward the mountain range. He saw the sky grow dark and wrap the peaks in a thickening blanket of gray.

"The goats are headed this way by now," he said to himself. "They'll come in all right." And he went on splitting the day's supply of stove wood.

Another hour passed, when a blinding storm suddenly chilled the air with driving sleet.

With quick decision Clint flung himself into the saddle and spurred his horse up the trail. Soon he was at the side of old Andres, the herder, helping him rush the flock ahead of the storm. The pattering of those nimble feet sounded down the rocky slopes like the music of many little hammers. The noise of the goats crashing through the dry brush sounded good to the boy entrusted with their safety.

With a sigh of thankfulness he swung to the ground beside the corral gate to count the goats as they scudded to shelter. Jose's five hundred from the lower camp were already penned.

"Help me, Jose!" he directed.

The younger herder stepped opposite. "One hundred." The rapid, accurate count tallied. Then "Two." Now "Three hundred!" And "Thirty."

In swift alarm Clint looked up. His eyes searched the near-by hills. Not another goat—anywhere!

"Andres!" he called to the old herder, who came limping after the last stragglers, "where are the rest of the goats? One hundred seventy missing!"

The old man dropped his staff and threw up both hands as he replied: "Who knows where they are!" He shrugged. "Who knows!" But snatching up his staff, the herder set off in a hurried trot up the slope.

Clint raced after Andres. "Come on, Jose!" he commanded. "We've got to find those goats!" Up, up he rode into the storm, the wind furiously lashing boy and pony. Night came on, black night. And still the three searchers combed the slopes, Clint far in the lead.

Higher, higher! At last, oh joy! He spied a line of huddled white at the foot of an overhanging cliff. Closer approach brought to sight other shivering creatures here and there, in twos and threes, under leaky clumps of oak brush, bleating piteously as he came upon them.

Having found the lost animals, his next problem was what to do with them. "We can't drive them to the pens," he told his men. "But they ought to be able to reach the cedar brake down in the flat. They can't hold out here much longer. Come on. The sooner we get them started the better."

But saying and doing are two different matters; for frightened, half-chilled goats cannot be driven. It proved an all-night job to drive them from under the flimsy bushes a few at a time. By dragging them out, giving them a pull and a forward shove, by goading them on, Clint and the herders kept the goats moving down the slippery rocks toward the shelter of the great cedars. Then the rescuers would scramble back after fresh relays, even carrying the fallen animals in their arms.

South of the cedar brake, at a safe distance from the trees, Clint ordered Andres to keep a big fire blazing. Here the old herder rubbed the chilled goats back to life as Clint and the young herder brought them down. In blinding sleet this work went on for hours. And still Clint kept old Andres piling on cedar boughs, which lighted the night weirdly; he kept Jose working shoulder to shoulder with him till all but twenty goats were in.

"They're hid out somewhere," Clint concluded. "We'll have to wait till daylight to make another round. Here's hoping they've found a cave."

RESCUING A HERO OF THE AIR

Suddenly, above the bleating of the goats and the crackle of the fire and the whistling of the wind, there sounded a distant droning. Clint listened intently. With an oncoming whir the noise zoomed through the ridge of the mountain. Now the roar was whirling close overhead. Through the driving sleet a light was exploring the flat in narrowing circles. Then zip! bang! An airplane flopped to the ground not a hundred yards away, and skipped into the clearing opposite the bonfire!

Clint ran forward. The plane wobbled; its motor stopped. A tall young man hopped out and jerked off his visor.

"We're safe!" he grinned. "Thanks to your signal fire!"

"Engine trouble?" asked Clint, stepping up and laying his hand on the disabled plane.

"No, sleet. The wings got iced and stopped working. I thought I would never find a landing place. It was hard to keep from hanging on those mountain jags. Through the ice drizzle, my flare wouldn't show me where to land, but your bonfire cleared things up for me."

The pilot was examining his plane, knocking the ice off the wings to find out how great was the damage.

"Need help, do you?" asked Clint, eager to put some of his book knowledge into practice.

"I surely do," replied the pilot looking about. "What is this place—a goat camp?"

Clint explained. With a sudden dart he snatched up a kid that had toppled over on its side. Then he knelt down and quickly shifted the position of an older goat that was scorching on one shoulder and shivering on the other.

"Andres, don't let them burn up!" he warned. "Jose, drive

those goats back under the cedars and help Andres with his charges." Then he turned to his guest. "This job keeps a fellow on the jump!" he exclaimed.

"I should say so!" The pilot nodded with understanding, stretching his palms to the fire. The light of the flames revealed a strong face glowing with admiration, the admiration of one hero for another. "You have had a life-saving night of it—a whole bunch of goats and then my ship and me for good measure! A real job!"

Suddenly the stranger dived into the plane after the tool kit. Then the two of them fell to work, Clint keeping one eye on the herders and their charges, and the other on the work in hand, managing both with growing skill.

Daybreak found the plane ready for flight.

"Thanks, my boy!" exclaimed the grateful flyer, as he

buckled on his parachute pack. "You should go in for aircraft yourself."

"I have decided to do that."

The pilot looked at him keenly. "You'll make good, I'm sure. Are you coming to the air meet today?"

The eagerness went out of Clint's face, the hope out of his eyes.

"I'd figured on it, big," he admitted. "But—" with a backward gesture toward the cloud-wrapped mountains—"there's another handful of goats to gather in. And"—his jaw squared —"Dad's counting on me."

As swift sympathy leaped into the pilot's eyes, Clint blurted it all out: his longing to fly, his hope for a chance at the scholarship, his present disappointment.

"Too bad, old scout." The pilot gripped his hand, then stepped into the cockpit. "You've got it in you, all right," he called back. "It takes more nerve to stay on a job like this than to hop off to—the moon."

And he was gone.

CLINT WINS THE CHANCE TO FLY

Inspired by the pilot's words of approval, Clint turned with fresh courage to the work in hand. Old Andres and Jose should keep guard here at the campfire; his job was to find the goats that were lost.

Toward noon the sun broke through the chill air, drying it quickly. Clint, discouraged, was returning from a fruitless search when he met the twenty lost animals.

Grimly he stumbled on after the browsing goats. Presently he lifted his eyes to the sound of a plane's motor. Why, it was coming back! All the planes were returning from the air meet. Arrow-swift they held their course, zooming with a burst of sound. Two planes circled now, then climbed and hung in mid-air. A third dipped and pin-wheeled to the earth. Clint caught his breath. His friend of the morning! He ran forward.

The pilot leaned clear out of the cockpit. "Hello!" he grinned. "The air meet was great. I surely wished you could have been there."

"The world pilot, was he there?" Clint wanted to know.

"Oh, yes. It was he that pulled the vote for you!"

"Me?"

"Yes. For the scholarship." He drew out an official-looking envelope.

"But the tests," faltered Clint. "I—I don't understand."

The pilot laughed. "You passed them last night and this morning. *Emergency test, endurance, skill-of-hand,* and *stay-on-the-job qualities* and all that sort of thing." He tossed the certificate to Clint and started his engine.

In a daze Clint read the certificate. At last he began to understand. His heart pounded unbelievingly.

"You!" cried the boy, running after, "are *you* the world flyer?"

The pilot answered with a mischievous twinkle. "See you the fifteenth," he grinned. "I am going to give instruction at the air school for a few weeks." With a friendly wave of the hand he soared upward to join his fellow planes.

"The world flyer!" repeated Clint, his eyes following the fascinating glint of wings. "And I too—shall fly!"

NOTES AND QUESTIONS

1. Four different tests for this air-school scholarship are mentioned on page 110. Write the names of these four tests in one column. Then write opposite each test the best reason, from the list below, why Clint was able to pass this test. Your first answer is: *(1) Emergency test. (a) He was a quick thinker.*

(a) He was a quick thinker.
(b) He was a polite, thoughtful boy.
(c) He could work all night in bad weather.
(d) He finished every job he started.
(e) He saved his money.
(f) He was handy with tools.

2. Which was the greater test of Clint's character?
(a) Working all night in a terrific storm.
(b) Staying on the job the next day.
Give a reason for your answer.

3. (a) In which part of our country did the events of this story take place—the Middle West, Northwest, or Southwest?
(b) Give one fact to prove your answer.

4. Reread carefully the paragraphs where the following words and phrases are used to see if you know their meanings. Write them in a column, and opposite each one write its meaning. If you cannot get the meanings from the story, use the glossary or a dictionary.

(a) barbecue, p. 103; (b) a wet norther, p. 103; (c) scudded, p. 105; (d) tallied, p. 105; (e) combed the slopes, p. 105; (f) cedar brake, p. 106; (g) fresh relays, p. 106; (h) exploring the flat, p. 106; (i) mountain jags, p. 107; (j) pin-wheeled, p. 110

5. Would you feel safe in a plane piloted by Clint Warren? Be prepared to give reasons for your answer.

Two good aviation stories are "Wings of Speed," Whitfield, and "Through the Storm," Collins (in *Skyward Ho!,* Mathiews).

HOW POTTS SAVED THE NIGHT EXPRESS

Ray Stannard Baker

The men who command our ships, pilot our airplanes, and run the great locomotives that pull our trains cannot be weaklings. They must be able to think and act with quickness and courage, for the lives of others depend upon them. Many a brave deed that these men do never gets into the newspapers, because such deeds are "all in the day's work" for them.

It was past midnight when Potts came out of Galesburg, Illinois, pulling the Chicago express from Burlington. There was a full moon, making the whole country almost as bright as day; the September air was warm and sweet with the smell of the woods. Harrison, the fireman, was swinging the black door of the fire-box and shoveling in the coal. Potts, with his left hand resting carelessly on the throttle lever, leaned out of the cab window and wished that all night runs might be made in nights like this one. Under him quivered the great steel giant that he had grown to love as a friend, and behind him trailed the long, dark, voiceless train.

There were eleven cars in all, four baggage cars, three day coaches, three sleepers, and a mail car, one of the heaviest trains on the road. Packed away inside of them were two hundred fifty persons or more, bound eastward from Burlington, Omaha, Denver, and the Far West. They dozed, secure in their faith that the steady but unknown hand that guided the engine would bring them safe into Chicago.

At the blinking of the Altona semaphore Potts drew down
on the whistle lever, and the engine gave one long cheer for
the little town which it intended to pass with no other notice.
As the train slowed to schedule speed, a few straggling buildings came up suddenly into the moonlight, stood for a moment
in plain view, and then darted backward again into the darkness. Altona was passed with a clear track and a long up-grade
ahead. A mile eastward blinked a semaphore, white and safe,
and to its left, close down to the track, there were three other
lights, a large one and two small ones.

"Tramp freight," said Potts to himself, as he saw the lights
of the stranger slowly brighten. There was no need of further
reducing speed. It was a double track all the way, and the
passenger must make time. The two trains would slip by each
other with the usual shrieks of friendly greeting.

An ordinary engineer might have rested on his arm pad and left the throttle wide open; but Potts leaned suddenly farther out, peering with wrinkled face up the track. Behind the headlight of the freight he saw the dark hulks of the box cars half shrouded in smoke from the engine stack. Behind them a long chain of tank cars, filled with gasoline, naphtha, and kerosene, was dimly outlined in the moonlit distance. To the engineer they looked, as they moved, like a continuous black cylinder.

"It's a long train," he muttered.

Then, as his quick eye traveled again from the yellow headlight back to the green lantern on the far-away caboose, he saw with a sudden sinking of his heart that the train was much too long. He knew that somewhere in the middle a coupling had broken, and the front end of the train with the engine was roaring down the grade with the rear end pursuing it. Sooner or later, unless the freight crew manned the brakes, there must be a terrible collision.

In the face of sudden danger an engineer's first impulse is to stop his train. Potts sprang back to his place. He jammed the throttle forward and drew back the quivering reverse lever. Then his hand closed on the brass handle that controlled the air brake. There was a deafening hissing and crackling, and the needle on the air-pressure indicator dropped from 70 to 65 to 60 pounds in two seconds. The wheels underneath whipped up a fountain of sparks, and the sleepers in their berths turned and grumbled at being disturbed.

Most difficult to believe, all these events had taken place within the bounds of a long breath. Now there were three biting shrieks of the whistle—Potts's cry of warning to the

freight engineer that his train was broken. Harrison, the fireman, who well knew the meaning of the signal, sprang to his
window on the left. His hair blew loose in the back draft.

"The break is among the tanks," he shouted, as he saw
the approaching freight.

The cab was dark except for the shaded light at the indicator, but Harrison saw the engineer nod grimly, and again
the three warning whistles cut the night air. He must do his
best to warn the crew of the freight. But the tank train continued to advance. Its engineer either failed to hear the signal
or else its fearful meaning did not impress him. He would
have known well enough, had he stopped to think, that a
collision meant an explosion such as would put to shame a
powder mill.

Suddenly Harrison drew in his head.

"She's slowing up to take water," he said sharply.

For a moment Potts was undecided. In a few seconds'
time he would be opposite the broken freight. The stopping
of its detached front end would hasten the collision. His
train had only partly slacked its terrific speed, although the
air indicator trembled at 55. If he waited to stop and back,
and there was a collision, what would become of his train?
He already saw in a flash of imagination the fiery burst of
the explosion, the heaps of crushed cars, tangled and twisted
with burning oil spluttering over them; and he heard the
agonized cries of the passengers pinned to their death under
the wrecked sleeping cars.

But in a moment excitement of the discovery passed. Potts
stood six feet one in his stockings, and he weighed two hundred twenty pounds. There was nerve in every inch of him.

Besides, he knew the huge, black, breathing machine under him, and he had confidence in her. He shut off the air brake.

"Coal her up," he shouted to Harrison.

"But you can't run by—there isn't time—"

"Coal her up," roared the voice again, and the engineer's huge height loomed up on his seat at the right of the cab. His hair was loose, and his face was smutty. He knew the risk of the attempt to drive his train past the danger point. He knew it might cost him his life, and he had a wife and baby at home in Burlington; but his hand never wavered.

Open came the throttle, the whistle screeched, and the engine leaped forward as if it fully appreciated the need of effort. Again the sleepers in the Pullman cars grumbled at being shaken up.

Harrison, the fireman, bent steadily from tender to fire pit, and each time he bent, the flames glowed more fiercely. All this happened within the space of a dozen seconds. At such a time an engineer must act as quickly as he thinks. The loss of one second may cost a hundred lives.

The head of the freight appeared alongside. Potts caught a glimpse of its engineer leaning lazily out of his window, unconscious of impending disaster. The detached end of the freight, as Potts saw it now, was well down the grade, rushing straight for the front end at terrific speed. The roar and jar of its wheels could be heard above the sound of his own train. Fifty thousand gallons of inflammable oil soon to collide with another fifty thousand gallons—and then!

Potts put on sand. The engine started forward more swiftly, its wheels biting the track with a firmer grip at every second of their progress. The throttle was now wide open. From the stack belched a fierce fountain of sparks, and the bell jangled continuously.

"She'll do it; she'll do it; she'll do it," said Potts to the beating rhythm of the piston rod.

The engineer knew the creature he was driving. He heard her pant with the exertion, he saw the flames belching from her nostrils, he heard her clamoring hoofs, he heard the "squeak, squeak" of a spot where the harness was wearing. The first half of the freight had now beaten past; there was the long flash of the open space soon to be filled with the wreck, and then tank cars again, the tank cars of the flying end of the train. Then a streak of green light, and Potts knew that his engine was clear of the caboose. But would he pull past far enough to save the last sleeper?

All this time the passengers slept quietly. The conductor was lounging in the baggage car, and the brakeman was joking with the newsboy. No one knew of the danger save the two quiet, stern men in the engine cab. And in the seconds which elapsed after Potts first scented danger, they lived a year.

Without warning there followed a terrific crash. The freight train came together, and far in the air a great splash of fire glowed bright against the black sky. Halfway down, as the exploded tank car fell, hissing with flame, it met another and another. The explosions shook the earth, blew great holes in the road bed, tore away the sanded rails over which the passenger had just thundered, hurled the sleepers from their berths, jarred out the lights, and swayed the fifty-ton Pullmans as if they had been cardboard playhouses.

Potts, dripping with perspiration, sank weakly to his seat. The train had come to a standstill. The engine breathed as if

exhausted with its race. The conductor came up on the run, white of face, and held up his lantern.

"It was a narrow escape," he said.

Potts, the engineer, smiled in his face. He laid his hand caressingly on the huge black side of the engine as though he feared it had been strained.

"We're behind two minutes, now," he said calmly, as if being on time was the most important thing in the world.

A mile back the tank train was going up, car after car, like a bunch of giant firecrackers. The oil was blazing on the houses of the town, and the panic-stricken engineer of the freight train was escaping up the track with his detached engine and a few of the box cars. In all, thirteen tanks of oil were exploded, two buildings were burned, and a man was killed. But the Chicago express was saved.

NOTES AND QUESTIONS

1. Engineer Potts had two duties to perform when he discovered the broken freight train. *(a)* What were they? *(b)* Which was the more important?

2. Potts had to decide which of two ways he would take to carry out his most important duty. What were the two ways?

3. Which word or phrase at the end of each sentence makes the correct ending?

    (a) Potts discovered the danger because he was   *brave honest alert.*

    (b) He saved his train because he   *understood engines was courageous could think quickly and correctly.*

4. *(a)* Why was the rear end of the freight moving so rapidly?

    (b) Just what did the engineer of the freight do that made a collision certain?

    (c) If he had known his train was broken, what might he have done to save a collision? (You will have to think a little to answer this question.)

5. To see whether you know some facts about railroading, tell what words belong where the letters *(a)*, *(b)*, *(c)*, etc., are below.

An engineer can signal and warn by means of the ....*(a)*........ and the ....*(b)*......... Another kind of signal along a track is called a ....*(c)*......... The steam in a locomotive is controlled by a lever called a ....*(d)*......... The power that works the brakes is ....*(e)*......... To keep the wheels from slipping when power is applied suddenly, ...*(f)*........ is put on the rails. In order to make steam there must be ....*(g)*........ and ....*(h)*.........

You would enjoy the book, *Historic Railroads,* by Holland, and the story "How Buckley Saved the Flyer," by Spearman (in *Child-Library Readers, Book Six*).

A BACKWARD LOOK

THE STORY of how men have planned and worked to find ways of traveling and sending messages swiftly and safely is a long one. It began centuries ago when the swiftest runner of the tribe was chosen to carry a message; when some daring person made the first boat by sitting astride a log and using a branch for a paddle; when some savage inventor found that he could take a round, flat piece of wood, bore a hole in the middle, put a stick through the hole for an axle, and thus make a wheel which would move things much more easily.

The driver of the slow-moving wagon train has given way to the engineer at the throttle of his iron horse and the air pilot in the cockpit of his plane. Where Indians waved blanket signals from hill tops and sent puffs of smoke signals into the air, telegraph wires now sing in the wind, and the radio sends its swift, unseen message.

What you have read in this part of your book has given you just a few little pictures from the great story of how men have learned to travel and send messages swiftly and safely. You have seen that daring men are needed for this work—men who, like Jonathan Adams and Humphrey Reynolds, have dared to risk failure and being made fun of; men who have dared to try out these new ways, often at the risk of their lives. Alert, clear-headed men are needed, because speed often means danger, and important decisions must be made in the flash of an eye.

If you want to read more of this great story of travel and communication, you will find on page 449 a list of books that will tell you many interesting things.

Part Three
Stories That Never Grow Old

MY BOOK TREASURES

NANCY BYRD TURNER

A book is like a magic box—
  Brimful of lovely treasures;
One quaint, old-fashioned key unlocks
  Good gifts in generous measure:
Gay songs, and words like jewels old,
  Tales carved from ancient times,
And shining legends set in gold,
  And chains of silver rhymes.

STORIES DO MANY THINGS FOR US

Stories do many different things for us: They make us laugh heartily; they bring real tears to our eyes. They take us through exciting adventures that thrill us almost as much as if we ourselves were having a part in them. They teach us valuable lessons, because they show us just how people have acted and thought, and what happened to them because of their actions.

Story-tellers—authors, as we call them—have two great gifts: Their eyes are quick to see, and their minds are keen to understand what they see. Then, they have the power to write about the things they see in such a way as to make them live for us on the printed page.

Now, certain authors have written so well that their stories have lived for long, long years and have been read by millions of people. Isn't it strange that we should enjoy tales that were written fifty, one hundred, even a thousand years ago by men who never dreamed of our world of automobiles, radios, and airplanes?

You have probably already read some of these stories that never grow old. Do you remember King Midas, whose touch turned everything to gold; the dwarf, Rumplestiltskin, who spun straw into fine gold for the princess; and little August, who so deeply loved the beautiful stove, Hirschvogel?

You will now read three more of these famous tales that everyone should know. See if you can tell why people for so many years have loved to read them.

PANDORA'S BOX

Nathaniel Hawthorne

You are now going to read a story that began over two thousand years ago in the times of ancient Greece. It explains why there are troubles on earth. Troubles, the Greeks believed, were sent among men and women by Zeus, father of the gods, as a punishment for stealing fire from Heaven.

Nathaniel Hawthorne, the author, was one of America's great story-tellers. Often he would take some old, old tale that had been known for hundreds of years and retell it in his own way for the boys and girls of his time.

PANDORA AND THE GREAT BOX

Long, long ago, when this old world was in its infancy, there was a child named Epimetheus who never had either father or mother. In order that he might not be lonely, another child, fatherless and motherless like himself, was sent from a far country to be his playfellow. Her name was Pandora.

The first thing that Pandora saw when she entered the cottage where Epimetheus dwelt was a great box. And almost the first question which she put to him, after crossing the threshold, was this:

"Epimetheus, what have you in that box?"

"My dear little Pandora," answered Epimetheus, "that is a secret, and you must be kind enough not to ask any questions about it. The box was left here to be kept safely, and I do not myself know what it contains."

"But who gave it to you?" asked Pandora. "And where did it come from?"

"That is a secret, too," replied Epimetheus.

"How provoking!" exclaimed Pandora, pouting her lip. "I wish the great ugly box were out of the way!"

"O come, don't think of it any more," cried Epimetheus. "Let us run out of doors, and play with the other children."

It is thousands of years since Epimetheus and Pandora were alive. Then, everybody was a child. Children needed no fathers and mothers to take care of them; because there was no danger or trouble of any kind, and there were no clothes to be mended, and there were always plenty of things to eat and to drink.

Whenever a child wanted his dinner, he found it growing on a tree; and if he looked at the tree in the morning, he could see the blossom of that night's supper; or at eventide he saw the tender bud of tomorrow's breakfast. It was a very pleasant life indeed. No labor to be done, no lessons to be studied; nothing but sports and dances and sweet voices of children talking or singing.

What was most wonderful of all, the children never quarreled among themselves; neither had they any crying fits; nor, since time first began, had a single one of them ever gone into a corner and sulked. Oh, what a good time was that to be alive in! The truth is, those ugly little winged monsters called Troubles, which are now almost as numerous as mosquitoes, had never yet been seen on the earth. Perhaps the very greatest uneasiness which a child had ever felt was Pandora's vexation at not being able to discover the secret of the mysterious box.

"Whence can the box have come?" Pandora continually kept saying to herself and to Epimetheus. "And what on earth can be inside of it?"

"Always talking about this box!" said Epimetheus at last, for he had grown tired of the subject. "I wish, dear Pandora, you would try to talk of something else. Come, let us go and gather some ripe figs, and eat them under the trees for our supper. And I know a vine that has the sweetest and juiciest grapes you ever tasted."

"Always talking about grapes and figs!" cried Pandora, pettishly.

"Well, then," said Epimetheus, who was a very good-tempered child, "let us run out and have a merry time with our playmates."

"I am tired of merry times, and don't care if I never have any more!" answered pettish little Pandora. "And, besides,

I never do have any. This ugly box! I am so taken up with thinking about it all the time. I insist upon your telling me what is inside of it."

"As I have already said fifty times over, I do not know!" replied Epimetheus, getting a little vexed himself. "How, then, can I tell you what is inside?"

"You might open it," said Pandora, "and then we could see for ourselves."

"Pandora, what are you thinking of?" exclaimed Epimetheus.

His face showed so much horror at the idea of looking into a box which had been given to him on his promise never to open it, that Pandora thought it best not to suggest it any more. Still, she could not help thinking and talking about the box.

"At least," said she, "you can tell me how it came here."

"It was left at the door," replied Epimetheus, "just before you came, by a person who looked very smiling and who could hardly keep from laughing as he put it down. He was dressed in an odd kind of cloak, and had on a cap that seemed to be made partly of feathers, so that it looked almost as if it had wings."

"What sort of staff had he?" asked Pandora.

"Oh, the most curious staff you ever saw!" cried Epimetheus. "It was like two serpents twisting around a stick, and was carved so naturally that I at first thought the serpents were alive."

"I know him," said Pandora thoughtfully. "Nobody else has such a staff. It was Quicksilver, and he brought me here as well as the box. No doubt he intended it for me;

and most probably it contains pretty dresses for me to wear, or something very nice for us both to eat!"

"Perhaps so," answered Epimetheus, turning away. "But until Quicksilver comes back and tells us so, we have neither of us any right to lift the lid of the box."

"What a dull boy he is!" muttered Pandora, as Epimetheus left the cottage.

THE KNOT OF GOLDEN CORD

For the first time since her arrival, Epimetheus had gone out without asking Pandora to accompany him. He went to gather figs and grapes for himself, or to seek whatever amusement he could find with other children. He was tired to death of hearing about the box, and heartily wished that Quicksilver had left it at some other child's door where Pandora would never have set eyes on it.

How she did babble about this one thing! The box, the box, and nothing but the box! It was really hard that poor Epimetheus should have a box in his ears from morning till night; especially as the little people of the earth in those happy days knew not how to deal with troubles. Thus a small trouble made as much disturbance then as a far bigger one would in our own times.

After Epimetheus was gone, Pandora stood gazing at the box. She had called it ugly over a hundred times; but in spite of all that she had said against it, it was a very handsome article of furniture. It was made of a beautiful kind of wood with dark and rich veins spreading over its surface, which was so highly polished that little Pandora could see her face in it.

The edges and corners of the box were carved with most wonderful skill. Around the edges there were figures of graceful men and women, and the prettiest children ever seen. But here and there, Pandora once or twice thought that she saw a face not so lovely, or something or other which stole the beauty out of all the rest. Nevertheless, on looking more closely and touching the spot with her finger, she could discover nothing of the kind. Some face that was really beautiful had been made to look ugly by her catching a sideways glimpse at it.

The most beautiful face of all was carved in the center of the lid. There was nothing else except the dark, smooth richness of the polished wood, and this one face in the center with a garland of flowers about its brow. Pandora had looked at this face a great many times and imagined that the mouth could smile if it liked, or be grave when it chose, the same as any living mouth. The features, indeed, all wore a very lively and rather mischievous expression.

Had this mouth spoken, it would probably have said something like this:

"Do not be afraid, Pandora! What harm can there be in opening the box? Never mind that poor, simple Epimetheus! You are wiser than he, and have ten times as much spirit. Open the box, and see if you do not find something very pretty!"

The box, I had almost forgotten to say, was fastened not by a lock but by a very fine knot of gold cord. There appeared to be no end to this knot, and no beginning. Never was a knot so cunningly twisted with so many ins and outs. And yet, by the very difficulty that there was in it, Pandora was the more tempted to examine the knot, and just see how it was made. Two or three times already she had stooped over the box and taken the knot between her thumb and forefinger, but without trying to undo it.

"I really believe," said she to herself, "that I begin to see how it was done. Nay, perhaps I could tie it up again after undoing it. Even Epimetheus would not blame me for that. I need not open the box, and should not, of course, without that foolish boy's consent, even if the knot were untied."

It might have been better for Pandora if she had had a little work to do so as not to be so constantly thinking of this one subject. But children led so easy a life before any Troubles came into the world that they had a great deal too much leisure. They could not be forever playing at hide-and-seek among the flower-shrubs, or at blind-man's buff with garlands over their eyes, or at whatever other games had been found out while Mother Earth was in her babyhood.

When life is all sport, toil is the real play. There was nothing to do. A little sweeping and dusting about the cottage, I suppose, and the gathering of fresh flowers and arranging them in vases—and poor little Pandora's day's work was over. And then, for the rest of the day, there was always the box!

After all, I am not quite sure that the fascinating box was not a blessing to Pandora in its way. It supplied her with so many ideas to think of, and to talk about, whenever she had anybody who would listen to her! When she was in good humor, she could admire the bright polish of its sides

and the rich border of beautiful faces that ran all around it.
Or, if she happened to be ill-tempered, she could give it an
angry push, or kick it with her naughty little foot. And
many a kick did the mischievous box receive, you may be
sure! But certain it is if it had not been for the box, little
Pandora would not have known half so well how to spend
her time as she now did.

GUESSING WHAT WAS IN THE BOX

For it was really an endless employment to guess what was
inside. What could it be, indeed? Just imagine, my little
hearers, how busy your wits would be if there were a great
box in the house, which you might suppose contained something new and pretty for your Christmas or New Year's
gifts. Do you think that you should be less curious than
Pandora? If you were left alone with the box, might you not

feel a little tempted to lift the lid? But you would not do
it. Oh, fie! No, no! Only, if you thought there were toys
in it, it would be so very hard to let slip an opportunity of
taking just one peep!

I know not whether Pandora expected any toys; for none
had yet begun to be made, probably, in those days, when the
world itself was one great plaything for the children that
dwelt upon it. But Pandora was certain that there *was* something very beautiful and valuable in the box, and therefore
she felt just as anxious to take a peep as any little girl would
have felt.

On this particular day, however, her curiosity grew so
much greater than it usually was that at last she approached
the box. She was more than half determined to open it,
if she could. Ah, naughty Pandora!

First, however, she tried to lift it. It was heavy; much
too heavy for the slender strength of a child like Pandora.
She raised one end of the box a few inches from the floor,
and let it fall again with a loud thump. A moment afterwards she almost thought that she heard something stir inside
the box.

She listened as closely as possible. There did seem to
be a kind of stifled murmur within! Or was it merely the
singing in Pandora's ears? Or could it be the beating of her
heart? The child could not be sure herself whether she had
heard anything or not. But, at all events, her curiosity was
stronger than ever.

Her eyes fell upon the knot of gold cord!

"It must have been a clever person who tied this knot,"
said Pandora to herself. "But I think I could untie it,

nevertheless. I believe I will at least try to find the two ends of the cord."

So she took the golden knot in her fingers and looked into it as sharply as she could. Almost without quite knowing what she was about, she was soon busily trying to undo it. Meanwhile, the bright sunshine came through the open window; as did also the merry voices of the children, playing at a distance, and perhaps the voice of Epimetheus among them.

Pandora stopped to listen. What a beautiful day it was! Would it not be wiser if she were to let the troublesome knot alone and think no more about the box, but run and join her little playfellows and be happy?

All this time, however, her fingers were busy with the knot; and happening to glance at the face on the lid of the enchanted box, she seemed to see it slyly grinning at her.

"That face looks very mischievous," thought Pandora. "I wonder whether it smiles because I am doing wrong! I have a great notion to run away!"

But just then, by the merest accident, she gave the knot a kind of twist; the gold cord untwined itself as if by magic, and left the box without a fastening.

"This is the strangest thing I ever knew!" said Pandora. "What will Epimetheus say? And how can I possibly tie it up again?"

She made one or two attempts to tie the knot, but soon found it quite beyond her skill. It had untied itself so suddenly that she could not in the least remember how the strings had been doubled into one another; and when she tried to recollect the shape and appearance of the knot, it seemed to have gone entirely out of her mind. Nothing was to be done, therefore, but to let the box remain as it was until Epimetheus should come in.

"But," said Pandora, "when he finds the knot untied, he will know that I have done it. How shall I make him believe that I have not looked into the box?"

And then the thought came into her naughty little heart, that since she would be suspected of having looked into the box, she might just as well do so at once. The enchanted face on the lid of the box looked at her bewitchingly, and she seemed to hear, more distinctly than before, the murmur of small voices within. She could not tell whether it was fancy or not; but there was quite a little tumult of whispers in her ear—or else it was her curiosity that whispered: "Let us out, dear Pandora—pray let us out! We will be such nice, pretty play-fellows for you! Only let us out!"

"What can it be?" thought Pandora. "Is there something alive in the box? Well!—yes!—I will take just one peep! Only one peep, and then the lid shall be shut down as safely as ever! There cannot possibly be any harm in just one little peep!"

HOW TROUBLES CAME INTO THE WORLD

But it is now time for us to see what Epimetheus was doing. This was the first time since his playmate had come that he had tried to enjoy any pleasure in which she did not take part. But nothing went right, nor was he nearly so happy as on other days. He could not find a sweet grape or a ripe fig; or, if ripe at all, they were overripe, and so sweet as to be distasteful. There was no gladness in his heart; he grew so uneasy and discontented that the other children could not imagine what was the matter with him. Neither did he himself know what ailed him, any better than they did.

For at the time we are speaking of, it was everybody's nature and habit to be happy. The world had not yet learned to be unhappy. Not a single soul or body, since these children were first sent to enjoy themselves on the beautiful earth, had ever been sick or out-of-sorts.

At length, discovering that somehow or other he put a stop to all the play, Epimetheus thought it best to go back to Pandora. But, with a hope of giving her pleasure, he gathered some flowers and made them into a wreath which he meant to put upon her head. The flowers were very lovely —roses and lilies and orange-blossoms, and a great many more, which left a trail of fragrance behind as Epimetheus carried them along; and the wreath was put together with as much skill as could be expected of a boy.

And here I must mention that a great black cloud had been gathering in the sky for some time past, although it had not yet overspread the sun. But, just as Epimetheus reached the cottage-door, this cloud began to cut off the sunshine, and thus to make a sudden darkness.

He entered softly; for he meant, if possible, to steal behind Pandora and fling a wreath of flowers over her head before she knew that he was there. But, as it happened, there was no need of his treading so very lightly. He might have trod as heavily as he pleased, as heavily as a grown man—as heavily as an elephant—without Pandora's hearing his footsteps. She was too interested in what she was doing. At the

very moment of his entering the cottage, the naughty child had put her hand to the lid, and was on the point of opening the mysterious box, when Epimetheus saw her.

But Epimetheus himself, although he said very little about it, had his own share of curiosity to know what was inside. Seeing that Pandora intended to find out the secret, he determined that his playfellow should not be the only wise person in the cottage. And if there were anything pretty or valuable in the box, he meant to take half of it to himself.

As Pandora raised the lid, the cottage grew very dark; for the black cloud had now swept quite over the sun and seemed to have buried it alive. There had, for a little while past, been a low growling and muttering which all at once broke into a heavy peal of thunder. But Pandora, unmindful of all this, lifted the lid nearly upright and looked inside. It seemed as if a sudden swarm of winged creatures brushed past her, taking flight out of the box, while at the same instant she heard Epimetheus calling as if in pain.

"Oh, I am stung!" he cried. "I am stung! Naughty Pandora! why have you opened this wicked box?"

Pandora let fall the lid, and, starting up, looked about her to see what had happened to Epimetheus. The thundercloud had so darkened the room that she could not very clearly see what was in it. But she heard a disagreeable buzzing, as if a great many huge flies, or giant mosquitoes, were darting about. And as her eyes grew more accustomed to the imperfect light, she saw a crowd of ugly little shapes, with bats' wings, looking very spiteful, and armed with terribly long stings in their tails. It was one of these that had stung Epimetheus. Nor was it a great while before Pandora herself began to scream in no less pain than her playfellow. An ugly little monster had settled on her forehead, and would have stung her if Epimetheus had not run and brushed it away.

Now, if you wish to know what these ugly things were which had made their escape out of the box, I must tell you that they were the whole family of earthly Troubles. There were a great many kinds of Cares; there were more than a hundred fifty Sorrows; there were Diseases, in a vast number of miserable and painful shapes; there were more kinds of Naughtiness than it would be of any use for us to talk about.

In short, everything that has since troubled our souls and bodies had been shut up in the mysterious box and given to Epimetheus and Pandora to be kept safely, in order that the happy children of the world might never be harmed by them. But by Pandora's lifting the lid of that miserable box, and by the fault of Epimetheus, too, in not preventing her, these Troubles have gained a foothold among us, and do not seem likely to be driven away in a hurry.

For it was impossible, as you will easily guess, that the two children should keep the ugly swarm in their own little cottage. The first thing that they did was to fling open the doors and windows in hope of getting rid of them. Sure enough, away flew the winged Troubles all abroad to torment the small people, everywhere.

And what was very strange, all the flowers and dewy blossoms on earth, not one of which had before faded, now began to droop and shed their leaves, after a day or two. The children who before seemed always young now day by day grew older and came to be men and women by-and-by.

WHAT HOPE DOES FOR US

Meanwhile the naughty Pandora and hardly less naughty Epimetheus remained in their cottage. Both of them had been grievously stung, and were in a good deal of pain, which seemed the more unbearable to them because it was the very first pain that had ever been felt since the world began. Besides this, they were in very bad humor, both with themselves and with one another. Epimetheus sat down sullenly in a corner with his back toward Pandora, while Pandora flung herself upon the floor and rested her head on the fatal box. She was sobbing as if her heart would break.

Suddenly there was a gentle tap on the inside of the lid.

"What can that be?" cried Pandora, lifting her head.

But either Epimetheus had not heard the tap, or was too

much upset to notice it. At any rate, he made no answer. "You are very unkind," said Pandora, sobbing again, "not to speak to me!"

Again the tap! It sounded like the tiny knuckles of a fairy's hand, knocking playfully on the inside of the box.

"Who are you?" asked Pandora. "Who are you, inside of this naughty box?"

A sweet little voice spoke from within: "Only lift the lid, and you shall see."

"No, no," answered Pandora, again beginning to sob, "I have had enough of lifting the lid! You are inside of the box, naughty creature, and there you shall stay!"

"Ah," said the sweet little voice again, "you had much better let me out. I am not like those naughty creatures that have stings in their tails. Come, come, my pretty Pandora! I am sure you will let me out!"

And, indeed, there was a kind of cheerful witchery in the tone that made it almost impossible to refuse anything which this little voice asked. Pandora's heart had grown lighter at every word that came from within the box. Epimetheus, too, though still in the corner, had turned half round and seemed to be in rather better spirits than before.

"My dear Epimetheus," cried Pandora, "have you heard this little voice?"

"Yes, to be sure I have," he answered. "And what of it?"

"Shall I lift the lid again?" asked Pandora.

"Just as you please," said Epimetheus. "You have done so much mischief already that perhaps you may as well do a little more. One other Trouble can make no very great difference."

"You might speak a little more kindly!" murmured Pandora, wiping her eyes.

"Ah, naughty boy!" cried the little voice within the box, in a laughing tone. "He knows he wants to see me. Come, my dear Pandora, lift up the lid. I am in a great hurry to comfort you."

"Epimetheus," exclaimed Pandora, "no matter what happens, I will open the box!"

"And, as the lid seems very heavy," cried Epimetheus, running across the room, "I will help you!"

So the two children again lifted the lid. Out flew a sunny and smiling little person, and hovered about the room, throwing a light wherever she went. She flew to Epimetheus and laid the lightest touch of her finger on the spot where the Trouble had stung him, and immediately the pain was gone. Then she kissed Pandora on the forehead, and her hurt was also cured.

After performing these good deeds, the bright stranger fluttered over the children's heads, and looked so sweetly at them that they both began to think it not so very much wrong to have opened the box, since otherwise their cheery guest must have been kept a prisoner among those naughty imps with stings in their tails.

"Pray, who are you, beautiful creature?" inquired Pandora.

"I am to be called Hope!" answered the sunshiny figure. "And because I am such a cheery little body, I was packed into the box to make up for that swarm of ugly Troubles which was to be let loose."

"Your wings are colored like the rainbow!" exclaimed Pandora. "How very beautiful!"

"And will you stay with us," asked Epimetheus, "for ever and ever?"

"As long as you need me," said Hope, with her pleasant smile, "and that will be as long as you live in the world. I promise never to leave you. There may be times now and then when you will think that I have vanished. But again, and again, and again, when perhaps you least dream of my being with you, you shall see the glimmer of my wings on the ceiling of your cottage."

Notes and Questions

1. Make up another title for this story that will tell what it is about.

2. Give at least one reason for believing that Nathaniel Hawthorne wrote this story especially for boys and girls rather than for "grown-ups."

3. In this story Hawthorne teaches some important lessons. Mention three such lessons. Give your answers in this way: *(1) We enjoy ourselves better when we have work as well as play.* Now give three others. Perhaps you can find more.

4. Select the correct ending for this sentence: Pandora called Epimetheus "stupid" and "foolish" because—

    (a) she really thought he was.

    (b) he was not kind to her.

    (c) she was angry with him.

5. What two things about the box kept drawing Pandora's attention to it?

6. What did Hawthorne do to make the reader feel that something terrible would happen when the box was opened?

7. *(a)* Name four Troubles that came from the box.

    (b) What was sent with Troubles? Why?

8. If Pandora had been able to tie the knot again, would she have done so and left the box unopened? Be ready to discuss this.

9. If she had found some nice things in the box, would she have taken just "one little peep"? Be ready to discuss this.

10. On page 125 find lines in which Hawthorne seems to be "poking fun" at children.

11. Find on page 130 a paragraph in which Hawthorne seems to be joking.

12. Hawthorne loved to tell stories to children. Do you feel as if he were talking to you in this story? What makes you feel that way? Perhaps something on page 130 gives you that feeling. If you think so, be ready to read the lines.

13. Quicksilver brought the box. Do you know who he was? If not, try to find out.

Other "stories that never grow old" are "Old Pipes and the Dryad," Stockton (in *Child-Library Readers, Book Six*); and "The Pygmies," Hawthorne, "The Clocks of Rondaine," Stockton, "The Giant Who Played Jackstraws," Jordan (all in *Child-Library Readers, Book Five*).

THE KING OF THE GOLDEN RIVER; OR, THE BLACK BROTHERS

John Ruskin

John Ruskin, the author of this story, was one of England's greatest writers and thinkers. He spent many years of his life and a great part of his wealth in helping poor people to have better homes and to live happier lives. Ruskin at one time said that being kind and true, helping needy or distressed people, and enjoying the beautiful things of the outdoor world were the only true riches.

Keep in mind what Ruskin said as you read this story of the strange adventures that happened to the three brothers—Schwartz, Hans, and Gluck.

CHAPTER ONE

A STRANGE VISITOR COMES TO TREASURE VALLEY

In a mountainous part of Styria there was, in old time, a valley of the most surprising fertility. It was surrounded on all sides by steep and rocky mountains which were always covered with snow. From the peaks of these mountains streams of water poured constantly in rushing waterfalls. One of these fell westward over the face of a crag so high that, when the sun had set and all below was darkness, his beams still shone upon this waterfall so that it looked like a shower of gold. It was therefore called by the people of the neighborhood, the Golden River.

It was strange that none of these streams fell into the valley itself. They all rushed down the other side of the mountains and wound their way through broad plains and past busy cities. But the clouds were drawn so constantly to the snowy

142

hills, and rested so softly in the valley, that in time of drought and heat, when all the country round was burned up, there was still rain in the little valley. Its crops were so heavy, and its hay so high, and its apples so red, and its grapes so blue, and its wine so rich, and its honey so sweet, that it was called the Treasure Valley.

The whole of this little valley belonged to three brothers called Schwartz, Hans, and Gluck. Schwartz and Hans, the two elder brothers, were very ugly men, with heavy eyebrows and small, dull eyes, which were always half shut, so that you could not see into them, yet you always thought they saw very far into you. They lived by farming the Treasure Valley, and very good farmers they were. They killed everything that did not earn its food. They shot the blackbirds because they pecked the fruit; they poisoned the crickets for eating the crumbs in the kitchen; and killed the locusts, which used to sing all summer in the trees. They worked their servants without any wages till they would not work any more, and then quarreled with them and turned them out-of-doors without paying them. They generally managed to keep their corn till it was very dear, and then sell it for twice its value; they had heaps of gold lying about on their floors, yet it was never known that they had given so much as a penny or a crust of bread to the poor. They never went to church, and were of so cruel and selfish a temper as to receive from everyone who knew them the nickname of the "Black Brothers."

The youngest brother, Gluck, was completely opposite in both appearance and character to his brothers. He was not above twelve years old, fair, blue-eyed, and kind to every living thing. He did not, of course, agree very well with his brothers, or rather, they did not agree with him. When there was any meat to roast, Gluck was usually given the task of watching it. And it was not often they had meat, for the brothers were just about as stingy with themselves as they were with other people. At other times he cleaned the shoes, the floors, and sometimes the plates.

Things went on in this manner for a long time. At last came a very wet summer, and everything went wrong in the country around. The hay had hardly been got in, when the haystacks were floated bodily down to the sea by a flood; the vines were cut to pieces with the hail; and the corn was all rotted. Only in the Treasure Valley all was safe. As it had rain when there was rain nowhere else, so it had sun when there was sun nowhere else. Everybody came to buy corn at the farm, and went away pouring curses on the Black Brothers, who made them pay a terrible price. Some of the poor people, who could only beg, starved at their very door.

It was drawing toward winter, when one day the two elder brothers had gone out with their usual warning to little Gluck, who was left to turn the roast, that he was to let nobody in and give nothing out. Gluck sat down quite close to the fire, for it was raining very hard, and the kitchen walls were by no means dry. He turned and turned, and the roast got nice and brown. "What a pity," thought Gluck, "my brothers never ask anybody to dinner. I'm sure when they have such a nice piece of mutton as this, and nobody else has so much as a piece of dry bread, it would do their hearts good to have somebody to eat it with them."

Just as he spoke, there came a double knock at the door, yet heavy and dull—more like a puff than a knock.

"It must be the wind," said Gluck; "nobody else would dare to strike double knocks at our door."

No, it wasn't the wind; there it came again very hard. Gluck went to the window, opened it, and put his head out to see who it was.

It was the strangest-looking little gentleman he had ever seen in his life. He had a very large nose, slightly brass-colored, and his cheeks were very round and very red. His eyes twinkled merrily through long, silky eye-lashes, his mustaches curled twice around like a corkscrew on each side of his mouth, and his hair, of a curious mixed pepper-and-salt color, hung far over his shoulders. He was about four-feet-six in height, and wore a pointed cap almost as high as himself, decorated with a black feather some three feet long. Hanging from his shoulders was an enormous black, glossy-looking cloak, which must have been very much too long in calm weather, as the wind, whistling round the old house, carried it clear out from the wearer's shoulders to about four times his own length.

Gluck was so perfectly paralyzed by the strange appearance of his visitor that he remained fixed without uttering a word, until the old gentleman turned round to look after his fly-away cloak. In so doing he caught sight of Gluck's little yellow head jammed in the window, with his mouth and eyes very wide open indeed.

"Hollo!" said the little gentleman, "that's not the way to answer the door. I'm wet; let me in."

And to speak truly, the little gentleman was wet. His feather hung down between his legs like a beaten puppy's tail, dripping like an umbrella; and from the ends of his mustaches

the water was running into his pockets and out again like a mill stream.

"I beg pardon, sir," said Gluck; "I'm very sorry, but I really can't."

"Can't what?" said the old gentleman.

"I can't let you in, sir—I can't indeed; my brothers would beat me to death, sir, if I thought of such a thing. What do you want, sir?"

"Want?" said the old gentleman, complainingly. "I want fire and shelter; and there's your great fire there, blazing, crackling, and dancing on the walls, with nobody to feel it. Let me in, I say; I only want to warm myself."

Gluck had had his head so long out of the window by this time that he began to feel it was really cold, and when he turned and saw the beautiful fire throwing long, bright tongues up the chimney, his heart melted within him that it should be burning away for nothing. "He does look very wet," said little Gluck; "I'll just let him in for a quarter of an hour." Round he went to the door and opened it; and as the little gentleman walked in, there came a gust of wind through the house that made the old chimneys totter.

"That's a good boy," said the little gentleman. "Never mind your brothers. I'll talk to them."

"Pray, sir, don't do any such thing," said Gluck. "I can't let you stay till they come; they'd be the death of me."

"Dear me," said the old gentleman, "I'm very sorry to hear that. How long may I stay?"

"Only till the mutton's done, sir," replied Gluck; "and it's very brown."

Then the old gentleman walked into the kitchen and sat himself down close to the fire, with the top of his cap reaching up the chimney, for it was a great deal too high for the roof.

"You'll soon dry there, sir," said Gluck; and sat down again to turn the mutton. But the old gentleman did not dry. He went on drip, drip, dripping among the ashes, and the fire fizzed, and sputtered, and began to look very black. Surely, never was there such a cloak; every fold in it ran water like a little river.

"I beg pardon, sir," said Gluck at length, after watching for a quarter of an hour the water spreading in long streams over the floor, "may I take your cloak?"

"No, thank you," said the old gentleman.

"Your cap, sir?"

"I am all right, thank you," said the old gentleman, rather gruffly.

"But—sir—I'm very sorry," said Gluck, "but—really, sir—you're—putting the fire out."

"It'll take longer to do the mutton, then," replied his visitor.

Gluck was very much puzzled by the behavior of his guest, who was sometimes bold and commanding and other times humble. He turned away for another five minutes.

"That mutton looks very nice," said the old gentleman at length. "Can't you give me a little bit?"

"Impossible, sir," said Gluck.

"I'm very hungry," continued the old gentleman; "I've had nothing to eat yesterday or today. Your brothers surely couldn't miss a bit from the knuckle!"

He spoke so sadly that his words quite melted Gluck's heart. "They promised me one slice today, sir," said he; "I can give you that, but not a bit more."

"That's a good boy," said the old gentleman again.

Then Gluck warmed a plate, and sharpened a knife. "I don't care if I do get beaten for it," thought he. Just as he had cut a large slice out of the mutton, there came a loud rap at the door. The old gentleman jumped up as if he had suddenly become too warm. Gluck fitted the slice into the mutton again, with every effort to make it look as if it had not been cut, and ran to open the door.

"What did you keep us waiting in the rain for?" said Schwartz, throwing his umbrella in Gluck's face. "What for, indeed, you little rascal?" said Hans, giving Gluck a box on the ear, as he followed his brother into the kitchen.

"Bless my soul!" said Schwartz, when he opened the door.

"Amen," said the little gentleman, who had taken his cap off, and was standing in the middle of the kitchen, bowing again and again.

"Who's that?" said Schwartz, catching up a rolling-pin, and turning to Gluck with a fierce frown.

"I don't know, indeed, brother," said Gluck, in great terror.

"How did he get in?" roared Schwartz.

"My dear brother," said Gluck, "he was so very wet!"

"Who are you, sir?" demanded Schwartz, turning upon the old gentleman.

"What's your business?" snarled Hans.

"I am a poor old man, sir," the little gentleman began, "and I saw your fire through the window; so I begged shelter for a quarter of an hour."

"Have the goodness to walk out again, then," said Schwartz. "We've quite enough water in our kitchen without making it a drying-house."

"It is a cold day to turn an old man out in, sir; look at my gray hairs." They hung down to his shoulders, as I told you before.

"There are enough of them to keep you warm," said Hans. "Walk!"

"I'm very, very hungry, sir; couldn't you spare me a bit of bread before I go?"

"Bread, indeed!" said Schwartz; "do you suppose we've nothing to do with our bread but to give it to such fellows as you?"

"Why don't you sell your feather?" said Hans. "Out with you!"

"A little bit," said the old gentleman.

"Be off!" said Schwartz.

"Pray, gentlemen—"

"Off, and be hanged!" cried Hans, seizing him by the collar. But he had no sooner touched the old gentleman's collar than away he went spinning round and round till he fell into the corner. Then Schwartz was very angry, and ran at the old gentleman to turn him out; but he also had hardly touched him when he went after Hans and hit his head against the wall as he too tumbled into the corner.

Then the old gentleman spun himself round in the opposite direction; continued to spin until his long cloak was all wound neatly about him; clapped his cap on his head, very much on one side; gave an additional twist to his corkscrew mustaches, and replied with perfect coolness: "Gentlemen, I wish you a very good morning. At twelve o'clock tonight I'll call again. After such unkind treatment as I have just received in your home, you will not be surprised if that visit is the last I ever pay you."

"If ever I catch you here again," muttered Schwartz, coming, half frightened, out of the corner—but before he could finish his sentence, the old gentleman had shut the house door behind him with a great bang; and there drove past the window, at the same instant, a ragged cloud that whirled and rolled away down the valley in all manner of shapes; turning over and over in the air and melting away at last in a gush of rain.

"A very pretty business, indeed, Mr. Gluck!" said Schwartz. "Dish up the mutton, sir. If ever I catch you at such a trick again—bless me, why, the mutton's been cut!"

"You promised me one slice, brother," said Gluck.

"Oh! and you were cutting it hot, I suppose, and going to catch all the gravy. It'll be long before I promise you such a thing again. Leave the room, sir; and have the kindness to wait in the coal-cellar till I call you."

Such a night as it was! Howling wind and rushing rain!

The brothers put up all the shutters and double-barred the door, before they went to bed. They usually slept in the same room. As the clock struck twelve, they were both awakened by a tremendous crash. Their door burst open so suddenly that the house shook from top to bottom.

"What's that?" cried Schwartz, starting up in his bed.

"Only I," said the little gentleman.

The two brothers sat up and stared into the darkness. The room was full of water; and by a misty moonbeam which found its way through a hole in the shutter, they could see in the midst of it an enormous foam globe, on which, as on a cushion, reclined the little old gentleman, cap and all. There was plenty of room for it now, for the roof was off.

"Sorry to disturb you," said their visitor. "I'm afraid your beds are damp. Perhaps you had better go to your brother's room; I've left the ceiling on there."

They required no second warning, but rushed into Gluck's room, wet through, and full of terror.

"You'll find my card on the kitchen table," the old gentleman called after them. "Remember, the last visit."

"Pray Heaven it may!" said Schwartz, shuddering. And the foam globe disappeared.

Dawn came at last, and the two brothers looked out of Gluck's little window in the morning. The Treasure Valley was one mass of ruin and desolation. The flood had swept away trees, crops, and cattle, and left in their place a waste of red sand and gray mud. The two brothers crept shivering and horror-stricken into the kitchen. The water had ruined the whole first floor; corn, money, almost every movable thing, had been swept away, and there was left only a small white card on the kitchen table. On it, in large, breezy, long-legged letters, were engraved the words:

Chapter Two
HOW THE BLACK BROTHERS BECAME GOLDSMITHS

Southwest Wind, Esquire, kept his word. After the important visit above described, he entered the Treasure Valley no more; and what was worse, neither did his relations, the other West Winds. So no rain fell in the valley from one year's end to another. Though everything remained green and flourishing in the plains below, the land of the Three Brothers was a desert. What had once been the richest soil in the kingdom became a shifting heap of red sand; and the brothers gave up their worthless farm in despair, to seek some means of gaining a livelihood among the cities and people of the plains. All their money was gone, and they had nothing left but some curious, old-fashioned pieces of gold.

"Suppose we turn goldsmiths?" said Schwartz to Hans, as they entered the large city. "It is a good trade. We can put a great deal of copper into the gold without anyone's ever finding it out."

So they hired a furnace and turned goldsmiths. But two things hurt their trade: first, that people did not like the coppered gold; second, that the two elder brothers, whenever they had sold anything, used to leave little Gluck to tend the furnace, and go and spend all the money for drink. So they melted all their gold without making money enough to buy any more. At last there was left only one large drinking mug, which an uncle of his had given to little Gluck, and which he was very fond of, and would not have parted with for the world.

The mug was very odd to look at. The handle was formed of two wreaths of flowing golden hair so finely spun that it looked more like silk than metal. These wreaths flowed into a beard and whiskers which surrounded and decorated a very fierce little face, of the reddest gold imaginable, right in the front of the mug. When it came to the mug's turn to be made into spoons, it half broke poor little Gluck's heart; but the brothers only laughed at him, tossed the mug into the melting-pot, and staggered out, leaving him, as usual, to pour the gold into bars when it was all ready.

When they were gone, Gluck took a farewell look at his old friend in the melting-pot. The flowing hair was all gone; nothing remained but the red nose and the sparkling eyes. He wandered sadly to the window, and sat down to catch the fresh evening air and escape the hot breath of the furnace.

Now this window gave a direct view of the range of mountains which, as I told you before, overhung the Treasure Valley, and more especially to the peak from which fell the Golden River. It was just at the close of the day; and Gluck saw through the window the rocks of the mountain tops all crimson and purple with the sunset. There were bright tongues of fiery cloud burning and quivering about them; and the river, brighter than all, fell in a waving column of pure gold from crag to crag, with a broad, purple rainbow stretched across it.

"Ah!" said Gluck aloud, after he had looked at it for a while, "if that river were really all gold, what a nice thing it would be."

"No, it wouldn't, Gluck," said a clear voice, close at his ear.

"Bless me! what's that?" exclaimed Gluck, jumping up. There was nobody there. He looked round the room and under the table and a great many times behind him, but there was certainly nobody there, and he sat down again at the window. This time he did not speak, but he could not help thinking again that it would be very nice if the river were really all gold.

"Not at all, my boy," said the same voice, louder than before.

"Bless me!" said Gluck again, "what is that?" He looked again into all the corners and cupboards, and then began turning round and round as fast as he could in the middle of the room, thinking there was somebody behind him. Then the same voice struck again on his ear. It was singing now very merrily; no words, only a soft, running melody, something like that of a kettle when it is boiling. Gluck looked out of the window. No, it was certainly in the house. All at once it struck Gluck that it sounded louder near the furnace. He ran to the opening and looked in; yes, it seemed to be coming not only out of the furnace, but out of the pot. He uncovered it, and ran back in a great fright, for the pot was certainly singing! He stood in the farthest corner of the room for a minute or two with his hands up and his mouth open, when the singing stopped and the voice became clear and distinct.

"Hollo!" said the voice.

Gluck made no answer.

"Hollo, Gluck, my boy!" said the pot again.

Gluck called up all of his courage, walked straight up to the crucible, drew it out of the furnace, and looked in. The gold was all melted, and its surface as smooth and polished as a river; but as he looked in, he saw, meeting his glance from beneath the gold, the red nose and sharp eyes of his old friend of the mug, a thousand times redder and sharper than ever he had seen them in his life.

"Come, Gluck, my boy," said the voice out of the pot again; "I'm all right; pour me out."

But Gluck was too much astonished to do anything.

"Pour me out, I say," said the voice, rather gruffly.

Still Gluck couldn't move.

"*Will* you pour me out?" said the voice sharply; "I'm too hot."

By a great effort Gluck managed to make himself move, took hold of the melting-pot, and sloped it so as to pour out the gold. But instead of a liquid stream there came out, first, a pair of pretty little yellow legs, then some coat-tails, then a pair of arms, and, finally, the well-known head of his friend, the mug; all which articles, joining together as they rolled out, stood up on the floor, in the shape of a little golden dwarf about a foot and a half high.

"That's right!" said the dwarf, stretching out first his legs, and then his arms, and then shaking his head up and down, and as far round as it would go, for five minutes without stopping. Gluck stood looking at him in speechless amazement. He was dressed in a garment of spun gold. Over this

his hair and beard fell full halfway to the ground in waving curls so delicate that Gluck could hardly tell where they ended; they seemed to melt into air. Finally the dwarf turned his small, sharp eyes full on Gluck and stared at him for a minute or two. "No, it wouldn't, Gluck, my boy," said the little man.

This was certainly a rather strange way to begin a conversation. It might refer to what Gluck had been thinking when he first heard the voice from the pot. But whatever it was, Gluck had no desire to dispute what he said.

"Wouldn't it, sir?" said Gluck, very meekly indeed.

"No," said the dwarf. "No, it wouldn't." And with that the dwarf stuck his thumbs in his belt, and took two turns, of three feet long, up and down the room, lifting his legs up very high and setting them down very hard. This pause gave time for Gluck to think a little, and seeing no great reason to fear his little visitor, he decided to ask a question.

"Pray, sir," said Gluck, timidly, "were you my mug?"

On which the little man turned sharp round, walked straight up to Gluck, and drew himself up to his full height. "I," said the little man, "am the King of the Golden River." Then he turned about again, and took two more turns some six feet long up and down the room. After this he again walked up to Gluck and stood still, as if expecting some reply to his last remark.

Gluck decided that he had to say something. "I hope your Majesty is very well," said Gluck.

"Listen!" said the little man. "I am the King of what you call the Golden River. The shape you saw me in was caused by the ill will of a stronger King, from whose enchantments you have this instant freed me. What I have seen of you and your conduct toward your wicked brothers makes me willing to serve you; therefore, attend to what I tell you. Whoever shall climb to the top of that mountain from which you see the Golden River springing forth, and shall cast into the stream at its source three drops of holy water, for him, and for him only, the river shall turn to gold. But no one failing in his first attempt can succeed in a second; and if anyone shall cast unholy water into the river, he will become a black stone."

So saying, the King of the Golden River turned away and deliberately walked into the center of the hottest flame of the furnace. His figure became red, white, dazzling—a blaze of light—rose, trembled, and disappeared. The King of the Golden River had evaporated.

"Oh!" cried poor Gluck, running to look up the chimney after him; "oh, dear, dear, dear me! My mug! my mug! my mug!"

CHAPTER THREE

HOW HANS AND SCHWARTZ JOURNEYED TO THE GOLDEN RIVER

The King of the Golden River had hardly disappeared before Hans and Schwartz came roaring into the house very drunk. The discovery of the total loss of their last piece of gold made them just sober enough to be able to stand over Gluck, beating him very steadily for a quarter of an hour. Then they dropped into a couple of chairs and requested to know what he had got to say for himself. Gluck told them his story, of which, of course, they did not believe a word. They beat him again till their arms were tired, and staggered to bed. In the morning, however, the steadiness with which he stuck to his story made them believe him, and immediately the two brothers began to quarrel as to which of them should be the first to make the journey to the Golden River. Soon they drew their swords and began fighting.

The noise of the fray alarmed the neighbors, who sent for the constable. On hearing this, Hans made his escape and hid himself; but Schwartz was taken before the judge, fined for breaking the peace, and was thrown into prison till he should pay. When Hans heard this, he was much delighted, and decided to set out immediately for the Golden River. How to get the holy water was the question. He went to the priest, but the priest could not give any holy water to such a man. So Hans went to vespers in the evening for the first time in his life, and pretending to cross himself, stole a cupful.

Next morning he got up before the sun rose, put the holy water into a strong flask, and two bottles of wine and some bread in a basket. These he slung over his back, and taking his staff in his hand, set off for the mountains. On his way out of the town he had to pass the prison, and as he looked in at the windows, whom should he see but his brother Schwartz peeping out through the bars and looking very down-hearted.

"Good morning, brother," said Hans. "Have you any message for the King of the Golden River?"

Schwartz gnashed his teeth with rage and shook the bars with all his strength; but Hans only laughed at him, and advising him to make himself comfortable till he came back again, shouldered his basket, shook the bottle of holy water in Schwartz's face, and marched off in great glee.

It was indeed a morning that might have made anyone happy, even with no Golden River to seek for. But on this object, and on this alone, Hans's eyes and thoughts were fixed. Forgetting the distance he had to travel, he set off at a rate of walking which greatly exhausted him before he had climbed the first range of the green and low hills. He was surprised on reaching their summit to find that a large glacier lay between him and the source of the Golden River. He mounted it, though, with the boldness of a trained mountaineer; yet he thought he had never in his life climbed so strange or so dangerous a glacier.

The ice was very slippery, and out of all its chasms came wild sounds of gushing water, changeful and loud, now rising into wild melody, then breaking off into short, sorrowful tones, or sudden shrieks, like those of human voices in distress or

pain. The ice was broken into thousands of shapes, but none, Hans thought, like the ordinary forms of splintered ice. Lurid lights played and floated about, dazzling and confusing the sight of the traveler, while his ears grew dull and his head dizzy with the constant gush and roar of the hidden waters. The ice crashed and yawned into fresh chasms at his feet; tottering spires nodded around him, and fell thundering across his path. Though he had repeatedly faced these dangers on the most terrific glaciers and in the wildest weather, it was with a new feeling of terror that he leaped the last chasm and flung himself, exhausted and shuddering, on the firm turf of the mountain.

He had been compelled to cast aside his basket of food, which became too great a burden on the glacier, and had no means of refreshing himself but by breaking off and eating some of the pieces of ice. This, however, relieved his thirst, an hour's rest renewed his strength, and he resumed his laborious journey.

His way now lay straight up a ridge of bare, red rocks, without a blade of grass to ease the foot, or a cliff to give an inch of shade from the south sun. It was past noon, and the sun's rays beat fiercely upon the steep path. Burning thirst was soon added to the bodily fatigue from which Hans was now suffering; glance after glance he cast at the flask of water which hung at his belt. "Three drops are enough," at last thought he; "I may at least cool my lips with it."

He opened the flask and was raising it to his lips, when his eye fell on an object lying on the rock beside him; he thought it moved. It was a small dog, apparently in the last agony of death from thirst. Its tongue was out, its jaws dry, its limbs extended lifelessly, and a swarm of black ants were crawling about its lips and throat. Its eyes moved to the bottle which Hans held in his hand. He raised it, drank, kicked the animal with his foot, and passed on. And he did not know how it was, but he thought that a strange shadow had suddenly come across the blue sky.

The path became steeper and more rugged every moment, and the high, hill air, instead of refreshing him, seemed to throw his blood into a fever. His thirst increased every moment. Another hour passed, and he again looked down to the flask at his side. It was half empty, but there was much more than three drops in it. He stopped to open it, and again, as he did so, something moved in the path above him. It was a fair child, stretched nearly lifeless on the rock, its eyes closed, and its lips parched and burning. Hans looked at it for a moment, drank, and passed on. And a dark gray cloud came over the sun, and long, snake-like shadows crept up along the mountain-sides. Hans struggled on. The sun was sinking, but its descent seemed to bring no coolness, but the goal was nearer. He saw the cataract of the Golden River springing from the hillside, scarcely five hundred feet above him. He paused for a moment to breathe, and sprang on to complete his task.

At this instant a faint cry fell on his ear. He turned, and saw a gray-haired old man stretched out on the rocks. His eyes were sunk, and his features deadly pale. "Water!" he stretched his arms to Hans, and cried feebly, "Water! I am dying."

"I have none," replied Hans; "thou hast had thy share of life." He strode over the body and darted on. And a flash of blue lightning rose out of the East, shaped like a sword. It shook thrice over the whole heaven, and left it dark with one heavy, black shade. The sun was setting; it plunged toward the horizon like a red-hot ball.

The roar of the Golden River rose on Hans's ear. He stood at the brink of the chasm through which it ran. Its waves were filled with the red glory of the sunset; they shook their crests like tongues of fire, and flashes of bloody light gleamed along their foam. Their sound came mightier and mightier on his senses; his brain grew dizzy with the prolonged thunder. Shuddering, he drew the flask from his girdle and hurled it into the center of the torrent. As he did so, an icy chill shot through his limbs; he staggered, shrieked, and fell. The waters closed over his cry. And the moaning of the river rose wildly into the night as it gushed over THE BLACK STONE.

Poor little Gluck waited very anxiously alone in the house for Hans's return. Finding he did not come back, he was terribly frightened, and went and told Schwartz in the prison all that had happened. Then Schwartz was very much pleased, and said that Hans must certainly have been turned into a black stone, and he should have all the gold to himself. But Gluck was very sorry, and cried all night. When he got up in the morning, there was no bread in the house, nor any money; so Gluck went and hired himself to another goldsmith, and he worked so hard and so neatly and so long every day that he soon got money enough together to pay his brother's fine. He went then and gave it all to Schwartz, and Schwartz got out of prison. Then Schwartz was quite pleased and said that Gluck should have some of the gold of the river. But Gluck only begged him to go and see what had become of their brother Hans.

Now when Schwartz, had heard that Hans had stolen the holy water, he determined to manage matters better. So he took some more of Gluck's money, and went to a bad priest, who gave him some holy water very readily for it. Then Schwartz was sure it was all quite right. He got up early in the morning before the sun rose, took some bread and wine in a basket, put his holy water in a flask, and set off for the mountains. Like his brother, he was much surprised at the sight of the glacier, and had great difficulty in crossing it, even after leaving his basket behind him.

The day was cloudless, but not bright; there was a heavy purple haze hanging over the sky, and the hills looked gloomy. And as Schwartz climbed the steep rock path, the thirst came upon him, as it had upon his brother, until he lifted his flask

to his lips to drink. Then he saw the fair child lying near him on the rocks, and it cried to him, and moaned for water.

"Water, indeed," said Schwartz; "I haven't half enough for myself," and passed on. As he went, he thought the sunbeams grew more dim, and he saw a low bank of black clouds rising out of the West. When he had climbed for another hour, the thirst overcame him again, and he would have drunk. Then he saw the old man lying on the path, and moaning for water. "Water, indeed," said Schwartz; "I haven't half enough for myself," and on he went.

Then again the light seemed to fade from before his eyes, and he looked up, and behold, a mist had come over the sun. The bank of black cloud too had risen very high, and its edges

were tossing and tumbling like the waves of the angry sea.
And they cast long shadows, which flickered over Schwartz's
path.

Then Schwartz climbed for another hour, and again his
thirst returned. As he lifted his flask to his lips, he thought
he saw his brother Hans lying exhausted on the path before
him, and, as he gazed, the figure stretched its arms to him
and cried for water. "Ha, ha," laughed Schwartz, "are you
there? Remember the prison bars, my boy. Water, indeed—
do you suppose I carried it all the way up here for you to
drink!" And he strode over the figure. When he had gone a
few yards farther, he stopped and looked back, but the figure
was not there.

A sudden horror came over Schwartz, he knew not why;
but the thirst for gold was stronger than his fear, and he
rushed on. The bank of black cloud rose high overhead, and
out of it came bursts of lightning, and waves of darkness
seemed to float between their flashes over the whole heavens.
The sky where the sun was setting was all level, like a lake of
blood; and a strong wind came out of that sky, tearing its
crimson clouds into fragments and scattering them far into
the darkness. And when Schwartz stood by the brink of the
Golden River, its waves were black, like thunder clouds, but
their foam was like fire; and the roar of the waters below and
the thunder above met as he cast the flask into the stream.
As he did so, the lightning glared into his eyes, the earth gave
way beneath him, and the waters closed over his cry. And
the moaning of the river rose wildly into the night, as it gushed
over the TWO BLACK STONES.

CHAPTER FOUR

HOW GLUCK MET THE DIFFICULTIES OF HIS JOURNEY

When Gluck found that Schwartz did not come back, he was very sorry and did not know what to do. He had no money, so he was obliged to go and hire himself again to the goldsmith, who worked him very hard and gave him very little money. After a month or two Gluck grew tired and made up his mind to go and try his fortune with the Golden River. "The little King looked very kind," thought he. "I don't think he will turn me into a black stone." So he went to the priest, and the priest gave him some holy water as soon as he asked for it. Then Gluck took some bread in his basket, and the bottle of water, and set off very early for the mountains.

If the glacier had caused his brothers a great deal of fatigue, it was twenty times worse for him, who was neither so strong nor so practiced on the mountains. He had several bad falls, lost his basket and bread, and was very much frightened at the strange noises under the ice. He lay a long time to rest on the grass, after he had crossed over, and began to climb the hill just in the hottest part of the day. When he had climbed for an hour, he became dreadfully thirsty, and was going to drink as his brothers had done, when he saw an old man coming down the path above him, looking very feeble, and leaning on a staff.

"My son," said the old man, "I am faint with thirst; give me some of that water." Then Gluck looked at him, and when he saw that he was pale and weary, he gave him the water. "Only pray don't drink it all," said Gluck. But the old man drank a great deal, and gave him back the bottle two-thirds empty. Then he gave Gluck his blessing, and Gluck went on again merrily. The path became easier to his feet, and two or three blades of grass appeared upon it. Some grasshoppers began singing on the bank beside it, and Gluck thought he had never heard such merry singing.

Then he went on for another hour, and the thirst increased on him so that he thought he should be forced to drink. But as he raised the flask, he saw a little child lying panting by the roadside, and it cried out piteously for water. Gluck struggled with himself, and determined to bear the thirst a little longer; and he put the bottle to the child's lips, and it drank it all but a few drops. Having done this, it smiled on him, got up, and ran down the hill. Gluck then turned and began climbing again. And behold, there were all kinds of sweet flowers growing on the rocks, bright green moss, with pale pink, starry flowers, and gentians more blue than the sky at its deepest, and pure-white transparent lilies. Crimson and purple butterflies darted hither and thither, and the sky sent down such pure light that Gluck had never felt so happy.

Yet after he had climbed for another hour, his thirst became unbearable again; and when he looked at his bottle, he saw that there were only five or six drops left in it, and he did not dare to drink. But just as he was hanging the flask to his belt again, he saw a little dog lying on the rocks, gasping for breath—just as Hans had seen it. Gluck stopped and looked at it, and then at the Golden River, not five hundred yards above him; and he thought of the dwarf's words, that no one could succeed, except in his first attempt. He tried to pass the dog, but it whined piteously, and he stopped again. "Poor little beast," said Gluck, "it'll be dead when I come down again." Then he looked closer at it, and its eye turned on him so mournfully that he could not stand it. "Confound the King and his gold, too," said Gluck; and he opened the flask and poured all the water into the dog's mouth.

The dog sprang up and stood on its hind legs. Its tail disappeared; its ears became long, silky, and golden; its nose became very red; its eyes became very twinkling. In three seconds the dog was gone, and before Gluck stood his old acquaintance, the King of the Golden River.

"Thank you," said the King, "but don't be frightened; it's all right. Why didn't you come before, instead of sending me those rascally brothers of yours, for me to have the trouble of turning into stones? Very hard stones they make, too."

"Oh, dear me!" said Gluck, "have you really been so cruel?"

"Cruel!" said the dwarf; "they poured unholy water into my stream; do you suppose I'm going to allow that?"

"Why," said Gluck, "I am sure, sir—your Majesty, I mean —they got the water out of the church font."

"Very probably," replied the dwarf; "but"—and his face grew stern as he spoke—"the water which has been refused to the cry of the weary and dying is unholy, though it had been blessed by every saint in heaven."

So saying, the dwarf stooped and plucked a lily that grew at his feet. On its white leaves there hung three drops of clear dew. And the dwarf shook them into the flask which Gluck held in his hand. "Cast these into the river," he said, "and go down on the other side of the mountains into the Treasure Valley. And so good speed."

As he spoke, the figure of the dwarf became indistinct. The colors of his robe formed themselves into a mist of dewy

light. He stood for an instant veiled with them as with a belt of a broad rainbow. The colors grew faint; the mist rose into the air; the monarch had disappeared.

And Gluck climbed to the brink of the Golden River; its waves were as clear as crystal and as brilliant as the sun. When he cast the three drops of dew into the stream, there opened where they fell a small whirlpool, into which the waters fell with a musical noise.

Gluck stood watching it for some time, very much disappointed because the river was not turned into gold, and its waters seemed less in quantity. Yet he obeyed his friend the dwarf, and went down the other side of the mountains toward the Treasure Valley; and as he went, he thought he heard the noise of water working its way under the ground. Now, when he came in sight of the Treasure Valley, behold, a river was springing from a new cleft in the rocks, and was flowing in streams among the dry heaps of red sand.

As Gluck stood gazing, fresh grass sprang beside the new streams, and creeping plants grew among the moistening soil. Young flowers opened suddenly along the river sides, as stars leap out when twilight is deepening. And thus the Treasure Valley became a garden again, and the lands which had been lost by cruelty were regained by love.

And Gluck went and dwelt in the valley, and the poor were never driven from his door; so that his barns became full of corn, and his house of treasure. For him the river had, according to the dwarf's promise, become a River of Gold.

To this day the inhabitants of the valley point out the place where the three drops of holy dew were cast into the stream, and trace the course of the Golden River under the ground, until it appears in the Treasure Valley. And at the source of the Golden River there are still to be seen Two Black Stones, round which the waters howl mournfully every day at sunset; and these stones are still called by the people of the valley The Black Brothers.

Notes and Questions

1. When John Ruskin wrote this story, which one of these three things do you think he was trying to do?

    (a) Tell the story of a brave thing a boy did.

    (b) Show that wicked people are always punished.

    (c) Show that unselfishness brings the truest happiness.

2. Name four things Gluck did that show his unselfishness.

3. *(a)* What did Gluck expect to happen when he poured the drops of water into the river?

    (b) What far better thing happened?

4. *(a)* Who do you think the old man, the child, and the dog really were?

    (b) Why were they along the path to the Golden River?

5. *(a)* What did Southwest Wind really mean when he said he would never come again?

    (b) Why was this so serious to Treasure Valley?

6. You noticed that this story is divided into four chapters. Write the chapter titles across your paper, and then write under each title the items from the list below that belong there.

Treasure Valley becomes a desert.

Gluck's strange visitor.

Schwartz is put in jail.

Treasure Valley and the Golden River.

The strange visitor comes again.

Hans steals the holy water.

The golden dwarf visits Gluck.

Gluck gets the holy water and starts out.

The two black brothers.

The brothers become goldsmiths.

Hans journeys up the mountain.

The brothers meet the strange visitor.

Happiness comes again to Treasure Valley.

Gluck shares the water with the sufferers.

Schwartz journeys up the mountain.

The golden dwarf helps Gluck.

Gluck earns money to free Schwartz.

You would also like to read "The Golden Goblet," Stocking, and "The Three Brother Dwarfs," Beard (both in *Child-Library Readers, Book Six*). Another good story is "The King's Missionaries," Stocking (in *Query Queer*).

ABOU BEN ADHEM

Leigh Hunt

Abou Ben Adhem (may his tribe increase!)
Awoke one night from a deep dream of peace,
And saw, within the moonlight in his room,
Making it rich, and like a lily in bloom,
An angel writing in a book of gold.
Exceeding peace had made Ben Adhem bold,
And to the presence in the room he said,
"What writest thou?"—The vision raised its head,
And, with a look made of all sweet accord,
Answered, "The names of those who love the Lord."
"And is mine one?" said Abou. "Nay, not so,"
Replied the angel. Abou spoke more low,
But cheerily still, and said, "I pray thee, then,
Write me as one that loves his fellow men."
The angel wrote and vanished. The next night
It came again, with a great wakening light,
And showed the names whom love of God had blessed,
And lo! Ben Adhem's name led all the rest!

TOM AND HIS TREASURE CHEST

Howard Pyle

When we think of pirates, we think of buried treasure and of a map that tells us where the treasure can be found—if only we can understand the map. Although we like to read pirate stories, we probably should dislike very much to come upon pirates at night along a lonely ocean shore. But that is what happened to Tom Chist in his story, taken from Howard Pyle's famous *Book of Pirates*.

TOM TRAILS THE PIRATES

There had been a thunderstorm that afternoon, and Tom had gone down the beach to bail out the boat in readiness for the morning's fishing. It was full moonlight now, as he was returning, and the night sky was full of floating clouds. Now and then there was a dull flash to the westward, and once a muttering growl of thunder, promising another storm to come.

All that day the pirate ship had been lying just off the shore back of the Capes, and now Tom Chist could see the sails glimmering in the moonlight, spread for drying after the storm. He was walking up the shore homeward when he became aware that at some distance ahead of him there was a ship's boat drawn up on the little narrow beach, and a group of men clustered about it. He hurried forward with a good deal of curiosity to see who had landed, but it was not until he had come close to them that he could distinguish who and what they were. Then he knew that it must be a party who had come off the pirate ship.

They had evidently just landed, and two men were lifting out a chest from the boat. One of them was a negro, naked to the waist, and the other was a white man in his shirt sleeves, wearing petticoat breeches, a hunting cap upon his head, a red bandanna handkerchief around his neck, and gold earrings in his ears. He had a long plaited queue hanging down his back, and a great knife dangling from his side. Another man, evidently the captain of the party, stood at a little distance as they lifted the chest out of the boat. He had a cane in one hand and a lighted lantern in the other, although the moon was shining as bright as day. He wore jack boots and a handsome laced coat, and he had a long, drooping mustache that curled down below his chin. He wore a fine feathered hat, and his long black hair hung down upon his shoulders. All this Tom Chist could see in the moonlight that glinted and twinkled upon the gilt buttons of the captain's coat.

They were so busy lifting the chest from the boat that at first they did not notice that Tom Chist had come up and was standing there. It was the white man with the long plaited queue and the gold earrings that spoke to him. "Boy, what do you want here, boy?" he said in a rough hoarse voice. "Where d'ye come from?" And then dropping his end of the chest, and without giving Tom time to answer, he pointed off down the beach, and said, "You'd better be going about your own business, if you know what's good for you; and don't you come back, or you'll find what you don't want waiting for you."

Tom saw in a glance that the pirates were all looking at him, and then, without saying a word, he turned and walked away. The man who had spoken to him followed him threateningly for some little distance, as though to see that he had gone away as he was bidden to do. But presently he stopped, and Tom hurried on alone, until the boat and the crew and all were dropped away behind and lost in the moonlight night. Then he himself stopped also, turned, and looked back whence he had come.

There had been something very strange in the appearance of the men he had just seen, something very mysterious in their actions, and he wondered what it all meant, and what they were going to do. He stood for a little while thus looking and listening. He could see nothing, and could hear only the sound of distant talking. What were they doing on the lonely shore thus at night? Then he suddenly turned and cut off across the sand hillocks, but kept pretty close to the shore, his object being to spy upon them, and to watch what they were about from the back of the low sand hills that fronted the beach.

He had gone along some distance when he became aware of the sound of voices that seemed to be drawing closer to him as he came toward the speakers. He stopped and stood listening, and instantly, as he stopped, the voices stopped also. He crouched there silently in the glimmering moonlight, surrounded by the silent stretches of sand, and the stillness seemed to press upon him like a heavy hand. Then suddenly the sound of a man's voice began again, and as Tom listened he could hear someone counting. "Ninety-one," the voice began, "ninety-two, ninety-three, ninety-four, ninety-five, ninety-six, ninety-seven, ninety-eight, ninety-nine, one hundred, one hundred and one,"— the slow monotonous count coming nearer and nearer; "one hundred and two, one hundred and three, and one hundred and four," and so on.

Suddenly he saw three heads appear above the sand hill, so close to him that he crouched down quickly with a keen thrill, close beside the hillock near which he stood. His first fear was that they might have seen him in the moonlight; but they had not, and his heart rose again as the counting voice went steadily on. "One hundred and twenty," it was saying — "and twenty-one and twenty-two, and twenty-three, and twenty-four," and then he who was counting came out from behind the little sandy hill into the shimmering brightness.

It was the man with the cane whom Tom had seen some time before — the captain of the party who had landed. He carried his cane under his arm now. He was holding his lantern close to something that he held in his hand, upon which he looked closely as he walked slowly in a perfect straight line across the sand, counting each step as he took it. "And twenty-five, and twenty-six, and twenty-seven, and twenty-eight, and twenty-nine, and thirty."

Behind him walked two other figures; one was the half-naked negro, the other the man with the plaited queue and the earrings, whom Tom had seen lifting the chest out of the boat. Now they were carrying the heavy box between them, laboring through the sand as they bore it onward. As he who was counting pronounced the word "thirty," the two men set the chest down on the sand with a grunt, the white man panting and blowing and wiping his sleeve across his forehead. And immediately he who counted took out a slip of paper and marked something down upon it. They stood there for a long time, during which Tom lay behind the sand hillock watching them, and for a while the silence was not interrupted. In the perfect stillness, the washing of little waves beating upon the distant beach, and once the far-away sound of a laugh, could be heard.

One, two, three minutes passed, and then the men picked up the chest and started on again; and then again the other man began his counting. "Thirty and one, and thirty and two, and thirty and three, and thirty and four"—he walked straight across the open space, still looking at that which he held in his hand—"and thirty and five, and thirty and six, and thirty and seven," and so on, until the three men disappeared, and still Tom could hear the sound of the counting voice in the distance.

Just as they disappeared behind the hill there was a sudden

faint flash of light; and by and by, as Tom lay still listening to the counting, he heard a far-away muffled rumble of distant thunder. He waited for a while, and then arose and stepped to the top of the sand hillock behind which he had been lying. He looked all about him, but there was no one else to be seen. Then he stepped down from the hillock and followed in the direction which the pirate captain and the two men carrying the chest had gone. He crept along cautiously, stopping now and then to make sure that he still heard the counting voice, and when it ceased he lay down upon the sand and waited until it began again.

Presently, still following the pirates, Tom saw the three men again in the distance. Hurrying around back of a hill of sand covered with coarse grass, he came to a point where he could see a little open level space gleaming white in the moonlight.

The three pirates had been crossing the level of sand, and were now not more than twenty-five paces from him. They had again set down the chest upon which the white man with the long queue and the gold earrings had seated himself to rest, the negro standing close beside him. The moon shone as bright as day, full upon Tom's face. It was looking so directly at him that Tom drew back with a start, almost thinking he had been discovered. He lay silent, his heart beating heavily in his throat; but there was no alarm, and presently he heard the counting begin again. When he looked once more, he saw they were going away straight across the little open. A soft, sliding hillock of sand lay directly in front of them. They did not turn aside, but went straight over it, the leader helping himself up the sandy slope with his cane, still counting and still keeping his eyes fixed upon that which he held in his hand. They then disappeared again on the other side of the hill.

So Tom followed them cautiously until they had gone almost half a mile inland. When he saw them clearly, the white man who had helped to carry the chest was kneeling, busied at some work, though what it was Tom at first could not see. He was whittling the point of a stick into a long wooden peg. When he had finished what he was about, he rose and stepped to the place where the man who seemed to be the captain had stuck his cane upright into the ground as though to mark some particular spot. He drew the cane out of the sand, thrusting the stick down in its place. Then he drove the long peg down with a wooden mallet which the negro handed to him. The sharp rapping of the mallet upon the top of the peg sounded loud in the perfect stillness, and Tom lay watching and wondering what it all meant. The man drove the peg farther and farther down into the sand until it showed only two or three inches above the surface. Just as he finished his work, there was another faint flash of light followed soon by another rumble of thunder.

The two white men were now stooping over the peg, the negro man watching them. Then presently the man with the cane started straight away from the peg, carrying the end of a measuring line with him, the other end of which the man with the plaited queue held against the top of the peg. When the pirate captain had reached the end of the measuring line, he marked a cross upon the sand; and then again they measured out another stretch of space.

So they measured a distance five times over, and then, from

where Tom lay, he could see the man with the queue drive another peg just at the foot of a tall white sand dune which stood sharp and clear against the night sky behind. As soon as the man with the plaited queue had driven the second peg into the ground, they began measuring again. Still measuring, they disappeared in another direction which took them in behind the sand dune where Tom no longer could see what they were doing.

The negro still sat by the chest where the two had left him. So bright was the moonlight that from where Tom lay he could see the glint of its beams twinkling in the whites of the negro's eyeballs.

Presently from behind the hill there came, for the third time, the sharp rapping sound of the mallet driving still another peg. Then after a while the two pirates came from behind the sand dune into the space of moonlight again.

They came direct to the spot where the chest lay. The white man and the black man, lifting it once more, walked away across open sand, and on behind the edge of the hill, out of Tom's sight.

TOM FLEES IN TERROR

Tom Chist could no longer see what the pirates were doing, neither did he dare to cross over the open space of sand that now lay between them and him. He lay there wondering what they were about; and meantime the storm cloud was rising higher and higher above the horizon, with louder and louder mutterings of thunder. In the silence he could hear an occasional click as of some iron implement, and he supposed that the pirates were burying the chest, though just where they were at work he could neither see nor tell.

Still Tom lay there watching and listening; by and by a puff of warm air blew across the sand, when a thumping of louder thunder leaped from out the storm cloud, which every minute was coming nearer and nearer. Still Tom Chist lay watching. Suddenly, the three pirates came out again from behind the sand hill, the captain leading the way; the negro and white man followed closely behind him. They had gone about halfway across the sandy level toward the hillock behind which Tom Chist lay, when the white man stopped and bent over as though to tie his shoe. This brought the negro a few steps in front of his companion.

That which then followed happened so suddenly, so unexpectedly, so swiftly, that Tom Chist had hardly time to realize what it all meant before it was over. As the negro passed him, the white man arose suddenly and stood silently erect; and Tom Chist saw the white moonlight glint upon the blade of a great dirk knife which he now held in his hand. The white man took one, two silent, catlike steps behind the unsuspecting negro. Then there was a sweeping flash of the blade in the pale light, and a blow, the thump of which Tom could hear even from where he lay stretched out upon the sand. There was an instant yell from the black man, who ran stumbling forward, stopped, regained his footing, and then stood for a moment as though rooted to the spot.

Meantime the pirate captain had stopped, and now stood with his hand resting upon his cane, looking calmly on.

Then the black man started to run. The white man stood for a while glaring after him; then he, too, started after his victim upon the run. The black man was not very far from Tom when he staggered and fell. He tried to rise, then fell forward again and lay at length. At that instant the first edge of the cloud cut across the moon, and there was a sudden darkness; but in the silence Tom heard the sound of another blow and a groan, and then presently a voice calling to the pirate captain that it was all over.

He saw the dim form of the captain crossing the level sand, and then, as the moon sailed out from behind the cloud, he saw the white man standing over a black figure that lay motionless upon the sand.

Then Tom Chist scrambled up and ran away, plunging down into the hollow of sand that lay in the shadows below. Over the next rise he ran, and down again into the next black hollow, and so on over the sliding, shifting ground, panting and gasping. It seemed to him that he could hear footsteps following, and in the terror that possessed him he almost expected every instant to feel the cold knife blade slide between his own ribs.

So he ran on like one in a nightmare. His feet grew heavy as lead, he panted and gasped, his breath came hot and dry in his throat. But still he ran and ran until at last he found himself in front of old Matt Abrahamson's cabin, gasping, panting, and sobbing for breath.

As he opened the door and dashed into the darkened cabin (for both Matt and Molly were long ago asleep in bed) there was a flash of light, and even as he slammed the door shut behind him there was an instant peal of thunder. The doors and windows of the cabin rattled as though a great weight had been dropped upon the roof of the sky.

TOM CONFIDES IN PARSON JONES

Then Tom Chist crept to bed, trembling, shuddering, bathed in sweat, his heart beating like a trip hammer, and his brain dizzy from that long race of terror through the soft sand.

For a long, long time he lay awake, trembling and chattering with nervous chills, and when he did fall asleep, it was only to drop into horrible dreams.

Then came the dawning of the broad daylight, and before the rising of the sun Tom was up and out of doors to find the young day dripping with the rain of overnight. His first act was to climb the nearest sand hill and to gaze out toward the bay where the pirate ship had been the day before.

It was no longer there.

Soon afterward Matt Abrahamson came out of the cabin. He called to Tom to go get a bite to eat, for it was time for them to be away fishing.

All that morning the memory of the night before hung over Tom Chist like a great threatening cloud. Not for a moment was it lifted. Even when he was hauling in his dripping line with a struggling fish at the end of it, the memory of what he had seen would suddenly come upon him, and he would groan within himself at the recollection. When the boat reached the shore again, he leaped scrambling to the beach, and as soon as his dinner was eaten, he hurried away to find Parson Jones. He ran all the way from Abrahamson's hut to the parson's house, hardly stopping once. When he knocked at the door, he was panting and sobbing for breath. The good man was sitting on the back-kitchen doorstep, while his wife within was rattling about among the pans and dishes preparing their supper, of which a strong, porky smell already filled the air.

Then Tom Chist told his story, panting, hurrying, tumbling one word over another in his haste. Parson Jones listened, breaking every now and then into an exclamation of wonder.

"I don't see why they should have killed the poor black man," said Tom, as he finished his story.

"Why, that is very easy enough to understand," said the parson. " 'Twas a treasure box they buried!"

In his excitement Parson Jones had risen from his seat and was now clumsily pacing up and down.

"A treasure box!" cried out Tom.

"Aye, a treasure box! And that was why they killed the poor black man. He was the only one, d'ye see, beside they two who knew the place where 'twas hid, and now that they've killed him, there's nobody but themselves knows. The villains!"

"Why, then," said Tom, "it is indeed a wicked, bloody treasure, and fit to bring a curse upon anybody who finds it!"

" 'Tis more like to bring a curse upon the souls who buried it," said Parson Jones. "It may be a blessing to him who finds it. But tell me, Tom, do you think you could find the place again where 'twas hid?"

"I can't tell that," said Tom, " 'twas all in among the sand humps, d'ye see, and it was at night, too. Maybe we could find the marks of their feet in the sand," he added.

" 'Tis not likely," said the parson, "for the storm last night would have washed all that away."

"I could find the place," said Tom, "where the boat was drawn upon the beach."

"Why, then, that's something to start from, Tom," said his friend. "If we can find that, then perhaps we can find whither they went from there."

"If I was certain it was a treasure box," cried out Tom Chist, "I would rake over every foot of sand betwixt here and Henlopen to find it."

" 'Twould be like hunting for a pin in a haystack," said Parson Jones.

As Tom walked away home, it seemed as though a ton's weight of gloom had been rolled away from his soul. The next day he and Parson Jones were to go treasure hunting together; it seemed to Tom as though he could hardly wait for the time to come.

A SCRAP OF PAPER, KEY TO THE PIRATES' TREASURE

The next afternoon Parson Jones and Tom Chist started off together treasure hunting. Tom carried a spade over his shoulder, and the old gentleman walked along beside him with his cane.

As they jogged along up the beach, they talked together about the only thing they *could* talk about—the treasure box. "And how big did you say 'twas?" quoth the good gentleman.

"About so long," said Tom Chist, measuring off upon the spade, "and about so wide and this deep."

"And what if it should be full of money, Tom?" said the parson, swinging his cane around and around in wide circles in the excitement of the thought, as he strode along briskly. "Suppose it should be full of money, what then?"

"By Moses!" said Tom Chist, hurrying to keep up with his friend, "I'd buy a ship for myself, I would, and I'd trade with India and China, I would. Suppose the chest was all full of money, sir, and suppose we should find it; would there be enough in it, d'ye suppose, to buy a ship?"

"To be sure there would be enough, Tom; enough and to spare, and a good big lump over."

"And if I find it, 'tis mine to keep, is it, and no mistake?"

"Why, to be sure it would be yours!" cried out the parson, in a loud voice. "To be sure it would be yours!" He strode along in silence for a while. "Whose else would it be but yours if you find it?" he burst out. "Can you tell me that?"

"If ever I have a ship of my own," said Tom Chist, "and if ever I sail to India in her, I'll fetch you back the best chist of tea, sir, that ever was fetched from that land."

Parson Jones burst out laughing. "Thankee, Tom," he said; "and I'll thankee again when I get my chist of tea. But tell me, Tom, didst thou ever hear of the farmer girl who counted her chickens before they were hatched?"

It was thus they talked as they hurried along up the beach together, until they came to a place at last where Tom stopped short and stood looking about him. " 'Twas just here," he said, "I saw the boat last night. I know 'twas here, for I remember that bit of wreck yonder, and that there was a tall stake in the sand just where yon stake is."

Parson Jones put on his spectacles and went over to the stake which Tom had pointed out. As soon as he had looked at it carefully, he called: "Why, Tom, this hath just been driven down into the sand. 'Tis a brand-new stake of wood, and the pirates must have set it here themselves as a mark, just as they drove the pegs you spoke about down into the sand."

Tom came over and looked at the stake. It was a stout piece of oak nearly two inches thick; it had been shaped with some care, and the top of it had been painted red. He shook the stake and tried to move it, but it had been driven so deeply into the sand that he could not stir it. "Aye, sir," he said, "it must have been set here for a mark, for I am sure 'twas not here yesterday or the day before." Tom stood looking about him to see if there were other signs of the pirates. At a little distance there was the corner of something white sticking up out of the sand. He could see that it was a scrap of paper, and he pointed to it, calling out: "Yonder is a piece of paper, sir. I wonder if they left that behind them."

It was a happy chance that placed the paper there. There was only an inch of it showing, and if it had not been for Tom's sharp eyes, the paper would certainly have been overlooked and passed by. The next windstorm would have covered it up, and all that afterward happened never would have occurred. "Look, sir," he said, as he struck the sand from the paper. "It has writing on it."

"Let me see it," said Parson Jones. He adjusted the spectacles a little more firmly on his nose as he took the paper in his hand and began studying it. "What's all this?" he said; "a whole lot of figures and nothing else." And then he read aloud, " 'Mark—S. S. W. by S.' What d'ye suppose that means, Tom?"

"I don't know, sir," said Tom. "But perhaps we can understand it better if you read on."

" 'Tis all a great lot of figures," said Parson Jones, "without a grain of meaning in them so far as I can see, unless they be sailing directions." And then he began reading again: " 'Mark—S. S. W. by S. 40, 72, 91, 130, 151, 177, 202, 232, 256, 271'—d'ye see, it must be sailing directions—'299, 335,

362, 415, 446, 469, 491, 533, 544, 571, 598'—what a lot of them there are—'626, 652, 676, 695, 724, 851, 876, 905, 940, 967. Peg. S. E. by E. 269 foot. Peg. S. S. W. by S. 427 foot. Peg. Dig to the west of this six foot.'"

"What's that about a peg?" exclaimed Tom. "What's that about a peg? And then there's something about digging, too!" It was as though a sudden light began shining into his brain. He felt himself growing quickly very excited. "Read that over again, sir," he cried. "Why, sir, you remember I told you they drove a peg into the sand. And don't they say to dig close to it? Read it over again, sir, —read it over again!"

"Peg?" said the good gentleman. "To be sure it was about a peg. Let's look again. Yes, here it is. 'Peg S. E. by E. 269 foot.'"

"Aye!" cried out Tom Chist again, in great excitement. "Don't you remember what I told you, sir, 269 foot? Sure that must be what I saw 'em measuring with the line."

Parson Jones had now caught the flame of excitement that was blazing up so strongly in Tom's breast. He felt as though some wonderful thing was about to happen to them. "To be sure, to be sure!" he called out, in a great big voice. "And then they measured out 427 foot south-southwest by south, and then they drove another peg, and then they buried the box six foot to the west of it. Why, Tom—why, Tom Chist! if we've read this aright, thy fortune is made."

Tom Chist stood staring straight at the old gentleman's excited face. Were they, indeed, about to find the treasure chest? Tom thought to himself; but all the time he stood staring into the good old gentleman's face.

It was Parson Jones who first spoke. "But what do all these figures mean?" And Tom noticed how the paper shook in his hand. The parson began to read again. " 'Mark 40, 72, 91—.' "

"Mark?" cried out Tom, almost screaming. "Why, that must mean the stake yonder; that must be the mark." And he pointed to the oaken stick with its red tip blazing against the white sand behind it.

"And the 40 and 72 and 91," cried the old gentleman, in a voice equally shrill—"why, that must mean the number of steps the pirate was counting when you heard him."

"To be sure that's what they mean!" cried Tom Chist. "That is it, and it can be nothing else. Oh, come, sir—come, sir; let us make haste and find it!"

"Stay! stay!" said the good gentleman, holding up his hand; and again Tom Chist noticed how it trembled and shook. His voice was steady enough, though very hoarse, but his hand shook and trembled as though with a palsy. "Stay! stay! First of all, we must follow these measurements. And 'tis a marvelous thing," he croaked, after a little pause, "how this paper ever came to be here."

"Maybe it was blown here by the storm," suggested Tom.

"Like enough; like enough," said Parson Jones. "Like enough, after the wretches had buried the chest and killed the poor man, they were so blown about by the storm that the paper shook out of the man's pocket, and thus blew away without his knowing about it."

"But let us find the box!" cried out Tom Chist.

"Aye, aye," said the good man; "only stay a little, my boy, until we make sure what we're about. I've got my

pocket compass here, but we must have something to measure
off the feet when we have found the peg. You run across
to Tom Brooke's house and fetch his measuring rod. While
you're gone I'll pace off the distance marked on the paper
with my pocket compass here."

CAPTAIN KIDD'S BOX OF TREASURE

Tom Chist was gone for almost an hour, though he ran
nearly all the way back. When he returned panting, Parson
Jones was nowhere to be seen; but Tom saw his footsteps
leading away inland, and he followed the marks in the smooth
surface across the sand humps and down into the hollows.
By and by he found the good gentleman in a spot which he
at once knew as soon as he laid his eyes upon it. It was the
open space where the pirates had driven their first peg, and
where Tom had afterward seen them kill the poor black man.
Tom gazed around as though expecting to see some sign of
the tragedy, but the space was as smooth as a floor, excepting
where Parson Jones, who was now stooping over something
on the ground, had trampled it all around about.

When Tom Chist saw him the parson was still bending
over, scraping away the sand from something he had found.

It was the first peg!

Inside of half an hour they had found the second and third
pegs. Tom Chist stripped off his coat and began digging
like mad down into the sand, Parson Jones standing over
him and watching. The sun was sloping well toward the
west when the blade of Tom's spade struck upon something
hard. If it had been his own heart that he had hit in the
sand, his breast could hardly have thrilled more sharply.

It was the treasure box!

Parson Jones himself leaped down into the hole and began scraping away the sand with his hands as though he had gone crazy. At last, with some difficulty, they hauled the chest up out of the sand to the surface, where it lay covered all over with the grit that clung to it. It was locked and fastened with a padlock, and it took a good many blows with the blade of the spade to smash the bolt. Parson Jones himself lifted the lid. Tom Chist leaned forward and gazed down into the open box. He would not have been surprised to have seen it filled full of yellow gold and bright jewels. It was filled half full of books and papers, and half full of canvas bags tied around and around with cords of string.

Parson Jones lifted out one of the bags, and it jingled as he did so. It was full of money.

He cut the string, and with trembling hands gave the bag to Tom, who, dizzy with delight, poured out upon the coat spread on the ground a flood of shining silver money that rang and twinkled and jingled as it fell in a shining heap.

Parson Jones held up both hands into the air, and Tom stared at what he saw, wondering whether he was really awake. It seemed to him as though he was in a dream.

There were two-and-twenty bags in all in the chest: ten of them full of silver money, eight of them full of gold money, three of them full of gold dust, and one small bag with jewels wrapped up in cotton and paper.

" 'Tis enough," cried out Parson Jones, "to make us both rich men as long as we live."

The burning summer sun, though sloping in the sky, beat down upon them as hot as fire; but neither of them noticed

it. Neither did they notice hunger nor thirst, but sat there as though in a trance, with the bags of money scattered on the sand around them, a great pile of money heaped upon the coat, and the open chest beside them. It was an hour of sundown before Parson Jones had begun to examine the books and papers in the chest.

Of the three books, two were log books of the pirates who had been lying off the mouth of the Delaware Bay all this time. The other book was written in Spanish, and was evidently the log book of some captured prize.

It was then, sitting there upon the sand, the good old gentleman reading in his high cracking voice, that they first learned from the bloody records in those two books who it was who had been lying inside the Cape all this time, and that it was the famous Captain Kidd.

NOTES AND QUESTIONS

1. In the stories by Hawthorne and Ruskin you found that these authors wrote the stories for a definite purpose. Do you think Howard Pyle had a different reason for writing this story? What was he trying to do for his readers?

2. When an author writes a story, he has to keep many things in mind if his story is to seem real.

   (a) Why did Howard Pyle have this adventure happen on a quiet, moonlight night?

   (b) Why did he have a storm come up during the night?

You will have to do a little thinking to answer these questions. Something on page 186 will help you answer question *(b)*.

3. What do you think were the two most exciting moments in the story?

4. Why would you think that Parson Jones was Tom's closest friend?

5. On page 187 there is something that tells you on what part of the Atlantic coast the events of this story happened. In what state is this place? You may have to use your geography or some reference book to find out.

6. After Parson Jones and Tom had found the paper and the first stake, what two things did they need to locate the chest?

7. *(a)* What kind of ships had the pirates been capturing?

   (b) Where were these ships getting the gold? (What you have read in your history books will help you to answer this question.)

8. Find and be ready to read lines that—

   (a) Describe the pirates.

   (b) Tell the most exciting moment in the story.

   (c) Tell how frightened Tom was.

9. Make up a title for each picture in the story.

Other exciting stories you would like to read are *"Stolen Treasure,"* Pyle; *Treasure Island,* Stevenson; *Jim Davis, or the Captive of the Smugglers,* Masefield.

A BACKWARD LOOK

OF COURSE, the three famous stories you have just read are only a few of the many such tales. As you go on through school, and in your reading outside of school, you will meet with other story-tellers and with other stories that almost everyone knows.

Which of the stories you have just read interested you most? Why was it the most interesting one to you? Without turning back to the stories, can you tell two or three valuable lessons these stories taught? In this part of your book there was a poem. What did that poem teach? Did one of the stories teach much the same lesson as the poem?

If you had to make one of these stories into a play, which one would you choose? Which would be the hardest to make into a play that could be acted in school? Why?

Your school reader can only introduce you to the famous story-tellers. You will have to get acquainted with them yourself. Why not let Nathaniel Hawthorne entertain you with his *Wonder Book* and his *Tanglewood Tales?* Surely you will want to get Howard Pyle's *Book of Pirates* and learn of the strange way in which Tom Chist came to live with Matt Abrahamson, and of what he did after he found the treasure chest.

In the back of your book, on page 450, you will find a list of stories that never grow old. These books will give you many pleasant hours of reading. They are the kinds of stories that you will like to read over and over again, just as many other people have done for years. Remember that the librarian in your town or your school is always ready to help you find good books to read.

Part Four
Young American Citizens

TRUE CITIZENS

MARY E. McDOWELL

God hath made all the nations of men, and we are His children, brothers and sisters all. We are citizens of these United States, and we believe our flag stands for self-sacrifice for the good of all the people. We wish, therefore, to be true citizens of our great country, and will show our love for her by our works.

Our country asks us to live for her good; so to live and so to act that her government may be pure, her officers honest, and that every home within her boundaries shall be a place fit to grow the best kind of men and women to rule over her.

YOU HAVE CITIZENSHIP DUTIES

You have probably many times said, "I pledge allegiance to my flag and to the Republic for which it stands." Did you mean what you said? And if you meant it, did you understand what you were promising? You promised to be faithful to your country. What can you do to show that you are faithful? What are your duties as a young American citizen?

You cannot vote; you cannot be an officer of your city, county, or state. But you have duties that are just as important. You are a partner with your parents in making your home a happy place in which to live. You have important lessons to learn at school—lessons that will help you and make you happier all through your life. Even in sports and games there are ways in which you can show what kind of citizen you are. When you help cheerfully at home, do your school-work faithfully, and play games just as hard as you can and with good sportsmanship, you are doing the things your country most needs of you.

The stories in this part of your book tell you of young American citizens—boys and girls like yourself. You will read of Joseph and Priscilla Harris, who thought quickly and acted bravely. You will see Washington and Lincoln in their boyhood days. You will meet Marion Andrews, who never allowed difficulties to stop her, and Rodney, a true captain and leader of his team. What duties may you, as a citizen, be called upon to perform, and how can you prepare for them?

YOUTHFUL PATRIOTS OF COLONIAL TIMES

Janet P. Shaw

Oftentimes boys and girls can do just as important work as grown-up people, especially if they are quick-witted and brave. In this story you will read how Joseph and Priscilla Harris rendered a great service to our country in the days when we were fighting for our freedom.

LEAFING DAY

If there was one holiday which Joseph and Priscilla Harris liked better than the others, it was the one called "leafing day," that delightful time in the autumn when all the colonial boys and girls went out to the woods to gather leaves to use in the ovens during the winter when their mothers baked delicious loaves of bread and flaky, golden-brown pies.

At that time everybody in the colonies used what they called "Dutch ovens." These were nothing but big boxes of stone built into the wall of the chimney, and could be heated only by being filled with hot coals from the fireplace. When the ovens were very hot, the coals were raked out. Then as the walls were apt to be smoky, the ovens were lined with green leaves to make them all neat and clean. And last of all, the white loaves of bread and fragrant pies and puddings were placed on the leaves and left to bubble and bake until they were all brown and delicious and ready to be eaten.

All summer, of course, the leaves for the Dutch oven were cut fresh every baking. But when winter came and the trees were bare, then dried leaves had to be used, and every housewife had to have bundles and bundles of leaves stored away some place for the winter's baking. And that was the reason for "leafing day."

Ever since Joseph and Priscilla could remember, they had gone on "leafing day" picnics, and they loved them dearly. But when the war came, and General Washington and his brave men were fighting for the very life of the new nation, and no one knew what might happen from day to day, such jolly good times seemed almost impossible even to think of. But fortunately for the boys and girls, the mothers of the village said that they needed *more* leaves than usual during war times, for most of them were baking bread for the soldiers as well as for their own families.

And that's how it happened that one day in late autumn, when the leaves were broad and green and shiny from all the scrubbings which they had received during the fall showers, Joseph and Priscilla heard their teacher say, "If you all have your lessons perfectly this morning, you may spend the afternoon gathering leaves in the woods for your mothers."

"Leafing day!" whispered the children to each other happily. Then, when they had clapped and clapped their hands, they all began to study very hard. By noon every lesson was learned better than usual. Then, very soon afterwards, every child in the whole village was on his way to the woods.

THE ENGLISH LAY THEIR PLANS

Although the children did not know it, a great many important things were happening that beautiful "leafing day."

General Washington's headquarters at that time were located a few miles south of the village, and he was waiting there with his small, poorly clothed, and poorly armed troops, hoping to avoid a battle with the English troops until more of his soldiers arrived.

And on this very day the English, who had a camp several miles north, decided to attack the little American army, take General Washington and his brave men captives, and, if possible, end the war—and the new nation!

Last of all, as the village lay halfway between the armies, the English planned to capture that first and thus prevent the inhabitants from sending word to Washington about their plans. And so, not long after the leaf-gatherers went gayly toward the woods, the English soldiers marched into the little village from the other direction and quickly made prisoners of all the people they could find! If they thought it was queer that the village had no children in it, they said nothing about it.

General Washington knew nothing about the plans of the English, and the enemy might easily have succeeded in capturing him if a brave boy and girl, Joseph and Priscilla Harris, had not found out their plans in time and carried the news to the General.

All afternoon Joseph and Priscilla had a delightful time with the other children, cutting great branches from the trees, trimming them down, and tying them in bundles which could be carried in their arms, or balanced on their heads, or fastened on their backs, or tied on somewhere. And when at last they were ready to go home and were walking down the road, you could hardly believe they were children unless you saw their bright eyes peeping out through the leaves. They looked exactly like some new kind of dwarf tree out taking an airing,

perhaps, before the winter winds robbed them of their pretty green dresses. About sunset the other children said "good-by" and hurried home. Of course, they were immediately shut up with their mothers by the English soldiers. But Joseph and Priscilla loitered along until it was quite late, for they knew that their mother had left that morning to make a visit in another town and would not be home for several days.

Their house was in a lonely place, half a mile from the village, and of course they expected to find it dark and deserted. But when they reached the yard, to their surprise they found every window lighted! A great fire, also, had been built in the fireplace, and sparks were flying from the big chimney, sprinkling the yard with ashes.

"Somebody has started too big a fire," said Joseph anxiously, as he caught sight of the house.

"Oh, dear, maybe Mother has come home from her visit and will be worried because we are so late," cried Priscilla, a little frightened.

"Not much chance of that," answered Joseph, who was a little ahead. "Look, the yard is full of horses—that means soldiers. But, friends or enemies, I can't tell which. Let's creep up to the house and find out. Hold your bundles of leaves in front of your face, and if anybody comes near, just stand still where you are. I'm sure we'll be safe. They'll think we're bushes—or Christmas trees, perhaps."

Priscilla giggled a little at that and forgot to be afraid as she crept along behind Joseph until they were near enough to see the men inside the house.

THE ENEMY'S PLANS ARE DISCOVERED

"They are British!" cried Joseph as he caught sight of their red coats. "What do you suppose they're doing here? I wish I could find out. The men outdoors are of course only common soldiers, and they would not know. But the leaders are probably talking over their plans in the room there by the fire."

"Perhaps we can find out what they are saying if we creep around to the back of the house," suggested Priscilla. "You know Father built an extra door to the Dutch oven there to make it easier to rake out the ashes. If you climb into the oven, you can hear everything that is said in the room."

"Hooray!" cried Joseph softly. "You're a bright girl to think of a plan like that. I'd forgotten all about the outside door to the oven." And he began to move quietly toward the house with Priscilla close behind him.

A minute later, however, their plans almost came to grief. It was so dark under the trees that it was hard to see where they were going, and all of a sudden Priscilla found herself held fast. She had brushed the body of a sleeping soldier without knowing it. The man rolled over and caught hold of her, but when he found that he had only a handful of leaves for his trouble, he probably thought he had rolled into a bush in his sleep, for he soon let her go and went to sleep again. After that they were more careful and soon reached the back of the house.

Both Joseph and Priscilla had often hidden in the old oven when they were playing hide-and-seek, and they knew just how to manage. And so a minute later, when Joseph had taken off his bundles of leaves and piled them into a shelter under which Priscilla could keep watch, he crept carefully into the oven.

Fortunately for him there were air holes in the oven door through which the steam from the cooking could escape into the room, and through these he could both see and hear all that was going on in the room. It did not take him very long to find out something important, for in about ten minutes he slipped out of the oven and, breathing very hard, whispered excitedly to Priscilla.

"Oh, Prissy, they're planning to surprise the Americans at daybreak. The advance guard is already watching their camp fires from Wilson's Hill so that they can't escape. These men are waiting for a large body of soldiers to join them tonight, and then they will creep up on our men and destroy the whole army if they can. Washington and his little army won't have a chance unless they are warned beforehand.

JOSEPH WARNS GENERAL WASHINGTON

"I'll have to borrow Zack Brown's old plow horse and ride as fast as I can to the camp to tell them about the plans of the British. But I don't know what to do about you," he added with a worried air.

"Oh, I'll be all right," answered Priscilla bravely, though she felt very small and lonely when she thought of her brother riding away into the darkness and of the men, whose voices she could hear through the open oven door. Then a plan came to her, and she looked at the oven again. "Why can't I stay in the Dutch oven," she asked, "while you are gone? No one will think of looking for a girl in there."

"That's the best place to hide I can think of," answered Joseph slowly, "but I don't like to leave you. You know I wouldn't if I wasn't sure you would be safe."

"Of course not," whispered Priscilla, as he hurried away. Then she put a bundle of leaves in the oven for a pillow and climbed in after it, and, like the wise girl she was, she soon went sound asleep.

Exactly what happened that night the British soldiers never found out. The sentries on Wilson's Hill kept watch all night. Washington's camp fires burned as brightly as usual, and a few lights were to be seen in the tents and sentry boxes; everything seemed to be quiet in the camp of the Americans. But when the British made the attack at daybreak, not a gun answered them in the camp, and not an American soldier could be found! The place was as empty as a toy village.

When the soldiers went cautiously from tent to tent, they found the fires heaped high with ashes, and the candles were ringed around with melted wax as if they had burned all night long. Who had tended the fires and kept the candles burning, they could not discover, for there was no one in the camp to ask. Half a mile down the road, however, they came upon a sleepy boy with his head pillowed on a big bundle of crumpled leaves and a tired old plow horse grazing not far away. But of course, neither of them could tell them anything about the escape of the Americans.

"Humph!" said the disappointed British commander as he led his men back to their camp. "I thought I surely had the Americans in my power at last. But there's no use trying to get the best of that man Washington. He has his spies every place."

PRAISE FROM GENERAL WASHINGTON

Of course Joseph was not able to tell General Washington how he had learned of the plans of the British when he gave him the warning. But a few days later he was invited to visit the new camp, and this time Priscilla went along, and together they told the whole story. In fact, they told it many times— first to General Washington and his officers, and then to the men whose lives they had saved.

At dress parade in the camp that afternoon, the children were the guests of honor and reviewed the troops with General Washington. And after the drill was over, the General made a speech to the soldiers in which he told them of the bravery and wisdom of Joseph and Priscilla, and thanked the children on behalf of the whole country. After that he mentioned many other brave deeds which the children of the colonies had performed, and he said that they had many times proved that they were loyal and true to their country.

And then, at the very end of his speech, General Washington said something so beautiful that Joseph and Priscilla never forgot it.

"You and I," he said earnestly to the soldiers, "may finally be beaten by the English. But while our country has sons and daughters as brave as these two children, she can never be conquered!"

NOTES AND QUESTIONS

1. *(a)* What two things did the children do which show that they were brave?

   (b) What three things show that they could think quickly?

2. *(a)* If Joseph and Priscilla had not been brave, what might they have done?

   (b) If they had not been quick-witted, what might have happened to them?

3. In their quick thinking, the children asked themselves certain questions. Make a list of five important questions they had to ask and answer. Begin this way: *(1) Why is our house all lighted up?*

4. *(a)* How were the British trying to make sure that the American soldiers would not get away without their knowing it?

(b) What did General Washington do to fool the British?

5. Why was the brave act of Joseph and Priscilla so important to the American colonies?

6. Name at least one other story in this book that shows how important it is to be able to think quickly.

7. Tell in one sentence what this story is about.

8. There are five different parts to this story. Write the titles of the parts, reread the parts carefully, and under each title write two or three short sentences that tell what happened in that part. Your outline might start like this:

Leafing Day

(1) Leaves are needed to line the Dutch ovens.

(2) The children go to gather the leaves.

Other good stories of colonial days are: "The Bulb of the Christmas Tulip," Price, and "Belinda in the Fore-Room," Parton (in *Revolutionary Stories Retold from St. Nicholas*); "The Little Black-Eyed Rebel," Carleton (in *Child-Library Readers, Book Six*); and "The Deacon's Grasshopper," Bailey (in *Boys and Girls of Colonial Days*).

YOUNG GEORGE WASHINGTON

FREDERICK TREVOR HILL

We all know of George Washington as the wise and brave commander of the American army in our war for freedom, and as the first president of the United States. Both in war and in peace he served our country. But what was he like as a boy? What did he enjoy doing; what lessons did he learn that helped him become a great leader of his people?

THE PLANTATION PLAYGROUNDS

George Washington was a country boy. His father, Augustine Washington, owned three large farms or plantations, not far distant from each other in Virginia. On one of these plantations, which was later called "Wakefield," Washington was born on February 22, 1732.

The farmhouse which the family then occupied was a queer little two-story structure, with a steep sloping roof, two big chimneys, four rooms on the ground floor and perhaps as many more in the attic. It was built close to the Potomac River, between two streams known as Bridge's Creek and Pope's Creek, and all around it lay tobacco and corn fields fringed with forests. In later years this place became very familiar to the boy, but while he was still a mere baby, his family moved up the Potomac to another of his father's farms. Here George lived until he was nearly eight years old.

This plantation was then known as Hunting Creek. It was well named, for its creeks and rivers were fairly alive with fish, and the surrounding woods were full of quail, grouse, wild turkeys, foxes, and deer. Indeed, the whole country was famous for its game, and from the Indians who lived in the neighboring forests Washington undoubtedly learned something about shooting and fishing. The Indians were expert hunters, and knew far more about the habits of wild animals and fish than any of the white men. But fond as he was of such sport, the boy was still more fond of horses; he probably never remembered the time when he first sat astride of a pony. Certainly he began learning to ride at a very early age, and he had no lack of good instructors, for Virginians prided themselves on their horsemanship, and most of the planters were in the saddle from morning till night.

Altogether, the farm on Hunting Creek was a delightful spot for a lad like Washington who loved sport and adventure, but it would have been a bit lonely had it not been for his brothers and sisters. The nearest house was far away, and there were no schools or common meeting places for children. Fortunately, however, Washington had a sister and a brother old enough to be very companionable, and two still younger brothers who later proved excellent playmates. Besides, in the servants' quarters there were a number of boys and girls who joined the Washington children in all their games. For five years the woods about the plantation, which was later named "Mount Vernon," echoed with the shouts and laughter of a very merry company of youngsters. Then one day the house burned down, and the family moved to another farm on the Rappahannock River, almost directly opposite the little town of Fredericksburg.

This plantation, sometimes called the "Ferry Farm," closely resembled the others. The house was a small, plain, wooden

building, very simply but strongly constructed and painted a dark red. Around it lay tobacco, wheat, and corn fields, surrounded, as at the other homes, with dense woods. Until he arrived at Ferry Farm, Washington had been allowed to run free, without schooling of any kind, and it is doubtful if he then knew even his letters, although he was already in his eighth year.

He had, however, learned much that is not taught in books. He knew how to take care of himself in the open, how to make friends with horses and dogs, how to ride and fish and swim, how to lay out camps and build campfires, how to recognize the tracks of wild animals, how to blaze or mark a trail—all the thousand and one things which a quick-witted, outdoor boy learns from country life. Best of all, he had grown tall and strong and hardy from his life in the open air, storing up strength and health for the time when a sound body was essential for the work he had to do. And with these advantages his schoolboy days began.

GEORGE WASHINGTON'S SCHOOL DAYS

Washington's first school was not much more than a hut in the woods, in charge of a schoolmaster who knew very little more than his pupils. In those days it was difficult to find good school-teachers in Virginia. The instructor selected for this "old field school," as it was called, was a man known as Hobby, who had come over from England. How much Washington learned from this queer schoolmaster is not known. But it is certain that he was soon taught to write, for he scrawled his name all over a volume of sermons when he was eight or nine years old. That book, with his boyish writing, can be seen today in one of the Boston libraries. Indeed, Washington, like a great many other boys, was rather fond of scribbling, and some of his books which have been preserved are said to be adorned with pictures of birds, animals, people, and other drawings.

Hobby claimed in later years that his famous pupil received his best education in the little cabin schoolhouse, but it is certain that the most valuable things the boy learned in those early years he owed to his father and mother. They brought him up strictly but sensibly, teaching him the importance of obedience, manliness, courage, and honesty. Unfortunately for Washington, his father died when he was only eleven, but his mother proved a wise friend and counselor, and shortly after her husband's death she sent him to an excellent school kept by a Mr. Williams near "Wakefield."

It was not books nor book learning, however, that did the most for young Washington; it was his companionship with his half-brothers, Augustine and Lawrence. Up to this time he had seen very little of these young men, for they had been at school in England for several years. After their return Lawrence, the elder, had been made a captain in the English army and had gone to the West Indies, while Augustine had settled as a planter on the "Wakefield" farm.

Washington spent much of his time in the company of his brothers, and they took a great fancy to him. He was then a bright, promising lad, rather large for his age, fond of all outdoor games, and an exceptionally good horseman. He was also a good shot, a daring huntsman, and a keen woodsman, ready for any sport or adventure. It is no wonder that Lawrence and Augustine Washington were pleased to have young George with them. They were both educated, honorable men who had seen more of the world than most Virginians, and it was fortunate for Washington that he had their guidance and advice during these years. Doubtless they were proud of his skill in hunting and riding, and encouraged him, but they also showed him that he was expected to be something better than a horse trainer or a hunter. They set him an excellent example of useful work and decent living.

Captain Lawrence Washington proved a strong influence in making his brother into a gentleman, and some of the happiest hours that the lad ever knew were passed at the plantation on Hunting Creek, which Lawrence had received from his father, and which he had named Mount Vernon. Here Washington met many of his brother's comrades. Here he frequently met officers of the Royal Navy and of the big merchant ships which sailed into the Potomac, and listened to many a story of adventure on land and sea. So it is not at all surprising that George soon began to think he would like to be a sailor. Had his mother not interfered, he would certainly have gone to sea at the age of fourteen, for Captain Lawrence encouraged the idea. Fortunately, however, Mrs. Washington promptly forbade the plan, and her son returned to "Ferry Farm" to finish his schooling under a man named James Marye, who taught him a little Latin and generally improved his education.

Washington was not a solemn "old man" of a boy. He was a lively, quick-tempered, companionable youngster who wrestled with the boys and romped with the girls, but had plenty of good, hard common-sense. His schoolmates quickly learned this, and he was often selected to decide disputes, not as an outsider, but as a fellow who could be serious when it was necessary and was known to play fairly and squarely at every kind of sport.

Although he was not particularly studious, Washington could work as hard as he could play, and he was clever enough to know that if a thing is worth doing, it is worth doing well. One of his schoolbooks, called "The Young Man's Companion," is still in existence. From its exercises anyone can see where he acquired his good, clear handwriting, and how faithfully he stuck to its figures and accounts until he trained himself to exactness and order. There were plenty of boys in Virginia who were quite as well educated and promising as he was at the age of sixteen, but the little he had learned from books, he had learned thoroughly.

NOTES AND QUESTIONS

1. Write in a column the words that belong in the blank spaces.

George Washington, the son of ___(a)___ Washington, was born in the state of ___(b)___ in the year ___(c)___. At that time the family home was on a ___(d)___, later named ___(e)___, near the ___(f)___ River. While he was still a baby, the family moved to another place called ___(g)___. This later came to be known as ___(h)___. A second move took the family to ___(i)___ on the ___(j)___ River near the town of ___(k)___. Washington did not go to school until he was over ___(l)___ years of age. While at school he studied ___(m)___ (Name four things).

2. About how long ago was Washington born—75 years, 200 years, or 150 years?

3. Name five things Washington learned as a boy, which are not taught in books.

4. Make a list of twelve words or phrases from pages 213 and 214 which tell what kind of boy George Washington was.

5. From the list you have just made, choose five qualities that you think were most valuable to Washington when the time came for him to lead his country.

6. Mention an important thing that his outdoor life did for him.

7. Find and be ready to read lines that—

   (a) Tell about a valuable lesson that Washington's brother taught him.

   (b) Show he had learned obedience.

8. If anyone in your class has visited Mount Vernon, have him tell what he saw there.

You can learn more about George Washington by reading "The Washington Monument," and "Nellie Custis, the Girl Who Liked to Celebrate Washington's Birthday," Fox (in *Washington, D. C., a Book for Young People*); "Washington," Turner (in *Child Life*, February, 1930); *On the Trail of Washington*, Hill.

ABRAHAM LINCOLN GROWS UP

CARL SANDBURG

George Washington was the son of a rich and well-known family; Abraham Lincoln grew up in poverty. Yet each man became a great and beloved leader of his people. How Abraham Lincoln grew to manhood is told for you by Carl Sandburg, one of America's great writers. Sandburg spent many years studying about Lincoln and talking with people who knew him; then he wrote *Abe Lincoln Grows Up*, from which this story is taken.

When he was eleven years old, Abraham Lincoln's young body began to change. As the months and years went by, he noticed his lean wrists getting longer, his legs, too, and he was now looking over the heads of other boys. Men said, "Land o' Goshen, that boy air a-growin'!"

As he took on more length, they said he was shooting up into the air like green corn in the summer of a good corn-year. So he grew. When he reached seventeen years of age, and they measured him, he was six feet, nearly four inches high from the bottom of his moccasins to the top of his skull.

These were years he was handling the ax. Except in spring plowing-time and the fall fodder-pulling, he was handling the ax nearly all the time. The insides of his hands took on callus thick as leather. He cleared openings in the timber, cut logs, split firewood, built pig-pens.

He learned how to measure with his eye the swing of the ax, so as to nick out the deepest possible chip off a tree-trunk. The trick of swaying his body easily on the hips, so as to

217

throw the heaviest possible weight into the blow of the ax—he learned that.

On winter mornings he wiped the frost from the ax-handle, sniffed sparkles of air into his lungs, and beat a steady cleaving of blows into a big tree—till it fell. He sat on the main log and ate his noon dinner of corn bread and fried salt pork—and joked with the gray squirrels that frisked and peeped at him from high forks of near-by walnut trees.

He learned how to make his ax flash and bite into a sugar-maple or a sycamore. He could guess close to the time of the year, to the week of the month, by the way the leaves and branches of trees looked. Often he worked alone in the timber all day long with only the sound of his own ax, or his own voice speaking to himself, or the crackling and swaying of branches in the wind and the cries and whirs of animals, of brown and silver-gray squirrels, of partridges, hawks, crows, turkeys, sparrows, and the occasional wildcats.

The tricks of the sky, how to read clear skies and cloudy weather, the creeping vines of ivy and wild grape, the recurrence of dogwood blossoms in spring, the ways of snow, rain, drizzle, sleet, the visitors of sky and weather coming and going hour by hour—he tried to read their secrets; he tried to be friendly with their mystery.

So he grew, to become hard, tough, wiry. He found with other men he could lift his own end of a log—and more too. One of his neighbors said he was strong as three men. Another said, "He can sink an ax deeper into wood than any man I ever saw." And another, "If you heard him fellin' trees in a clearin', you would say there were three men at work by the way the trees fell."

He was more than a tough, long, rawboned boy. He amazed men with his man's lifting power. He put his shoulders under a new-built corn crib one day and walked away with it to where the farmer wanted it. Four men, ready with poles to put under it and carry it, didn't need their poles. He played the same trick with a chicken house; at the new, growing town of Gentryville near his home, they said that the chicken house weighed six hundred pounds, and only a big boy with a hard backbone could get under it and walk away with it.

So he grew, living in that Pigeon Creek cabin for a home, sleeping in the loft, climbing up at night to a bed just under the roof, where sometimes the snow and the rain drove through the cracks, eating sometimes at a table where the family had only one thing to eat—potatoes. Once at the table, when there were only potatoes, his father spoke a blessing to the Lord for potatoes; the boy murmured, "Those are mighty poor blessings." And Abe made jokes once when company came, and Sally Bush Lincoln brought out raw potatoes, gave the visitors a knife apiece, and they all peeled raw potatoes and talked about the crops, politics, and religion.

Days when they had only potatoes to eat didn't come often. Other days in the year they had "yaller-legged chicken" with gravy, and corn dodgers with shortening, and berries and honey. They tasted of bear meat, deer, coon, quail, grouse, prairie turkey, catfish, bass, perch.

Abe knew the sleep that comes after long hours of work out of doors. He worked in those young years clearing timberland for pasture and corn crops, cutting loose the brush, piling it and burning it, splitting rails, pulling the crosscut saw and whipsaw, driving the shovel-plow, harrowing, planting, hoeing, pulling fodder, milking cows, churning butter, helping neighbors at house-raisings, log-rollings, corn-huskings.

He found he was fast, strong, and keen when he went against other boys in sports. On farms where he worked, he held his own at scuffling, knocking off hats, wrestling. The time came when around Gentryville and Spencer County he was known as the best "rassler" of all, the champion. In jumping, foot-racing, throwing the maul, pitching the crowbar, he won against the lads of his own age always, and usually against those older than himself.

He earned his board, clothes, and lodgings, sometimes working for a neighbor farmer. He watched his father, while helping make cabinets, coffins, cupboards, window frames, doors. Hammers, saws, pegs, cleats, he understood first-hand, also the scythe and the cradle for cutting hay and grain, the corn-cutter's knife, the leather piece to protect the hand while shucking corn, and the horse, the dog, the cow, the ox, the hog.

And the hiding-places of fresh spring water under the earth crust had to be in his thoughts. He helped at well-digging; the wells Tom Lincoln dug went dry one year after another; neighbors said Tom was always digging a well and had his land "honey-combed," and the boy, Abe, ran the errands and held the tools for the well-digging.

When he was eighteen years old, he could take an ax at the end of the handle and hold it out in a straight horizontal line, easy and steady—he had strong shoulder muscles and steady wrists early in life. He walked thirty-four miles in one day, just on an errand, to please himself, to hear a lawyer make a speech. *He could tell his body to do almost impossible things, and the body obeyed.*

Growing from boy to man, he was alone a good deal of the time. Days came often when he was by himself all the time except at breakfast and supper hours in the cabin home. In some years more of his time was spent in loneliness than in the company of other people. It happened, too, that this loneliness he knew was not like that of people in cities who can look from a window on streets where faces pass and repass. It was the wilderness loneliness he became acquainted with. He lived with trees, with the bush wet with shining raindrops, with the burning bush of autumn. The faces of open sky and weather, the ax which is a one-man instrument, these he had for companions, books, friends, talkers, chums of his endless changing thoughts.

His moccasined feet in the winter time knew the white spaces of snowdrifts piled in queer shapes against timber slopes or blown in levels across the fields of last year's cut corn stalks; in the summer time his bare feet toughened in the gravel of green streams, while he laughed back to the chatter of bluejays in the red-haw trees, or while he kept his eyes ready in the slough grass for the cow-snake, the rattler, the copperhead.

He rested between spells of work in the springtime when the upward push of the coming out of the new grass can be heard, and in autumn weeks when the rustle of a single falling leaf lets go a whisper that a listening ear can catch.

And so he grew.

NOTES AND QUESTIONS

1. Under the headings "Lincoln" and "Washington," write the words and phrases from the list below that tell about each man. You may want to put some of the phrases under both names.

Rich parents   Happy, carefree boyhood
Lonesome boyhood   Poor parents
Expert hunter   Skillful axman
Good horseman   Had many companions
Crude log cabin   Healthy and strong
Knew out-door life   Respected by others
Boyhood of hard labor   Understood farming
Lived in the country   Comfortable plantation home

2. Name three of the sports in which Lincoln took part.

3. What four incidents does Carl Sandburg tell about to make us realize how strong Lincoln was?

4. Mention two or three facts that tell you that Lincoln grew up in a new and unsettled country.

5. If you had visited the part of Illinois where Lincoln grew up, what would you have seen on the farms—such as buildings, crops, and animals? Name seven such things.

6. Did the people of those times depend entirely on the farm for food, or did they get food in other ways? Prove your answer.

7. Find and be ready to read lines that—

   (a) Show what an expert axman Lincoln was.

   (b) Show how strong he was.

   (c) Tell of his love of the out-of-doors.

8. Which story—the one about Washington or the one about Lincoln—gave you the clearer understanding of the man's boyhood days? Why? Be ready to discuss this in class.

You would like to read "A Pioneer Boy," Tarbell (in *The Boy Scout's Life of Lincoln*); "A Backwoods Boy," Moores (in *The Life of Abraham Lincoln for Boys and Girls*); and "The Gingerbread Muster Day," Shaw (in *Child Life,* April, 1930).

A LITTLE SONG OF LIFE

LIZETTE WOODWORTH REESE

Glad that I live am I;
   That the sky is blue;
Glad for the country lanes,
   And the fall of dew.

After the sun the rain;
   After the rain the sun;
This is the way of life,
   Till the work be done.

All that we need to do,
   Be we low or high,
Is to see that we grow
   Nearer the sky.

TO TOIL AND BE KIND

MARY CAROLYN DAVIES

To toil and to be kind
These are the chores I find.

To work and to be gay—
This rule for every day.

To take life unafraid—
This task on me is laid;

On you too. Let us, then,
Do our task well. *Amen.*

IF LOVE WERE MINE

ANNETTE WYNNE

If love were mine, if love were mine,
  I know what I would do,
    I'd take it, spare it,
    Give it, share it,
Lend it, spend it, too.

If beauty I could claim for mine,
  To hold, to cherish, too,
    I'd strive to spread it,
    Pour it, shed it,
Till it flowed the whole world through.

But toil—just common toil—is mine;
  And so what I shall do
    Is strive to take it,
    Carve it, make it,
Into love and beauty, too.

Reprinted by permission from *For Days and Days: A Year-round Treasury of Verse for Children* by Annette Wynne, copyright 1919, Frederick A. Stokes Company.

MARION ANDREWS, LIFE SAVER

Mildred Augustine

Marion Andrews was not a good enough swimmer or diver to take part in the water-carnival contests; but when the carnival was over, she was the most important person of the day. She had shown that she could think quickly, act bravely, and use what she had learned.

A PLUCKY LITTLE SWIMMER

A girl came swimming toward the shore with easy, graceful strokes, but strokes which cut the water with great strength for a girl of her size. She reached shallow water, waded up the beach, and, as she approached the boathouse, shook the water from her eyes and jerked off her bathing-cap to free a bobbed mass of dripping hair.

"O-h," she shivered. "Water's like ice this morning."

"Big Bob" Brenton, life-guard at Coronado Beach, nodded and glanced out upon the river, where only a few of the most enthusiastic bathers were swimming.

"Two more weeks will finish the season. People are going back to the city already."

"And I suppose you'll be leaving too?" Marion Andrews spoke a trifle sadly, for when Bob returned to his work at the city Y. M. C. A. pool, it meant the end of the swimming lessons he had been giving her. In the two summers that he had guarded Coronado Beach he had taught her life-saving, and had greatly improved her racing stroke, the crawl.

"I'm staying until after the Seals' swimming races; then I leave. You're to be in the carnival, I suppose?"

Marion became sober, and a look of disappointment came into her eyes for an instant. Then she laughed.

"I'm helping to decorate the floats, and I'm to be in one of the water pyramids."

"But aren't you swimming in the races, or diving, or taking part in the canoe-tilts?"

"I'm not good enough, Bob. You see, I've been practicing life-saving most of the summer, and my diving isn't as good as it should be. My racing stroke isn't so bad, but there are three other girls larger for their age than I, and they make better time than I do; so they're to swim."

The Seals' Club, a swimming club to which Marion belonged, gave a thrilling water carnival each summer at Coronado Beach, and the festival usually marked the end of the summer-resort season. The carnival was one of the big events, and thousands of persons always crowded the river banks to watch the spectacular stunts. Only the best swimmers, divers, and canoeists took part in the events.

In spite of the fact that Marion was not to have an active part in the carnival, she found plenty of work to do during the week before the regatta. A pageant was to be given as the opening event, and elaborate floats had to be decorated. Marion furnished many useful ideas, and it was she who went here and there, gathering bunting, renting rafts and canoes for the big day, securing boards and odds and ends that never seemed to be on hand, but which were necessary.

"I wish I had worked on my diving this summer," Marion said a trifle regretfully to Bob the day before the swimming carnival. "Margaret Howard is to do fancy high-diving, and she will carry off all the honors."

"Well, perhaps." Big Bob, who had saved the lives of more than thirty bathers, had little respect for diving. "Personally, I'd rather be a good swimmer. It doesn't help you any to know how to dive when some drowning man gets you by the neck."

"I think I'll try a high dive," said Marion. "I'm scared to death of that board, but I want to see if I've got the nerve to do it. You watch me, Bob, and pick up the pieces if I come down all at once."

Marion always felt compelled to try the things which were the most difficult, the things she most feared. To the people of Coronado Beach she was still known as "the kid that fights her way"; for those who had seen her play basketball never could forget the plucky way in which she had fought to overcome her lack of strength and size, and had battled until she had won a position on the team. She had won success in other sports with the same grim determination.

It was fear of striking the water flat, and not the fear of the distance from the diving-board to the water, that made the girl hesitate. As she had often expressed it, "Even soft water is hard, if you hit it all in a heap."

"Oh, well, here I go." Marion stepped to the edge of the board, poised an instant, then jumped without allowing herself time to think about it. She felt her feet going over as she neared the water and she tried to obey the shouted warning from Bob: "Head up, Marion."

As she struck the water, she seemed to feel every pound of her body's weight; her feet splashed over, twisting her back slightly. She came to the surface of the water, and swam slowly back to where Bob stood.

"Too bad, Marion! That must have hurt. Keep your head up, or you'll flop over every time."

"I think I'll call it a day. I'm willing to let Margaret Howard have the diving honors."

CARNIVAL DAY ON CORONADO BEACH

As in previous years on the day of the Seals' regatta, an enthusiastic crowd of people strung themselves along the Coronado River. Marion was on hand in the morning at an early hour, for she did not mean to miss a single feature of the program. Bright banners waved in the wind; the band played; privately owned canoes, gaily flying their colors, skimmed up and down the river, and in front of the diving boards, where the main part of the swimming program was to be presented, all sorts of craft were parked.

The early part of the day was occupied with a water pageant, canoe and swimming races, and water-polo. Comedy was furnished by a tub-race, a canoe-tilt, and an old-clothes race. Then came the floating pyramids, in which Marion took part. Together with twenty other girls, who looked very much alike in trim black bathing-suits and red caps, she swam out into the water. The girls banded themselves together, holding hands, and floated down the river upon their backs. From the shore, the effect was that of a moving mass of solid red.

The exhibition completed, two motor-boats plowed down the river, the girls were hauled aboard, and brought back. Marion took a place on a float near the high-diving board, for fancy diving was the last event on the program, and she did not wish to miss it. She watched Margaret Howard, the first diver, as she mounted the ladder.   Margaret was the star diver of the club, and all eyes were upon her.

Margaret stood ready at the edge of the board.   For an instant Marion removed her eyes from the girl and glanced at the water beneath the platform.   She gave a sudden start and leaned forward in an attempt to get a clearer view.   She could see the indistinct outline of a dark object below the surface, and realized what had happened.

A log, in drifting down the river, had caught at one corner of the standards of the diving platform and was being held just below the surface of the water.   It reached out toward the spot where Margaret Howard would surely dive!   Fear paralyzed Marion for the moment; then she cried out in warning: "Stop her!"

A THRILLING RESCUE

The persons who were near Marion looked at her in surprise, and a few of them smiled, but Margaret did not hear. She poised on the board and sprang upward and out, spreading her hands for the swan dive.   A moment her body seemed to remain motionless at a point above the board, then she shot downward.   She struck the water, and what would have been a perfect dive ended in an awkward flop.   There was no thud, no crash, and not until a jagged log floated free on the water did those who were standing near the platform understand what had happened.

Quick as a flash Marion sprang from the float.   A dozen powerful strokes brought her to the spot where she had seen Margaret go down.   Holding to the slippery log with one hand, she peered down into the water and tried to catch a

glimpse of the girl. She thought she saw a form below her, but could not be certain. Drawing her body into a ball, she let go of the log, ducked her head, straightened her body with a sudden snap, and shot down into the water in a perfect surface dive. In working for her life-saving badge, she had mastered that dive.

Marion kept her eyes open, and the moment she was well below the surface, began to swim toward the dark object. Her hand reached out and clutched Margaret by the strap of her bathing-suit. Wasting not an instant, she swung the limp body into position for the cross-chest carry, and, with one arm free, began to lift the form to the surface. She was nearly out of breath, but not for a minute did she think of releasing the body that hung like a dead weight upon her. Then, just as it seemed that she could no longer hold her breath, her head emerged and she gulped in the fresh air.

She could see other swimmers in the water near her, and before she could take a stroke toward shore, Big Bob had reached her to take charge of Margaret.

"Keep the people back!" Big Bob warned as he stretched Margaret out on the sand. "Give her a chance."

Members of the Seals' Club and other swimmers formed a protecting circle about the unconscious girl and held curious and frightened persons from crowding in upon her. A hurried examination told the life-guard that Margaret had struck her hands on the log and had suffered only a glancing blow upon the head. One arm hung limp, and it was evident that it was broken.

"She's coming around now," Bob announced after he had worked with her for a few minutes. "We'll get a car and take her to the hospital, where she can have medical treatment. She'll be all right as soon as her arm is set."

When Bob had placed Margaret in the doctor's hands, he returned to the waterfront, for his duty as life-guard made it necessary for him to be on the beach. The crowd was rapidly melting away, but small groups of persons were still standing near the diving-board where the accident had taken place. Bob glanced searchingly up and down the beach. Then as he turned, he saw Marion, dressed in street clothes, coming toward him from the direction of the bath-house.

"Hello there, Marion. Come here. What do you mean by running off when everyone wants to congratulate you?"

Marion opened her eyes wide; then a flush of pleasure came over her face. Big Bob, seeing her surprised look, knew that Marion had not counted upon being the heroine of the day. He laughed.

"Why, Marion, you funny kid! Don't you know that your rescue of Margaret was the most thrilling event of the carnival? You had the greater part of the whole thing. And if you think you can sneak home without having me tell you so—well, you're mistaken, that's all!"

Notes and Questions

1. We often think that bravery means being not at all afraid. From what you have read about Marion Andrews, what would you say bravery might also mean?

2. What quality besides bravery made it possible for Marion to save Margaret's life?

3. Tell—

   (a) Two things that show Marion's bravery.

   (b) Something that shows her good sportsmanship.

   (c) Something that shows her modesty.

4. Marion was small for her age. How did she make up for her small size in the various games she played?

5. Tell exactly what it was that caused the accident to Margaret Howard.

6. In diving, what must a person be careful to avoid doing?

7. If anyone in the class understands what the crawl stroke and the cross-chest carry are, have him explain them to the class.

Three other good stories that you would enjoy reading are: "Florence Nightingale," Mabie, "A Young Hero of the Beach Patrol," Drysdale (both in *Child-Library Readers, Book Six*); and "Becky's Christmas Turkey," Skinner (in *Girl Scout Stories, Second Book*).

THE WILL TO WIN

Russell Gordon Carter

Do you know what it means to be beaten by your own self? It is this: You get the idea that you can't win, you can't learn this lesson, or you can't do that hard job. Then you are surely beaten. But people can do wonders when deep down in their hearts they resolve that they will not give up. Let us see what Rodney Owen and his team-mates did because they had "the will to win."

WHAT RODNEY'S TEAM NEEDED

Rodney Owen raced down the left side of the basketball court and leaped into the air. The ball, passed high and swift, smacked against his upstretched hands, and, dodging the opposing guards, he sent it flying toward the basket.

The spectators, crowded on both sides of the court and in the gallery of the Middleton gymnasium, held their breath as they watched the ball rise toward the rafters and then fall in a graceful curve. It struck the backstop and bounded downward against the iron rim; it sprang upward again and fell against the rim a second time. There it hesitated as it made some tiny bounces; then it rolled lazily off to the right and dropped toward the floor. At that moment the whistle blew, announcing the end of the first half of the game between Georgeburgh and Middleton—the final game to decide the high-school championship of western Ohio.

"Hard luck, Rod!" someone shouted.

"Good try, Rod, old man!" added another consoling voice. "Pretty work if it had gone in!"

From Russell Gordon Carter's *Three Points of Honor*. Copyright, 1929, by Little, Brown & Company.

"Yes, but it didn't!" replied a Middleton supporter. "Poor old Georgeburgh! Twenty-four to nine—some score!"

Rodney grinned when he heard these remarks, but in his heart there was anger. It was only the end of the first half, yet everybody seemed to think his team was hopelessly beaten —not only the Middleton supporters, but even the little band of Georgeburgh rooters who had made the long trip to see the game! He threw his sweater across his shoulders and followed his team-mates toward the locker room set aside for them. When he reached it, they were lying stretched out on the benches looking weary and dejected. It was clear that they, too, considered themselves hopelessly beaten.

Rodney sat down and mopped the sweat from his face.

"Listen, fellows! Do you know what the score is?" His voice was hard, and his sea-blue eyes, usually so mild, flashed with anger.

Frank O'Connor, the other forward, grinned. Bill Zimmerman and Ed Brown, the guards, made no sign of having heard. Paul Stearns, the tall center, pushed himself to a sitting position, slowly rubbing a bruised shoulder.

"Sure, we know the score," Stearns replied in a gloomy voice, "twenty-four to nine—and it will be a lot worse at the end of the second half!"

Ed Brown gazed straight upward at the gray ceiling. "Luck is against us, Rod. Take that last shot of yours—it missed the basket by a millionth of an inch!"

Rodney's teeth came together with a click. He passed a hand impatiently through his moist brown hair, thrusting it back from his forehead. "The second half is going to be different!" he cried.

He was on his feet now—a tall, loose-jointed, broad-shouldered boy with fists clenched in front of his chest. "We're not beaten! We're not even half beaten! Listen, now—do we want to win this championship? Of course we do! But we'll never win it if we just talk about hard luck and how big the final score's going to be!"

"Sure, that's right," agreed O'Connor, frowning. "We've got to go into the second half and fight!"

"We've got to do more than that!" retorted Rodney, thumping a fist against the palm of his hand. "We've got to start the second half with the will to win! And we can do it. Listen, fellows!" His voice quivered with feeling. "Do you remember that talk on General Foch we heard at one of the scout meetings last year? Do you remember what Foch said? He said, 'Victory is a thing of the will. Victory goes always to those who deserve it by the greater force of will.' And, certainly, General Foch ought to know!"

The others were all sitting up now, gazing with a sort of unwilling interest at their leader. They had never before seen him roused to such determination; they had never before seen his eyes flash with such fierce-burning fire. This was altogether a different boy from the good-natured, easy-going Rodney Owen who had led them through victory after victory to the very point of a championship. They just stared at him, not knowing what to say.

"Listen, now!" continued Rodney. "To-night we will be in camp with the gang. What'll they say if we're defeated badly? What will they think of us?"

At this moment Mr. Fisher, the coach and Scoutmaster of the Georgeburgh troop to which all five of the boys belonged, appeared in the locker room at the farther end of the aisle. It was his intention to speak to his boys, to encourage them as best he could; but seeing Rodney standing before them with fists clenched and face almost the color of his jersey, the coach paused, and then quietly left. At that moment he was not needed—and he knew it!

"Well, what do you say?" demanded Rodney. "Are you going to let Middleton beat us?"

Ed Brown was the first to find his voice. "I guess they won't beat us by much—"

"You're right they won't!" Rodney interrupted him fiercely. "They won't beat us at all! What are fifteen points? Nothing! Absolutely nothing! Come on, now, make up your minds we are going to win! I know you're tired. So am I! But let's forget how tired we are! Let's forget everything except that we are going to cut down that lead and win the game! I tell you we are a better team than Middleton! The will to win—that's all we need! And then tonight at camp we can face the gang with heads up!"

O'Connor glared at the rows of green lockers. "If I could only shake off that little guard, Martinelli—"

"Yes," Stearns interrupted him, "and if I could only get the jump once in a while on that tall Art Baker—"

"You'll do it!" exclaimed Rodney. "You'll both do it! And Ed and Bill will stick to Mason and McLaren—stick right to them all the time!" he added, shaking his fist. "And I'll take care of Gregg. Remember Foch, fellows! Remember: Victory equals will! And if anybody feels like quitting—"

"Who's going to quit?" Brown demanded angrily.

"Nobody!" replied O'Connor quickly.

"You're right they won't!" declared Stearns.

Rodney felt a sudden pride in his teammates. No, they would not quit; they would not slow up. It would be altogether a different team in the second half. There was a new look in their eyes!

GEORGEBURGH'S FIGHTING PLAYERS

A shrill whistle sounded in the gymnasium.

"Let's go!" cried Rodney.

And crowding close, the Georgeburgh team hurried back to the basketball court—five quick, determined boys in red jerseys. To the surprise of the onlookers they ran to their positions, and, "on their toes," began to dance about, exercising arms and legs and shouting words of fierce encouragement to one another.

"Huh!" remarked a Middleton rooter. "Looks as if old Georgeburgh meant to hold the score down this half."

A boy beside him grinned. "Sure," he added, "they're supposed to go to Scout Camp after it's over, and I guess they think the doors will be locked on them if they get a bad licking!"

The Middleton team, clad in white jerseys, came forth with great noise and confidence. Homer Gregg, the right guard, grinned as he took his place beside Rodney. "You'll need lots of 'pep' in this half! We're going to run away from you!"

Rodney slid his right foot back, signaling that he would go in for the ball. He kept his eyes fixed on the referee.

"Ready, Middleton?"

Art Baker nodded.

"Ready, Georgeburgh?"

"We are ready," said Rodney.

The referee tossed the ball up and blew his whistle. The two centers leaped into the air, and for the first time Stearns got the jump on his opponent. Rodney secured the ball and, slipping by his guard, whirled and sent it flying toward O'Connor, who had crossed to the left of the floor. He picked it out of the air, took a step that carried him free from the charge of little Johnny Martinelli, and with a forward push of his right hand shot it into the basket. A burst of cheers went up from the group of Georgeburgh supporters. It was a pretty play from signals, a pretty pass, a pretty shot!

"Come on, now, everybody!" cried Rodney as they lined up again. He slid his left foot back, and when the whistle sounded, he raced across the court.

Again Stearns got the jump. O'Connor secured the ball and whirled to pass it to Rodney; but Rodney was covered by both guards. O'Connor dribbled the ball toward the basket, and then, as Baker crashed into him, passed it to Stearns. Gregg, coming forward, was on the center in a flash; but Rodney was free now, and taking the ball on a short pass, he scored from almost under the basket.

A second roar of approval rose from the side lines—a louder roar than the first one. It set Rodney's blood to tingling. Again he gave O'Connor's signal, but on the next play Stearns missed the jump, and Mason secured the ball. A rapid succession of passes carried it down to Georgeburgh's goal, but there Brown and Zimmerman each covered his man so well that the ball went outside.

Stearns caught the pass from Brown, got away from Baker and Mason, and passed the ball to Zimmerman, who dribbled it to the center of the court before sending it to Rodney in one corner. Cries of "Shoot! Shoot!" came from the side line. Rodney hesitated, then crouched with careful aim. But even as he was about to shoot, he saw O'Connor, closely followed by Martinelli, racing down the other side of the court in a wide curve toward the basket. Suddenly straightening, he sent the ball toward his teammate. O'Connor caught it on his chest a dozen feet from the basket and, rising like a bird, dropped it into the iron circle.

The score was now twenty-four to fifteen, and some of those who had felt sure of a bad beating for Georgeburgh were willing to admit that they had a slim chance to win. But soon after the next toss-up Art Baker got loose from his opponent, made a long dribble and then a quick pass to

McLaren, received the ball again and scored from beside the basket. After that, in a scrimmage, the referee called a foul on Brown and Zimmerman, and Baker made the extra point. Rodney noticed the worried look on the faces of the two guards. "Never mind!" he shouted. "It couldn't be helped. Come on, now, on your toes! We'll show them! Up you go, Paul—way up this time!"

And Stearns got the jump again. He did more than that; taking a pass from Rodney, he made a long successful shot from the side. Then, a few minutes later, Bill Zimmerman, on a guard-forward play, received the ball from O'Connor and, with Gregg clawing desperately at him, made a short, one-handed shot that brought the Georgeburgh score up to nineteen; McLaren then scored two points for Middleton; but in the next few minutes Rodney and O'Connor each shot a basket, and Stearns followed with a goal from foul.

Slowly, fighting every point, Georgeburgh continued to gain. Rodney seemed to be everywhere on the court, blocking, passing, shooting, urging his team to greater efforts. And they responded as boys always respond to a leader who knows how to set an example by his deeds.

With three minutes left to play, the score was thirty-three to thirty-one in favor of Middleton, and the excitement of the crowd was at a fever pitch. That was what a championship game should be!

With two minutes to play, a foul was called on Middleton. Stearns had missed his last try for a point from foul, and now he looked doubtfully at his leader.

"Go ahead!" said Rodney. "Take your time. You'll make it!"

Stearns set his lips and with his eye carefully measured the distance. The ball rose, struck the backstop and swished downward through the basket. Thirty-three to thirty-two!

THE JOY OF VICTORY

"One minute to play!" came a voice from the sideline.

Rodney felt something almost like a panic. In one minute the game would be over! In one minute, unless Georgeburgh scored, the championship would be lost! Knowing that the time was passing swiftly, he gave O'Connor's signal and called upon Stearns to put all his strength into the jump.

In spite of Rodney's plea, Baker knocked the ball from Stearns's hand, but Bill Zimmerman, coming in before his forward, secured it and passed it to Brown, the only free man. Brown dribbled the ball a few yards, and then advanced it to O'Connor. Baker closed in upon the right forward, but O'Connor twisted free and passed to Stearns.

"Paul! Paul!"

The center whirled and saw Rodney, with Gregg and Martinelli on either side of him, racing across the court parallel with the backstop. Stearns took a desperate chance and made a high, swift pass.

Rodney seemed suddenly to climb into the air after the ball. The two guards jumped for it at the same time, but it was Rodney's fingers that touched it, held it—held it for a fraction of a second while over his shoulder he cast a quick glance toward the basket. Then his arms stiffened in an awkward sidewise shot—and the next instant he landed on hands and knees on the floor. A roar filled his ears, and looking up he saw the ball bound downward against the iron

rim and leap into the air. He saw it strike the rim a second time and hesitate in a number of bounces, and the sickening thought came to him that it was going to roll off after the manner of his final try at the end of the first half. He sprang to his feet, and as he did so, the ball made one more bounce and dropped through the netting.

Rodney's whole body was quivering with nervous excitement. Thirty-four to thirty-three! One point ahead! He ran to his position. "Hold them, fellows!" he pleaded. "Stick close, everybody! Everybody watch his man!"

The referee put the ball into play, and Rodney went forward after it. Again Stearns was out-jumped, and this time Mason got the ball; but as he turned to pass to McLaren, Rodney was upon him—and at that instant the timekeeper's whistle shrilled above the shouting. The game was over!

A sudden rush of boys from the sidelines sent Rodney staggering. They pushed him and thumped him on the back. They shouted his name in a roar that almost deafened him. Few though they were, compared with the Middleton supporters, they made more noise than Middleton had made at any point during the game. He struggled free from them at last; then they turned their enthusiasm loose upon O'Connor and Stearns and the two guards.

It was not until ten minutes later, after receiving the congratulations of the Middleton players, that the Georgeburgh team was once more together in the locker room; there, in the joy of victory, they hugged one another. And then at last O'Connor gasped, "But it was Rod who did it—"

"You bet!" cried Stearns. "He did it with that last shot—and by what he said to us between the halves—"

"Stop the fuss!" protested Rodney, struggling out of his jersey. "Just think of that final goal. Every one of us had the ball! Great teamwork—that's what did it!"

But the others would not listen to him. Well they knew that at the end of the first half they were a beaten team, that they would have been a beaten team at the end of the second half except for the words and example of their leader.

Rodney felt like shouting forth his joy. It was not the victory alone that was so sweet, but rather the manner in which it had come—through the power of the will to win in spite of great difficulties! He felt that in leading his team to success he had found some hidden strength of which he had been ignorant. The thought was new and brought with it a thrill of mastery that he had never in his life felt.

"Boys, I'm proud of you!" exclaimed Mr. Fisher as he

joined them. "I haven't the words to tell you how much! You did it all alone—"

"Thanks to your coaching," added Rodney.

Notes and Questions

1. Which one of these three reasons tells why the Georgeburgh team was being beaten?

(a) They were playing a better team.

(b) They had been poorly coached.

(c) They got a bad start and lost faith in themselves.

2. What does this story best show?

(a) We can always win if we make up our minds to do so.

(b) It is a disgrace to be defeated.

(c) Victory often depends upon determination.

3. In what two ways did Rodney make his team feel ashamed? (Pages 236 and 237 will help you.)

4. Mention two ways in which Rodney helped his team to win.

5. Rodney helped his team-mates win two victories; one was over Middleton.

(a) What was the other?

(b) Which was the more important victory?

6. Be ready to read the lines that describe Rodney as he looked while talking to the team.

7. Find on page 240 a paragraph that tells how Rodney led the team during the second half of the game.

8. Be ready to read the lines that tell how Rodney felt after the victory.

You would enjoy reading the book, *Three Points of Honor,* Carter; "How a Boy Saved the Third Troop," Hildreth (in *Child-Library Readers, Book Six*); and *The Builder of the Dam,* Heyliger.

OUR COUNTRY—AMERICA

MARGARET E. SANGSTER

By the sweep of rejoicing rivers
   That rush to the mighty sea,
By the waves on our coasts that thunder,
   By the winds that are wild and free,
By the stars in heaven above us,
   By the forests of pine and palm,
By the strength of the hearts that love us,
   By the valor serene and calm
Of our young men strong for toiling
   Of our old men, wise and brave,
By the Glory of days departed,
   By many a hero's grave;
Oh, blessed, beautiful Country,
   We pledge thee our deathless faith.

A BACKWARD LOOK

THE STORIES you have just read are samples. In your town or school library and in magazines written especially for young American citizens, you will find countless stories about boys and girls like yourself. It is always interesting to learn what others like ourselves are doing. Sometimes we are surprised to find that they have experiences very much like our own; at other times we learn new things or get new ideas that help us.

Perhaps you know of a baseball, basketball, or football team that has "come from behind" and won a game when it seemed certain of defeat. When a team goes into a game feeling sure of victory, what danger does it face? In addition to Rodney, was there a person in one of these stories that you think would have made a good leader?

You have just read about the boyhood days of two of our country's great men. Is there another great person about whose youthful days you know? It would be interesting to write a little story or prepare a little talk about that person's boyhood or girlhood days.

You have been told that young American citizens have duties to perform at home and at school. There are also ways in which boys and girls can help make the town or city a better place in which to live. It would be worthwhile for you and your classmates to suggest and talk over some of these ways. For example, is it right to destroy or damage property on Halloween?

On page 450 you will find a list of books that tell of American boys and girls. You will surely want to read some of them.

Part Five
Boys and Girls of Other Lands

THE SEA THAT COMES
TO MEET MY HAND

ANNETTE WYNNE

The sea that comes to meet my hand
Is rolling on some foreign land;
And some small child in that far place
Is looking out to see my face.

Reprinted by permission from *For Days and
Days: A Year-round Treasury of Verse for
Children* by Annette Wynne, copyright 1919
by Frederick A. Stokes Company.

ALL NATIONS ARE NEIGHBORS

OUR NEIGHBORS are those who live near us. Generally we know them best; often they are our closest friends. Have you ever stopped to think that slowly but surely all the people of the world are coming to be neighbors? Swift airplanes and trains, giant steamships, the radio and the telegraph are bringing the nations of the world closer and closer together.

The people of Japan suffer death and destruction from a terrible earthquake. In a few hours the whole world knows about it, and nations rush to the rescue with food, money, and messages of sympathy.

Boy Scouts from all over the world meet in a great "jamboree," and James Brown from America finds that Ivor Stannik from Poland, Giacomo Spadoni from Italy, and Ole Sjostrand from Sweden are much like himself and the boys he knows at home.

In times of long ago, before the news of the world could travel so swiftly and people could journey great distances so easily, every stranger was an enemy. Tribes and nations were almost always at war. But now we live so close together that we must be friends if this is to be a happy world. We must understand and respect the people of other nations. When you read about people of foreign lands, notice that they have qualities that make you want to be friends with them. You may find some of them much like yourself.

In the stories you are now to read, you will visit some young citizens of other countries. Think of them as distant but friendly neighbors.

THE SPANISH BOOTBLACK

CAROLINE MABRY

When you studied the history of America, you read a great deal about Spain and the Spaniards. You remember those great explorers—De Soto, de Leon, and Coronado. Perhaps you remember also that when we won our freedom, Spain owned nearly all the land from the Mississippi River to the Pacific Ocean. Even today there are thousands of Spanish-speaking people in our country.

The story you will now read tells something of life in Spain today. In the company of Pepin, the bootblack, you will travel to Seville and Granada, two of the most famous cities in the world.

NO WORK IN RONDA

Pepin was a bootblack in Spain. He lived in Ronda near the great bridge which stretches across a chasm so deep that on one side four hundred steps are carved in the rock leading down to the valley. They are old steps, cut in an early day when the Romans had besieged Ronda, and they were made so that the water carriers could slip down them secretly and bring water from the stream to the thirsty town. Now Ronda lay peacefully in the sunshine, and boys played on the steps, hiding in the caves along the way.

Pepin, usually the jolliest of them all, had not joined the boys today. His heart was heavy. He stood leaning over the high bridge looking out across the valley where the river turned the wheels of the grist mills. In his pocket was only one "little dog," which is a small coin with a lion on it. It was the last one Pepin had, for there had not been many boots

to black lately in Ronda. They needed blacking just as they had before, for the paths of Spain are dusty and rough with pebbles. But the crops had not been good this summer, and everyone was poor—too poor even to pay Pepin a few pennies to shine dusty shoes.

He stood now with his work box set on the railing of the bridge, begging the passers-by to let him polish their shoes. But they shook their heads, and with a kind word went on their way. Up the steep road that led from the valley, Pepin could see his older brother coming from the grist mill where he worked. With lagging steps, Pepin went to meet him. As they stopped at the door of their house right at the edge of the bluff, Pepin sighed.

"Why are you so sad today?" his brother asked kindly.

"No work. I ask and ask, and there's nothing to do," Pepin answered. "If I could only go to some other town, to one of the cities, where there are more people and where they aren't so poor!"

"Why can't you?" his brother asked.

"No money, only one little dog, and it wouldn't take me far on the train, hardly to the next station."

"Pepin, could you go if I'd loan you my donkey?" his brother asked.

"Yes, but how would you get back and forth to the mill?"

"I'll walk," his brother offered.

THE WONDERS OF GRANADA

A few days later Pepin set out toward the mountains, on the donkey. His mother had filled one of his saddle bags with food enough to last until he could earn more money, and in the other bag he carried an old quilt to cover him when he slept along the road at night. Behind him was strapped his boot-blacking box, ready for any work he might pick up along the way.

For several days Pepin rode steadily westward through the mountain passes toward Granada. He was sure he could get work there; it was a larger city than Ronda, and many travelers came to see its fine old palace, the Alhambra. Snow-covered peaks rose high above Pepin's head, as the donkey with sure feet made its way over the stony paths. At last they came to Granada.

On a hill above the town, Pepin could see the palace walls. As he rode toward them, he stopped before a shop with em-broidered shawls and brass candlesticks in the window. A man was coming out of the door, followed by two ladies, and from their talk Pepin knew that they were Americans, for he had heard other Americans talking, who had come to see the bridge in Ronda. In soft Spanish words Pepin asked to black their shoes. They did not understand what he said, but they saw his box and knew its meaning.

"Here's a bootblack wanting a job," the man said, turning to the others. "We may as well stop for a shine."

Pepin tried to catch the word he had used, but he couldn't quite say it. Still, he tried as he rubbed the dust from the man's shoes.

"Bo——ot," was as far as Pepin could go.

"Bootblack," the man repeated.

"Bootblack," Pepin said, his brushes flying.

He said it over and over again, for if he knew a word familiar to Americans, it would be easier to persuade them to let him shine their shoes. With the pennies from his work jingling in his pocket, Pepin rode up the hill and through the gate that leads to the mountain on which the palace stands. Trees arched over his head, and streams trickled down the hill, making soft music. It was easy to find the road, for many were going toward the Alhambra. As he came to the outer wall, Pepin found a place to tie his donkey. He passed under the Gate of Justice, with its hand carved in stone, and mounted a flight of steps.

He faced a garden with a fountain playing in it. There were travelers resting on the stone benches. He polished some of their shoes. He saw people coming and going through the door that led into the palace, and he joined them. But there he found that he would have to pay to enter. He was out of food now, and he needed to save his money. Through the palace door he could see a long hall leading to an archway shaped like a horse shoe, and the walls gleamed with tiles of many colors. He wanted to enter, but he turned away. Some other time perhaps.

Pepin found a cottage near by facing an olive grove, and the owner of the cottage would let him stay there for a few cents a day. And so Pepin made it his home while he was in the city. It was a three-room plaster house, and his room opened on a balcony that looked over the town of Granada, far below. In the hillside between him and the town there were gypsy caves, and at evening the gypsies came out to dance. Gray-green olive trees stretched beyond the house, and flowers bloomed under his balcony. To the left he could see snow-covered mountains, and he often watched the sunset turn them to pink and gold.

Every day he went to the palace gate to polish shoes. His pennies were growing, for the Americans liked the little boot-black who could ask for work in their own language. And then the day came when he felt he could spare the money to pay for a ticket at the palace door. Pepin had never seen anything so wonderful. Fountains splashed in the courtyards, and the walls gleamed with little tiles set with jewels. Their plaster was covered with delicate designs so that every inch of them was beautiful.

Pepin wandered from room to room, stopping beside the pools to look up at the latticed windows, from which prin-cesses had peeped when the Moorish kings lived here. He found the Court of Lions, where twelve stone lions guard the fountain. They are very old, and have guarded it for

many, many years. He looked through arched windows into the courtyards. Pepin's heart was filled with beauty.

PROSPEROUS DAYS IN GAY SEVILLE

But less happy days followed. The crowds who came to see the palace had grown very small. There was less work to do, and when Pepin asked the reason, he was told that all the world was going to Seville for Holy Week. There the streets would be crowded with people. Well, then, he must go to Seville. It was a long journey, but Pepin mounted the donkey and urged it on so that he would not be late. For a number of days the road led through mountain passes and valleys; then finally it made its way down to the low, broad plain of the Guadalquivir River, on whose banks the city of Seville is situated.

When he reached Seville, it was crowded with more people than Pepin had imagined there were in the world. All day long through the streets parades of masked men were coming and going. They followed floats on which some figures of the Virgin Mary were carried.

The figures wore rich velvet robes embroidered in jewels, and they were borne on the shoulders of many men. Beside them ran boys like Pepin, carrying goat skins of water to quench the thirst of those who marched.

Pepin was so interested in the crowd that he followed all the way to the cathedral. Inside, the shadows were lighted by hundreds of candles. Boys wearing red robes trimmed with lace were marching and singing. Others were ringing bells that hung above the choir. The organ pealed, and its rich music was mingled with the voices of the singers.

Pepin stood near the tomb of Columbus, who had discovered the land from which Pepin had learned the word "bootblack." Four statues of trumpeters bore the tomb of Columbus on their shoulders, and one of their long trumpets stretched above Pepin's head. A black veil was drawn over the gilded altar, but as the choir boys went toward it singing the veil parted. Pepin looked on with wondering eyes.

As the crowds came and went, he strolled with them past the bell tower—the tallest in all the world. In its belfry chimes were ringing, and all of Seville was glad and joyous. Pepin wandered through a garden where roses climbed the hedges around him and peacocks spread their tails before a fountain. There was so much to see that it was hard to stop and work, but remembering the box hanging from his shoulder, Pepin turned back to the crowded streets.

He came to the Street of the Serpents, so narrow that only foot passengers were allowed within it, and yet it is the main shopping street of Seville; Pepin knew that he would find work here. He took up his stand near the post box, where letters were dropped through the mouth of a carved lion. And now Pepin was busy cleaning shoes. He rubbed and polished, and his pockets jingled with pennies.

Easter passed, but the crowds still lingered in Seville, for now it was time for the fair. The streets were hung with flowers and colored lights. Booths had been built along the way, where friends greeted friends. There were dancing and singing. There were merry-go-rounds and slides for the children. Every one was happy, and shoes must be polished neatly so as not to shame the gay shawls and lace head-dresses which the Spanish girls wore so prettily. Pepin worked and played and worked some more.

When the fair was over, he had earned enough money to last him through the summer. He hid the money in his saddle bag, and remounted the donkey. Then he turned its head toward Ronda, and began his long journey, for he must take the donkey back to his brother who had been walking to the grist mill so that Pepin could ride.

NOTES AND QUESTIONS

1. From what is said on page 249, how would you know that Ronda is a very old town?

2. On what do most of the people in and around Ronda depend for a living?

3. If you went to Ronda, what two things would you want to see?

4. Through what kind of country did Pepin travel on his journey to Granada?

5. Write the words "Seville" and "Granada," and under each write from the list below the things Pepin saw in that city.

Alhambra	fountain with stone lions
tomb of Columbus	a great cathedral
Holy Week parades	boys with goatskins of water
Court of Lions	a tall bell tower
Gate of Justice	gypsy caves
Street of Serpents	a fair

6. From this story what do you think is the most famous building to see in Granada?

7. How do you know that the mountains Pepin saw are very high?

8. At what time of year did Pepin make his journey? There is one sentence on page 256 that tells you almost exactly when he visited the cities.

9. From a geography map draw or trace the southern part of Spain. Show Ronda, Granada, and Seville and a large river on which Seville is located. Draw lines to show Pepin's journey.

10. Be ready to read lines that tell—

   (a) What Pepin saw in the Alhambra.

   (b) What he saw in the cathedral.

11. On page 253 mention is made of the Moorish kings. If you do not know who they were, find out something about them—where they came from, when they ruled in Spain, etc.

Two stories you would enjoy are "Spanish Magic," Mabry (in *Child Life*, March, 1930) and *The Boy with the Parrot*, Coatsworth.

RIMFA, AFRICAN HERD-GIRL

Erick Berry

In the first story in this book you went to Africa with Martin Johnson to photograph wild animals. Now you will journey again to that great continent. This time you will visit a little African herd-girl, see something of life in her village, and learn how she proved her courage, skill, and faithfulness in a time of great danger. Perhaps you will feel that Rimfa was not so different from the boys and girls in our country.

HERDING THE CATTLE

It was yet three hours until the time of sundown and driving in the cattle. Now was the hottest part of the long day in West Africa. Rimfa, the little herd-girl, yawned as she lay in the shade of a huge tree, the only large tree in sight for miles and miles. Before her spread out her father's herd of cattle, fifty slow-moving white cows, each with horns a man's height across and a huge hump between its shoulders. They lay now in such small shade as they could find, contentedly chewing their cud and calmly looking out over the blazing plain. A cowbird, crowds of which follow the cattle herd, hopped nearer, and made bold by Rimfa's stillness, pecked at a weed near her foot; but at this, Biri, her pet monkey, suddenly sprang up and let out a shrill chatter of rage.

Herding would have seemed a dull life to anyone not accustomed to it, but Rimfa preferred it to the usual work

From "The Winning of Moy" in *Girls in Africa* by Erick Berry. Permission of The Macmillan Company, publishers.

of the girls of her tribe, to pounding corn and spinning, and cooking over the tiny fire in front of a hut in the narrow little village. Herding cattle was boys' work. At present her brother, Burum, was down with the measles. For this reason the only daughter of the family was allowed the task of watching the herd.

The little African girl was tall for her age. The girls of her tribe are very slim, and their skins are lighter than the usual African native's. She wore a cloth of brilliant blue, wound round and round her hips like a short skirt. Lying in the shade of the tree, she had taken off her headcloth, and her crisp black hair was braided in the two plaits which came in front of the huge, round, brass earrings which all the girls wore. Brass finger rings and a green bead necklace completed the hot-weather costume.

As the sunset began to turn the sky into a great ceiling of gold, and purple shadows lay over the brown stubble of the land, Rimfa stretched herself. Clicking to her pet, she jerked Biri's short strap, and the monkey leaped lightly to her shoulder. The largest animal of the herd, old Moy, clambered slowly to his feet, a signal for the other cattle to follow. Moy was a huge beast. His horns spread more than six feet from tip to tip, and his beautiful white coat was spotted with black. He stood waiting patiently for Rimfa to mount him. No other man or woman could approach him, not even her brother who usually tended the herd. But Rimfa had clung to his tail, clambered to his hump since she was a small ginger-colored baby, and he understood almost everything that she said to him.

Now she leaped to a place just behind his hump, and hung

on to it, her bare heels digging sharply into his side to urge
him forward. The monkey chattered, and Moy shook his
long horns angrily as at some pestering fly. He hated Biri;
and long ago he would have gored the little beast with his
huge horns if the monkey had not been far too nimble for
him and hid behind Rimfa's skirts.

LIFE IN RIMFA'S VILLAGE

Slowly the herd gathered and fell in behind Moy and the
little girl, wandering leisurely back across the darkening
plain toward the village above it. A collection of beehive-
shaped huts of roughly woven straw showed dark against the
sunset. Cooking fires lighted up, briefly, a face or a moving
figure, as the village women bent over the evening meal or
passed to and fro carrying wood for the fires. A larger group

showed where the men squatted together, smoking and talking in quiet tones.

Rimfa was hailed by various members of the tribe as she rode in. Driving the cattle within the small corral of thorn bushes, she tied Moy's rope to a stake and found her way to her own fire, as she was hungry after her long day in the open. The African native eats only two meals a day as a rule.

That night, after the dinner was finished, Rimfa's father said, "Your brother will be well enough in a few days now to take over the care of the herd."

"But father—" she commenced in protest, but her father broke in:

"It is more fitting that you stay at home and learn the duties of a woman. You are almost of the marriage age. No man will care for a wife that has worked as a boy works, and knows nothing of household duties."

"But I can spin, and pound the corn as well as any girl in the village," Rimfa replied.

"It is near the time for the tornado," her father went on to explain. "It is the task of a man, not a girl, to drive the cattle in the storm season. It is enough. I have spoken."

"It isn't as though the herd were not safe with me," thought the little girl as she walked away. "He *knows* I can take as good care of it, better, in fact, than any boy in the village."

Only a few more days of her life under the hot blue sky; of watching the crown birds flap heavily, with shrill voices, across the sun-baked country; of drowsily lying, almost asleep, yet awake for every movement of the herd, beneath the shade of the huge tree; of watching the tornadoes sweep up across the plains. It was early in the season yet, and the rains had not, so far, touched the plain. Only a few more long golden sunsets, and windy dawns when the sun came up golden through a haze of desert dust. Then back to the life of the village, shut in by hot high walls of matting. To Rimfa, long hours at the spindle or working on the little farm back of the village were hateful. Worst of all, she would see her favorite Moy only for the few brief moments when he was brought in at night. Between her and the huge beast there was a close friendship, and with no one else was he so gentle, so well behaved.

RIMFA MANAGES THE RUNAWAY HERD

It was late in the afternoon several days later, and Rimfa lay under the big tree, the monkey asleep at her feet—facing the south. She turned slowly, rolling over on her elbow, and glanced back at the sky, then sprang to her feet. A dark thick cloud was rising rapidly in the east. Long tongues of lightning flickered from it into the band of solid gray beneath, a gray band that meant rain. She watched it for only a moment. It was quite surely not going to swing north as the others had done, and it held the first of the season's tornadoes, that swift, terrible storm full of destructive wind and lightning.

Even as she watched it, the cloud spread, and the flashes increased. Already the cattle were commencing to stir uneasily. Moy came slowly and clumsily to his feet.

"Come, Biri, we must run for shelter," Rimfa cried, and jerking the monkey to her shoulder, she fled down the short slope to where the herd, now thoroughly aroused, was scrambling up. Moy awaited her impatiently. She pushed through the others, hitting them lightly with a short stick, pushing their rough dust-stained sides, and swung to Moy's back.

"Forward! Go! Swiftly!" she commanded him, though he was already breaking into an easy run.

Low rumbles of thunder came from the ever-growing cloud behind her. The darkening plain was hushed. There was no sound of cricket or bird, and the white flock of cow-birds that usually chattered so cheerily, flew low and silently, though still following the herd. If they hurried, they might yet reach the village before the windstorm broke, certainly before the rain came.

Moy swung into a long lope that covered the ground rapidly, and the rest of the herd, with a swift stumble of hoofs followed close behind. They were halfway to the village, entering a hollow so that the houses were hidden from them and crowding along between two walls of grass that brushed against the girl's bare feet. She crouched closer to the hump of Moy, when suddenly Biri gave a shrill scream of terror. Moy, who at his best hated the pet, now made nervous by the approaching storm, threw up his head in fright. Almost as soon as the monkey he, too, had caught the scent, the stale, sharp odor of lion. Like a flash Moy turned and crashed, head down, into the bush, the herd pounding after.

A lion had undoubtedly passed through the grass that morning, but there was none in sight now; in fact, all sight was being rapidly blotted out. The sun was completely hidden. A chill wind, stronger every second, whipped at Rimfa's bare shoulders. For a moment the herd was partly sheltered by the tall grass, but this was not the way home.

"Moy! Moy!" she shrieked, above the voice of the storm, pounding desperately on his hump. Biri clung, with jabbering fear, to her skirts.

Following Moy blindly, the herd was rushing away from the smell that had frightened it. Below the level of the plain and between the grazing ground and the village, there was a watercourse, dry at this season of the year. Into this, the herd, led by Moy, bolted.

Rimfa continued to shout above the roar of the oncoming storm, but the thunder, together with the monkey's screeches, and the terrific wind, was too much for her. Since a slip would have sent her beneath the feet of the stampeding herd, she clung tight to Moy and waited.

The high grass had given way to low stubble, and then to the sandy bed of the stream. There was a brief lull in the wind, which foretold that the rain would soon be upon them. Rimfa was frightened, and her teeth chattered with cold. She clutched the monkey with one hand to keep him quiet for a moment and then held him tightly beneath one arm. With the other she still clung to Moy's neck.

Softly she began to coax and pat the great beast. "Moy, Moy," she begged, "be not afraid. It is I, Rimfa, that clings to thy back. Be still, great one. Be not afraid!" And she pushed hard on his left side with her knee, reaching out to give a similar push on his left horn. Gently she pushed again. Softly she coaxed.

Desperately she steadied herself on Moy's back. Knowing that the torrent of rain was not far off, she tried again. This time the great beast responded slightly, wheeling a bit to the right. Then more and more he changed the course

of the runaway herd. They were running now where the waterway spread out, to a firm shallow beach. Moy's pace slowed. Then a sharp spatter of rain stung Rimfa's back. There was a sudden blinding flash of lightning, and immediately a great crash of thunder seemed to split the sky apart.

Moy tore forward again, but it was no longer in a straight line. He kept turning to the right, and the herd, following as always, turned with him, till soon the cattle crashed against the sandy wide banks of the watercourse.

The stampede was over. Rain was coming in torrents, but the big cattle were used to rain, with flash after flash of lightning making an almost continuous flare across the sky. By this light, Rimfa, breathless and shaken, slid to the ground and stood leaning a moment against Moy's soaked flank. Her knees were shaking with fatigue and excitement, but there was a feeling of triumph. No boy of the village could have done better, nor, perhaps, as well.

RIMFA WINS MOY

She was too weary, when she finally drove the tired cattle into the corral, to seek her father that night, but gulping down a few handfuls of hot porridge and curling up in her blanket within the shelter of the hut, she went immediately off into a dreamless sleep to the sound of the cool pattering rain on the thatching.

In the morning when she woke, she could tell by the brilliant sunlight streaming in through the doorway that it was late. Why had they let her oversleep? Why had no one wakened her? Frightened and wondering, for the cattle always left at dawn, she wrapped her short skirt around her hips, tucking it in at the belt to keep it in place, and slipped out of the house. Breakfast was over long ago and the men were at work in the fields, but a covered gourd was set among the ashes, keeping her breakfast warm. The village seemed deserted, and when she looked out, the corral was empty. Moy and the others had been taken out for the day, and she was not with them!

Swallowing back her tears, she ate breakfast and looked up to see her father entering the yard. He came directly to her and sat down beside her on the warm ground.

Rimfa at once asked, "Is it then that my brother has taken out the cattle for the day, my father?"

"Ay-e-e. Yes. It is so." Her father smiled and paused. "My child," he said, "I am proud of you. Yesterday's work was well done." Rimfa looked up, surprised. "Two of the boys of the village saw what was done. They had found shelter under a tree above the bank when you turned the herd. They told me of it last night." Rimfa looked pleased, but the unspoken question was in her mind. Why, then, had he sent the herd out with her brother again?

Her father answered the question before she spoke. "I have decided to let you have your way," he said. "You shall have your herd, but it shall be your own, not your brother's. Stay quietly with your mother for the rest of the month till the new calves are older. Then you may have the calves for a herd of your own."

Rimfa's face showed her joy, but her father held up his hand. "One thing more. You shall have Moy for your own. I give him to you. Your brother couldn't drive him," he added with a laugh.

Notes and Questions

1. Make a list of eight things in this story that are very unlike things we see and do in our country.

2. Name two or three of our States where you would find country that looks like the country in which Rimfa lived.

3. If you were going to tell someone this story, there would be certain main points to remember. Others might be interesting but not so necessary. From the list below choose five points that would be most necessary in making someone else understand.

    (a) The kind of cattle Rimfa tended

    (b) What the village was like

    (c) Who Rimfa was

    (d) How she dressed

    (e) Why she was guarding the cattle

    (f) What caused the stampede

    (g) Rimfa's pet monkey

    (h) How Rimfa saved the herd

    (i) Rimfa's reward

    (j) What Rimfa's country was like

4. Now take each of the five points you have chosen, and in one sentence explain it. When you have finished, you will have a paragraph that will make clear what the story is about.

5. We in America might call Rimfa's people savages, but perhaps you can find in this story ways in which they acted and felt much as we do. Name two such ways.

6. In this story there are a number of "word pictures" in which the author makes us see as if we had been there. Choose one such picture and be ready to read it aloud.

7. Make a list of ten words or phrases that help us see, hear, or feel—words like *blazing plain, shrill chatter,* etc.

Erick Berry, the author of this story, has made a number of visits to Africa. You would enjoy her book, *Girls in Africa,* from which this story was taken. You would also enjoy "In the Wilderness," Upjohn (in *Friends in Strange Garments*); and "Aki's Left Hand," Sugimoto (in *Girl Scout Stories—Second Book,* Ferris).

THE WAY OF A POLISH LAD

HELEN COALE CREW

Now we shall go with Ivor and Marya Stannik to the old, old city of Krakow in Poland. Poland is only a little country. It is about the size of California or Montana, but it has been famous for over a thousand years. Krakow was an old city, known all over Europe for its university, when Columbus sailed on his great voyage. Ivor, a Polish boy of today, longed to study at that great university. Let us see how he won his heart's desire.

ARRIVAL IN KRAKOW

It was a bright, hot day in June, and Ivor Stannik, with his sister Marya, who was twelve, and two years younger than himself, was sitting on the driver's seat of his father's farm wagon, going slowly, but surely, to Krakow to see the Festival of the Wreaths. They had seen it once or twice before with their parents; this time they were going alone. Jan Stannik knew he could trust his son, Ivor, to take good care of his sister, for it had always been Ivor's way to attend faithfully to any duty that was laid upon him.

It was the twenty-fourth of June. Every year on that date Krakow held the Festival of Wreaths in honor of a long-ago princess, the daughter of a famous chief who was ruler of that southern section of Poland. Her father had fortified a hill, around which the city of Krakow came to be built.

An old story tells us that this princess, Wanda by name, was very beautiful, and that when her father died she ruled his province with great ability. Now it happened that a German prince, hearing on all sides of the great loveliness of Princess

Wanda, desired to marry her, and thus join her Polish province to his own country. But by the messenger he sent asking her to marry him, she returned a refusal; she knew that if she married the prince, her province would lose its independence, and this her people did not wish. The prince replied that if she did not agree to marry him, he would conquer her country and marry her by force. Quickly she gathered together an army, went out to meet the army of the prince, and defeated it. Then, fearing that her great beauty might cause further trouble to her country, she threw herself into the Vistula River. And to this day, yearly, on the twenty-fourth of June, the people of Krakow cast wreaths of flowers upon the river in memory of the unselfish deed of the lovely Wanda.

So Ivor and Marya jogged along, sometimes down in the valley of the Vistula River, whose silver water flowed through a great plain where wheat fields ripened and potato patches were like little dark-green forests; sometimes along a ridge covered with oaks and poplars, and here and there a grove of aspens or pines. So clear was the day that they could see, far off on the southern horizon, the faint blue outlines of the Carpathian Mountains.

Arriving at Krakow about noon, they drove eastward out Copernicus Street nearly to the Botanical Gardens, and there, on the corner of Vladimir Alley, Ivor drew up before a modest little house with a bakery shop in front. Out came Uncle Ludwik Kemmel, in his white baker's cap and apron, followed by Aunt Anni, to welcome them. Their son Lothar, a boy of about fifteen, stood scowling in the doorway. He was a big lazy boy who thought pretty well of himself, and he was not at all pleased at the thought of having to amuse his country cousins. For it was Lothar's way to amuse himself first of all. And indeed, Ivor and Marya were not at all anxious to be amused by Lothar. He had done so much boasting and made such poor efforts at entertaining them once before, that all they wanted now was to get away by themselves and see the city that always thrilled them. In particular they wished to see their Grandfather and Grand-mother Stannik.

When, therefore, Aunt Anni's good dinner of red-beet soup, goulash of meat, potatoes and peppers, and stewed pears and spice cake, was at last ended, Ivor and Marya slipped quietly away. Half walking, half running, they hastened along Copernicus Street to the Old City, and entered the one ancient gate that is still standing, and presto! they were back in the Middle Ages.

There was no difficulty at all in knowing just what were the boundaries of the Krakow of the time when Marco Polo was having his great adventure in Asia, or the time when Copernicus, the great astronomer, was a student at the Krakow University and Christopher Columbus was crossing the Atlantic Ocean. For, although a century ago the old wall that surrounded the city was pulled down, a beautiful boulevard was planted where it had stood.

It takes just one hour to walk about the boulevard (or Planty as it is called), and all that time one is walking under great shade trees. At one place, on the south, the Planty makes a loop around the Wawel, a high hill, well-fortified, on which stands the old castle of the kings of Poland, and the great Cathedral of the Wawel, in which most of those kings were buried.

VISITING GRANDFATHER STANNIK

Once inside the gate, Ivor and Marya went to the left around the Planty, and soon came upon Grandfather Stannik, a slender, kindly old man in blue overalls, busily raking up leaves and sticks and bits of paper from both walk and grass.

"Ho, Grandfather!" cried Ivor. "Here we are again. Now give me the rake and you just watch!"

He seized the rake from the old man and raked the grass with swift strokes. Grandfather, smiling contentedly, walked along, his arm in Marya's, keeping up with his grandson, and pretending to find fault with his raking.

"How does school go, lad?" asked Grandfather as they progressed around the Planty.

Ivor's mind leaped back to the little country school near his father's farm, and saw as in a picture the long bare room with whitewashed walls, and rough benches and desks.

"Well, Grandfather," said Ivor, "if you must know, I think I've outgrown the school."

"Indeed!"

"Yes, sir, and I'd like to go to the University of Krakow."

"You would, would you?"

"Yes, sir, I would." Ivor stabbed at an orange peel on the walk as though it were his greatest enemy.

"Well, there's the new building of the University," said Grandfather. And while Ivor looked longingly at the new building set behind its iron fence, Grandfather thought over a little sum of money he had been hoarding in the bank, and which was slowly growing. With it he was intending to help either Lothar or Ivor to go to the University. It is true that Lothar was the older, but Ivor was the more energetic

and ambitious. Often he had tried to settle in his mind which boy it should be, but the question was still unsettled.

So, laughing and chatting, the three walked along. Twice every day Grandfather and his rake made a complete circuit of the Planty. At the going down of the sun he usually sat quietly for a while on a bench near the one old gate that remains, to smoke his pipe and think about his bank account before he went home.

On this particular morning the happy old man, with a grandchild at each elbow, turned off the Planty into Anna Street and hastened up the block to the Old University library. They looked into the beautiful cloister, in the midst of which stood a statue of Copernicus. This great astronomer, born in the fifteenth century, was the son of a Krakow merchant. It was Copernicus that first taught the world that the earth

revolves around the sun. Here, greatly to Grandfather's pride,
Ivor was able to read some of the Latin words upon the bronze
tablet that told how Copernicus was the most famous student
who had ever graduated from the University.

At last Ivor and Marya bade Grandfather "goodbye until
this evening," and went off to see Grandmother. Down the
narrow streets they went—one can almost jump across them
with one mighty leap. They came presently to the open
square which is the very heart of the old city, with streets
leading into it from all directions.

In the very middle of the square stands the old Cloth Hall,
a long building with quaint towers at one end and an open
arcade along the sides. On the second floor under those
arcades, and occupying the whole ground floor, a thriving
business is carried on at little stalls. There you can buy
aprons, handkerchiefs, muslins, woolen goods, toys, clothing,
shoes, dried fruits, candy, and all those many trifles that nobody really wants but that everybody buys. No doubt in the
thirteenth and fourteenth centuries, here in the very heart of
Europe, men were coming from long distances to buy and
sell at the Cloth Hall at Krakow, and doubtless people speaking different languages were buying and selling there. For
wherever there was a hall in a good-sized city suitable for
the purpose, the people of those times set up a yearly Fair.

Ivor and Marya went through the Cloth Hall and then
crossed the Square to the great church that stood at one
corner of the square. And here they visited Grandmother,
who was happy to see them. No, she was not in the church,

but at the door of it, in an old wheel chair, for she could not walk. Grandmother Stannik held a very exalted position there. The city had granted her permission to sit at the door of the church with her hand held out for alms. Beggar? No, indeed! It was because she was old, not well, and could not walk a step that she was given this privilege. All over Europe, at each cathedral or great church door, sits such an old woman—sometimes an old man. And when a penny was put into Grandmother's hand, her quavering voice, sweet though trembling, put up a bit of prayer for the giver, and the giver entered the church with his heart softened toward all suffering and needy people.

How her face did light up when she saw Ivor and Marya! Her pleasures were few, and seeing these two grandchildren was perhaps the greatest of them all. She was eager to hear about the farm. Was the wheat ripening? How many acres had her son Jan put into potatoes? So Ivor was in his last year at school. He's a man, this Ivor! And so Marya did the churning, helped with the chickens, and could heel a stocking as well as Mother. Well, well, what a fine girl!

"Grandmother," asked Ivor, "are you not going to the Festival?"

A cloud gathered on her face.

"No, lad. 'Tis too hard for your grandfather to push my chair away down the river."

"Listen!" said Ivor. He leaned down to whisper something in her ear, then changed his mind.

"You just wait!" he said, and winked slyly at her. She guessed his thought and smiled happily at him. It was Ivor's way, she knew, to think of others besides himself.

THE FESTIVAL OF WREATHS

And now it was seven o'clock, and all of Krakow had had its evening meal, and nearly all of Krakow was getting ready to go down to the river, near the Wawel, to celebrate the Festival of Wreaths. The people put on their best clothes —fine suits and dresses for the city folk, and quaint, old-fashioned Polish costumes for the country folk. Bright spots of color they made, those striped skirts and bright shawls of the country women, and white, embroidered, sleeveless jackets and polished high boots of the men. And on the arm of every woman and of almost every child there hung a wreath. Some of the wreaths were made of paper or muslin, some of roses or poppies from the gardens and meadows.

The Vistula is a wonderful river. It rises in those Carpathian Mountains that make the high, green, southern boundary of Poland, flows northward, with three great bends, through the great wheat plain, and for the last hundred miles of its journey flows directly northward into the Baltic Sea. About midway of its long length it passes under the three bridges of Warsaw, the capital of the country.

As twilight came on and deepened into night, the great mass of people at the river's edge sang songs—the Polish national song and many others. When at last the moon lifted up its bright face over the mud-flats to the east of the river, there went up a great shout. Then there were merry struggles to get to the water's edge and launch the wreaths. Those up on the top of the Wawel tossed theirs down, and these did not always fall into the river, but there were plenty of willing hands to take them up and throw them in. Many of those who had paper or muslin wreaths lighted them first,

and when they were burning brightly, set them afloat. They were like red stars upon the moonlit water. They bobbed about in the river until their flames were put out, or floated down its main currents, some flaming, some lying on the water's surface like great water-lilies.

GRANDFATHER MAKES HIS DECISION

Meanwhile, amidst the crowd, Uncle Ludwik and Aunt Anni were wondering where their son Lothar could be. They had asked him to go with them to the Festival, but when the time had come to start for the river they could not find him. They were quite used to that, for Lothar could not be depended upon. Quite near them was Marya, arm in arm with Grandfather, the two of them laughing like happy children together. Near by, Ivor was pushing Grandmother in her old wheel chair. He had gone early to get her, knowing that the chair had a habit of moving on a slant instead of straight ahead. And indeed it took a long time to reach the Wawel from the little house in a narrow street near the square where Grandfather and Grandmother lived.

When the Festival was over, Ivor pushed Grandmother home again, and when they arrived at her door, the muscles of his arms and legs ached. But he said cheerfully, "We had a good time, didn't we, Grandmother? I'll take you again next year, if I'm here." For that was always Ivor's way—to make the best of things.

It was ten o'clock by the time Ivor and Marya, after a late supper at Uncle Ludwik's house, left Krakow and started home. It was midnight when at last they caught sight of the farmhouse, its chimney visible above a line of willow trees silver in the moonlight. And it was just as the Town Hall clock of Krakow struck twelve at the same time with the clocks of the Cloth Hall and of the University—twelve great booming strokes—that Grandfather, who hadn't yet fallen asleep, suddenly made up his mind concerning something he had been thinking about all evening.

He must have made up his mind rather decidedly, for with each stroke of the great clocks he beat with his fist upon the head of his bed. After that he said in a loud voice, "Ivor it shall be; he can always be depended upon!" Then, with the matter settled in his mind, he lay down and peacefully fell asleep.

Just those words he said, no more. But surely it isn't hard to guess what he had in mind when he uttered them.

NOTES AND QUESTIONS

1. Make a list of the people, or characters, in this story and tell who they were. Begin this way: *(a) Ivor, a Polish boy from the country.*

2. Who were the two most important characters in the story?

3. From the following list choose the words that describe each boy and write them in columns under each name: *kind-hearted, ill-natured, selfish, reliable, unselfish, ambitious, lazy, boastful, cheerful, hard-working.*

4. *(a)* What dream of Ivor's did Grandfather make come true?
   (b) Why did Grandfather decide the way he did?

5. Name four famous things you would see if you went to Krakow.

6. *(a)* Who was the greatest man that ever studied at the University of Krakow?
   (b) What great truth did he discover?

7. On the Polish farms and along the roads, what things would you see that you could also see in our country? You should be able to name at least five things.

8. List all the towns, rivers, and mountains named in this story. Then look them up in your geography so that you can point them out on the wall map.

9. How long did it take Ivor and Marya to make their journey? Near the end of the story there is something that tells you.

10. Be ready to tell why the Festival of Wreaths is held each year in Poland.

11. Read the part that describes the Festival of Wreaths.

Helen Coale Crew, the author of this story, lives in Evanston, Illinois. She has many times visited the countries of Europe, and she is always interested in what the boys and girls of those lands do. The story you have just read was written especially for this book.

You would like Helen Crew's book, *Under Two Eagles.* Another good story is "Michael Makes Up His Mind," Upjohn (in *Friends in Strange Garments*).

MINA AND KARSTEN OF NORWAY

Caroline Mabry

You have read a story of Spain in southern Europe and one of
Poland in central Europe. Now you will travel to the far north to the
little country of Norway, famous for its sturdy fishermen and
sailors and the wild beauty of its scenery. Of course you remember
Lief the Lucky, that bold viking who sailed to America nearly five
hundred years before Columbus. Let us spend a little time with
Mina and Karsten, two viking children of today.

VISITING UNCLE NORDAHL IN BALHOLM

It was ten o'clock at night, and it was broad daylight. In
Norway the midsummer sun does not set, and the nights are
like the days. Mina and Karsten lived in the Flaam valley.
The high walls of the mountains came down to enclose it,
and many waterfalls trickled down into the valley. The
children's red house stood facing the fjord. Now they were
helping their father gather hay. It was thrown over racks
which stood near the barn like helter-skelter broken fences.
A rack stood here and another there, for there is so much
rain in Norway that the hay will not dry if piled on the
ground.

The children talked of the wonderful journey they were
to have tomorrow. When they'd carried the last arm load
of hay to the barn, they ran to the house, and their mother
said they must go to sleep early so that they'd awaken
for their journey tomorrow morning. As if they could
oversleep! They were going to visit their uncle who lived

in Balholm, and the visit was a great event to them. Their clothes were already packed in a brown cloth bag with a shawl strap around it. It lay in the corner looking like a giant sausage.

When the children wakened the next morning, the boat whistle was already sounding. Mina and Karsten hurried on board with their bag, and the boat pulled out into the fjord. The water looked miles deep, and the children knew that in places it was. The mountains were as high as the water was deep, and there was a great stillness in the air. Almost the only sound was that of the boat as it cut through the quiet water. Now and then could be seen a little Norwegian village with its red and brown wooden houses hugging the shore; but most of the way there was no shore to hug, for the mountains dropped straight into this long, narrow arm of the sea.

Toward evening, as the children stood at the prow of the boat, they sighted Balholm. It is one of Norway's summer resorts, and a colony of artists live there in pretty red houses stretched along the shore. There is a big white hotel by the boat landing, but the children were looking eagerly toward the houses.

"I wonder which is Uncle Nordahl's," Mina said. "I'm sure it's the one with the carved vikings on the roof."

"There's Uncle Nordahl now," Karsten answered. "And we'll soon know which is his house."

Uncle Nordahl greeted them and led the way past the hotel to his small red house facing the fjord. A tree stood beside it, and he had built a tree house where he often sat to paint. From this high studio he could see far out over the fjords and study the ships, the image of which he caught for his pictures. But now he led the children inside the house. It had wood carving all about the window frames, and the curtains were embroidered in bright-colored yarn flowers. The children sat in the window seat while Uncle Nordahl told them stories of the vikings. No matter how often they heard viking stories, Mina and Karsten wanted to hear more, for the vikings were their heroes, and the whole history of Norway was made up of their daring adventures.

Uncle Nordahl told the children of a viking ship he had seen recently in Oslo, the capital city of Norway. Living as they had in the quiet valley, Mina and Karsten had never seen the ship that had been found only a few years before buried in the sea.

"I've been making a model of it," their uncle said, as he finished the story.

He brought the little ship and laid it across Karsten's knees. It was carved of wood. It had a figurehead in front, as the real ships had, and racks along the sides where the shields were carried when they were not in use. There were four pairs of oars, and at the back a long, oddly shaped paddle which the sailors could move back and forth as a rudder to guide the ship.

"Tomorrow, if you like, you may go down to the fjord and sail it," Uncle Nordahl said.

"But what if it sails away and never comes back?" Mina asked, fearing they'd lose the beautiful little boat.

"I'll tie a string to it," Karsten said, "and then we can pull it back to us."

They spent the next morning sailing the boat, while their uncle climbed to the tree-house and painted. And then he told them of a surprise he had in store for them. A magician had come to the hotel near by to amuse the guests, and that evening Uncle Nordahl planned to take the children to see Zippo, the Great. They were to have their evening meal in the hotel, and this in itself was a great treat to the children, who had seldom been out of their green valley.

GLIMPSES OF HOTEL LIFE IN NORWAY

When they entered the hotel dining-room that evening, they saw that the servant girls wore tight red velvet bodices over their white waists, and the front of these bodices had heavy bright colored beading. A big round silver pin that had danglers like tiny doll spoons held the blouse together at the throat. It was the national costume which the children did not often see now. Their mother had one which she wore only for festivals, and she kept it packed away in a carved wooden chest. Mina and Karsten were delighted with the pretty serving girls in their bright dresses, and the children were so busy watching them that at first they could hardly eat.

Everyone now was seated at little tables about the room, and the maids were bustling about the tables with little baskets lined softly with wool. Each guest was given a boiled egg out of the warm basket. Then bread and coffee were passed. In the center of the room stood a long table loaded with food. There were two large brown bricks standing at each end of the table. They looked very important, for each had a piece of embroidery tied around the

center with a ribbon. Mina and Karsten knew that the bricks were goat cheese, for they'd eaten it since they were babies, but they had never seen it dressed up like this before. Besides the goat cheese, there were on the table dishes and dishes of fish, little and big. It was pickled and stewed and cooked every other way, so that each guest could choose it the way he liked best.

Presently everyone in the dining-room arose and lined up around the long table. Then they began to reach for this and that. Everybody took slices of the goat cheese. There wasn't a plate came back that didn't have goat cheese on it, and of course Mina and Karsten had their share of it, too.

"I've got shrimp and lobster and sardines and salmon and herring, and so many other fish that I'll soon feel like a fjord," Karsten laughed as he laid a sardine on his slice of bread and popped it into his mouth.

Mina speared a pink shrimp and made a cushion of goat cheese for it, and just as she ate it, her uncle pointed out Zippo, the Great, standing in the doorway. Zippo had been going from one Norwegian hotel to another amusing the guests, and as soon as the children had finished eating, they joined the other guests, who were seating themselves in a circle around the edge of the big parlor. The space near the stove was the most popular, for it had grown chilly. Mina and Karsten took their places near the stove, which was high and thin and built in many sections like a tall nest of iron boxes.

And now Zippo, the Great, stood before the audience. Mina was surprised to see him way up here at the top of the world, and he did the most amazing tricks. She couldn't possibly see how Zippo did them. But Karsten, whose eyes were quicker than hers, watched the magician so closely that he saw what became of the handkerchief Zippo pretended he had lost. Zippo made such a fuss about the handkerchief that Karsten wanted to help him find it. To seem a little worried over where the handkerchief had gone was part of the trick, but Zippo looked so earnest that Karsten thought he really had forgotten what he'd done with it, and so right in the middle of the trick, Karsten, to help Zippo, called out, "There it is on the rubber strap under your coat."

Mina clapped her hand over Karsten's mouth to stop him, but the magician looked as if he could eat him alive. In fact, he had to stop that trick then and there, and talk as fast as a mad parrot to make the audience forget it and begin to think about a new one.

For the next trick, he needed a helper. "I'd like a polite courteous child to help me," he said, glaring at Karsten.

Then he smiled and pointed at Mina, and she stood up before everybody and helped him with all the rest of the tricks. Karsten would have left the room if there hadn't been so many people around the stove that he couldn't get out. He had to stand there and bear the angry looks of Zippo until the show was over.

OVER GLACIER AND SNOW FIELD AT FINSE

As they walked back to the house, Uncle Nordahl asked the children if they would like to see a glacier. Even though they lived in the land of glaciers, they had never seen one, and they were on tiptoe to go. And so the next morning Uncle Nordahl took them across the fjord by steamer. When they landed, they climbed into a high two-wheeled cart called a cariole, which took them to the railway station. They boarded the train for Finse.

Finse faces a glacier. It has a station and a hotel, and everything else is ice and snow. There are no trees and no birds and animals, except a nice shaggy dog which belongs to the guide who takes people up to see the glacier. It is a hard climb, and there are no paths to follow over the trackless snow. The way is marked by small piles of rocks called cairns. The guide took the children across a frozen lake and up to a point where they could see the glacier which reared its icy head far above them.

When they returned to the hotel that evening, the first person Karsten saw was Zippo, the Great. He wondered if the magician were still angry with him, but he decided the only way to find out was to meet Zippo face to face. So instead of ducking down the hall, Karsten went up to him and said, "Good evening."

Zippo, who hadn't seen him until now, wheeled around fiercely, and pulling him to one side said, "Look here, you imp, don't you dare give away any of my tricks tonight."

"I didn't mean to spoil the fun," Karsten explained, "You looked so solemn I thought you really had lost the handkerchief."

In a way this pleased the magician; so his voice was kinder when he answered.

"Very well, but you keep still tonight."

Karsten grew bolder, now that there seemed to be some chance of their being friends.

"If you need a helper tonight, I could do it."

Zippo made no promises, but later he selected Karsten. The boy was in his glory, and he stuck in an antic or two of his own, although he was careful not to give away any of the tricks. By then Zippo was so friendly that he loaned Karsten his skis to take a slide over the snow when the tricks were finished. The manager of the hotel found a pair for Mina, and the children ended their wonderful day skimming like birds over the snow field at the foot of the glacier.

Notes and Questions

1. (a) What country of which you have read in this part of your book is most unlike Norway?

(b) In what two or three ways is Norway different from that country?

2. Where in North America does it stay light all the time during the summer?

3. In Norway would you expect to find little farms or big farms? Why?

4. (a) Why would you expect to learn that many of the Norwegians are fishermen and sailors?

(b) What in this story would lead you to believe that fishing is important in Norway?

5. What three things do you think would be beautiful to see on a visit to Norway?

6. (a) From what animals do the Norwegians get much of their milk?

(b) Why do they use these animals instead of cows?

7. In each sentence below tell what word belongs where the blank is.

(a) A _____ is a deep inlet from the sea with steep, mountainous sides.

(b) In countries where there is much snow, _____ are used in traveling.

(c) A _____ is a great river of ice and snow moving slowly down a mountain.

8. Choose and be ready to read some part of this selection that you think is funny.

9. Choose a part that you think gives a good description of the scenery. Be ready to read it.

10. Are there many Norwegians in our country? If so, in what states do most of them live?

Other good stories of distant lands are "The Race for the Silver Skates," Dodge (in *Child-Library Readers, Book Six*); "A Child of the Vikings," Thompson (in *Normal Instructor and Primary Plans*, March, 1930); and "The Little Post Boy," Taylor (in *Boys of Other Countries*).

A BACKWARD LOOK

IN OLDEN days when a man made a journey, his return was eagerly awaited by his friends. Journeys were full of danger, and people knew almost nothing of distant places and peoples. Many a long hour would the returned traveler spend telling of the strange things he had seen.

Today our libraries are full of books that tell about almost every nook and corner of the earth. Travel stories have always been a favorite kind of reading. People who cannot travel like to read of places which they wish they could visit; people who are about to set out on a journey read books about the lands to which they are going.

You have just read stories of four different countries. Did you meet any boys and girls in these stories that you would like to have for friends? You know that thousands of people have come from distant lands to live in America. It would be interesting to find how many of the parents or grandparents of your classmates came from across the sea. What countries did they come from? Perhaps some of them came from one of these countries about which you have read.

The illustrations in these stories give you just a little idea of the things which may be seen in the lands that are described. It would be fun to collect pictures of Spain, Poland, Africa, and Norway. The class may be divided into four groups, and each group may gather pictures of one of these countries.

If you want to read more stories of boys and girls of other lands, you will find a list of interesting books on page 451. You will enjoy reading them.

Part Six
Workers and their Work

WORK

JAMES RUSSELL LOWELL

No man is born into the world, whose work
Is not born with him; there is always work,
And tools to work withal, for those who will;
And blessed are the horny hands of toil!

WORKERS ARE CONQUERORS

CONQUERORS of the world! When you hear these words, you think of famous men like Napoleon and Caesar—men who have led victorious armies to battle and have made nations bow to their rule.

But these men are not the true conquerors. Workers are the conquerors of the world; they are the ones who have harnessed the earth and made it give forth its riches so that men and women and boys and girls may live happier lives. From the depths of the earth workers send up iron, copper, lead, and other metals. In roaring furnaces and mills and in busy factories other workers turn these metals into ships, engines, bicycles, building materials, and the countless other things we need. In wonderful laboratories careful, patient workers experiment to find new ways of doing things and different uses for the materials they have found on this earth.

These, then, are the true conquerors of the world: the men and women who fight the battle against disease and suffering, who twist and turn and cut and hammer metal and wood into shapes that we can use, who harness the forces of water, electricity, and heat so that they will work for us, who till the soil and plant it with crops so that we may have food. The earth has great gifts for man—greater gifts than any Aladdin's lamp could bring him. But man must win them by study and work.

In this part of your book you will read stories of how some of the work of the world is done. You will also meet some of the workers and learn how they are conquering the world.

THOMAS ALVA EDISON: LIGHT'S GOLDEN JUBILEE

Edith A. Heal

Wizards and other workers of magic are supposed to have lived only in times of long ago, but here in our own country there lived a man, Thomas Edison, who was called "The Wizard." And indeed, he was a magic worker. The wizards of olden times worked their magic by rubbing lamps, waving wands, or some other trick, but Thomas Edison produced his wonders by long hours of hard, clear thinking and patient, careful work. The whole world has been made happier and more comfortable by his magic.

THE GOLDEN JUBILEE OF 1929

The story of our country has been told by its postage stamps. Whenever an event of great importance happens, the government issues a stamp in honor of it. In 1929, a new two-cent stamp appeared. At once stamp collectors all over the world pasted this stamp in their albums. It stood for one of the most wonderful events in history—the invention of the electric light. "Edison's First Lamp: Electric Light's Golden Jubilee, 1879-1929," the printing on the stamp read, and on it was pictured a single bulb shedding rays like the sun.

The Golden Jubilee was remembered in other ways besides that of the special stamp issue. On Monday, October 21, 1929, a world-wide celebration was held, because a half century before—on that very date—a lamp, as magic as Aladdin's, was given to the world by Thomas Alva Edison. Everywhere showy displays of electric lights made known the

Golden Jubilee.   Men of far-away Argentina, China, Peru, Porto Rico, and all European nations took part in the celebration.   Every newspaper carried long articles on its front page.   Some told of Mr. Edison; others gave the story of the marvelous lamp.   One showed in pictures the history of light, from the simple torch, stone lamp, metal lamp, oil lamp, and candle—up through kerosene and gas to the remarkable light that the great inventor had made with a glass bulb and a piece of cotton sewing-thread.

The most interesting celebration of the Golden Jubilee was the one in which Mr. Edison himself took part.   People in all parts of the world listened to the program over the radio. It was the result of many months of planning.   On the day of the Golden Jubilee, Mr. Edison and the President of the United States journeyed to the small town of Dearborn, Michigan.   Here a great museum had been built, called the Edison Institute of Technology, which was to be opened to the world on the fiftieth anniversary, Light's Golden Jubilee.

It was not an ordinary museum.   You picture at once a stern building showing many kinds of machinery, when the word "institute" is mentioned.   But this institute was not like that at all.   When Mr. Edison reached the grounds, he found a sight that made his eyes grow dim with tears.   Before him rose the very village and the workshop where he had made his first experiments with the electric light.   The little New Jersey town of Menlo Park had been brought all the way to the Middle West near Mr. Edison's boyhood home. Even the houses of Menlo Park had been brought.

This museum was prepared in love and honor of the greatest inventor America has ever had.   The new Menlo Park was an

exact reproduction of the old. There was the original office building, brick by brick, and the laboratory—board, shingle, foundation rock, and even the very soil it had stood upon. Seven carloads of red Jersey earth had been carried to Dearborn to spread over the ground so that the new Menlo Park would be true to the original village in every way. Eight carloads of old lamps and tools found in an old pond near Menlo Park were brought to the museum in Michigan. The boarding house of Sally Jordan was there. This was the first house in the world to be lighted by electric lamps. It was where Edison and his fellow workers lived, talking over their problems far into the night during that exciting time of experimenting with the first light.

Here in the museum the great inventor saw once again all the scenes that were connected with the search for the right

burner for the lamp.   When Mr. Edison could speak, he
said: "I wouldn't have believed it—it's amazing."

THE BOY EDISON

The Golden Jubilee in 1929 not only brought back these
pictures of the past for Mr. Edison; throughout the world it
awakened new interest in the great inventor. How had he
become so great a genius?

It all began far back in the days when a thoughtful child
asked many, many questions.   Edison's early surroundings
would have aroused the interest and curiosity of any boy in
the world.   There were the busy wharves of Milan, Ohio—
the busy shipping port where he was born.   A canal connected
the city with the Huron River and thus with great Lake Erie.
From his house on the bluff the little boy watched and listened
—hearing the singing of the deck-hands, their laughter, and
the loud commands of the captains.   Soon he was old enough
to go down into the ship-yards.   How often he must have
heard the cry, "Out of the way, boy," as he stood watching
the cargoes of grain being loaded.   Every day six hundred
ox-drawn wagons came in from the surrounding countryside.
The air was filled with bustling sounds—the thud of hoofs, the
grinding of wagon wheels, and the din from the warehouses
along the river.

Young Edison played near the water's edge where the
graceful sailing boats were anchored.   He was always under
the feet of the workers, searching for tools and examining the
ropes and bales.   And all the time he was asking questions—
questions.   The canal men and lumbermen answered him
until they became impatient.   Hurrying him off, they would

shrug their shoulders and say to each other that a boy who asked as many questions as little Al Edison did must be stupid. How wrong they were! At that very moment the boy was thinking over the answers they had given him.

Later, when his family moved to Port Huron, Michigan, there were the railway yards and machine shops of the Grand Trunk Railway. There were the same rough voices and dirty faces, the same "Out of the way, boy." All about him were the smell of steam and soot and fire, the noise of box-cars, engines, boilers, the mysterious workings of pistons, valves, levers, gears. Again the questions of young Edison poured forth, faster than men could answer. The boy collected all the bits of knowledge that the train-men let drop. He loved the steam locomotive, and whenever he got a chance, rode in the cab with the engineer of the train. Once the engineer slept and allowed the boy to run the engine himself.

What a thrill and adventure the boy had that day! The boiler was too full of water, and black sooty mud soon covered the whole engine and the young engineer. When Edison reached the yards, he was greeted with shouts of laughter. But those who laughed did not guess that the plucky boy was to have a great deal to do with the development of the future train. Someday he was to make an engine that would run by electricity and never have any boiler trouble.

So Edison reached the time when he decided to go into business for himself. He was eleven years old when he became newsboy and candy boy on the trains of the Grand Trunk Railroad between Port Huron and Detroit. At this time he was a well built boy with a head of thick brown hair. He was sturdy like his Dutch ancestors and had the good health that belonged to the Edisons. His grandfather had lived until he was one hundred three years old. The boy's family were well-to-do, and there was no reason for him to earn his own living. But he was tired of staying at home. Most of his education had been received from his mother, who had taught school before her marriage. There was nothing to do at home to occupy his busy young mind.

Finally his parents consented to his new plan. He began to sell fruit, peanuts, and papers on the train. When he was through with his duties, he set up a small laboratory in an empty express car of the train he traveled on. Here, if he wasn't experimenting with strange liquids and powders, he was printing a little paper that he had started, called the "Weekly Herald." It is not hard to imagine a young boy going through a train calling, "Papers—books—buy a book." But it is more difficult to picture him, alone in the empty car, printing some seven hundred copies of the little three-cent newspaper.

A sudden swaying of the train one day jarred a piece of phosphorus from a shelf in the boy's train laboratory, and the car took fire. The conductor was furious at the thought of the danger young Al's experimenting had caused; so he hurled the entire outfit, including the printing plant and the young inventor, off at the next station.

EDISON'S INVENTIONS

The next step ahead for young Edison was an opportunity to learn telegraphy. He had saved the life of a railroad man's little boy. The child had wandered onto the tracks, and young Edison had snatched him out of the way of the oncoming train.

The grateful father had no money to reward Edison; so he offered to teach him telegraphy. In a few days the boy had learned it, and had made a telegraph set of his own between his cellar and the house of one of his chums. Edison's inventions had begun!

From this point on he was always thinking of things to create. Often his inventions were such as to save time and labor. Once when he was working on night duty in a telegraph office, he was ordered to signal the main office every hour so they would know he was awake. He wished that there was something to signal for him so that he might steal a nap. He thought for awhile, and finally made a small wheel with notches on the rim. He attached it to the clock so that every hour a signal was sent automatically. Later, when Edison invented the "repeater" for the telegraph, which took down the dots and dashes so that the operator could go back and copy them at his leisure, it was because he could not take news reports fast enough to get all of them.

Edison had a strong sense of humor which led him to invent many clever tricks. One day he wired up a workshop of the Cincinnati Indianapolis Railroad so that every man who went to wash his hands received an electric shock that threw his arms up over his head. Once he hid a machine in a guest's room. Just as his friend got into bed, a voice said, "Eleven o'clock, one hour more." The visitor was startled, but as nothing further happened he lay down to sleep. When midnight chimed, the voice came again: "Twelve o'clock, prepare to die!" The scream of the visitor brought Edison to the room with a laughing explanation of what had happened. The ghost was only a phonograph.

Throughout the long years of his early inventions and experiments, Edison was poor most of the time. He lived the life of a genius—which means half-starving one day and having plenty of money the next. He spent every cent he made to buy materials and tools for his workshop. His life was for the most part made up of hard work and study. He stayed until all hours of the night at his laboratory, snatching his sleep—an hour at a time, on a chair or a pile of sawdust. His wonderful ability to get along without sleep made the number of working hours in his lifetime many more than those of most men.

EDISON THE MAN

Thomas A. Edison was about five feet, nine inches tall. His features were large, his head well-shaped and covered with a mop of hair that usually fell down over his forehead. His eyes were light gray. His expression was happy and calm. One of the workers in the crew at Menlo Park described him as follows:

"I like best to think of Edison in the old laboratory on the Jersey sand. It was at Menlo Park that through his genius the telephone spoke out loud and clear; that the first electric railway swung in curves around the lot; that the phonograph sang with a human voice; that the electric lamp threw its steady beam across the world. In memory I see Edison, his black hair straggling over his forehead, a careless leg thrown across the arm of his chair, around him the noisy gang of his 'boys' —Edison either sunk deep in thought or looking up at some bit of fun, with his rare and hearty laughter that came upon us like a clap of applause."

Edison led a very busy life, and accomplished great things, but he never rushed. He believed in making speed by not wasting time. He never ordered his crew to hurry, but let them stop by the way to joke and make merry. He had one of the finest qualities in the world—that of patience.

During the strain of searching for the right burner or filament for the electric lamp, he never showed impatience. The first lamp that he made had a cotton thread for a filament, and it could burn for only forty-five hours. A filament had to be discovered that would be still glowing at the end of six hundred hours. The search began, and it led to all parts of the earth. Men went to the jungles of Ceylon, to India, and throughout the valley of the Amazon River in search of different kinds of bamboo. Over six thousand kinds of material were tested in thirteen months. One hundred thousand dollars were spent. Hope, despair, and disappointment followed one upon another, until finally one kind of bamboo was found that would burn for a long, long time.

An old copy of a Chicago newspaper, dated December 31, 1879, printed the following two telegrams which tell the story of the interest the world took in the experiments Edison was making for a filament that would last:

> December 30, 11 A. M., 1879
> To Prof. Thomas A. Edison
> Menlo Park, N. J.
> How long have your first lighted carbon horse-shoe electric lamps given continuous light?
>
> Editor, *Tribune*

> Dec. 30, 4 P. M., 1879
> To Editor *Chicago Tribune*
> Chicago, Ill.
> One week today and still burning.
>
> Edison

There are 168 hours in a week; so men knew that the electric lamp had come to stay. No matter what the cost was, a lamp that would burn this long was worth producing.

WHAT THE GOLDEN JUBILEE MEANS TO US

The electric lamp today burns many more hours than anyone ever dreamed it would, and its cost is low enough for all to afford its use. Light's Golden Jubilee proved to the world that Edison's lamp was a miracle—a miracle that has grown more wonderful during the years since it was invented.

On the day of the Golden Jubilee, Mr. Edison and the President of the United States rode from Detroit to Dearborn in an old wood-burning train of 1872. The "Sam Hill," as the old passenger coach is called, stopped at Smith's Creek Depot, where a conductor once threw a young boy and his train laboratory off on the platform. While he rode on the train, Mr. Edison played at being candy-boy again. He took a large basket of fruit and walked the aisles of the old-fashioned car. When the party left the train, they made their way to Menlo Park laboratory, where Mr. Edison went through the steps by which he made the first lamp. It is not often that a great inventor lives to celebrate the fiftieth anniversary of his greatest invention, for usually he spends a lifetime in creating it.

Light's Golden Jubilee celebrated Thomas Alva Edison's great gift to the world. Men will never forget the picture of the inventor re-living his youthful days in riding on a wood-burning train to Dearborn. This picture enables us to realize how marvelous is present-day travel by electric train, and the brilliant rays of our modern lamp call to mind that far-off time when a young inventor toiled by the light of flickering gas to free the world from darkness.

NOTES AND QUESTIONS

1. What words belong where the blanks are in sentences *(a)* to *(h)*? See how many of the sentences you can complete without rereading the story.

(a) Edison was born in _____ (town) _____ (state).

(b) While he was a boy, the family moved to _____ (town) _____ (state).

(c) He went to work at _____ years of age as _____ on a train.

(d) He was taught .... by a man whose son he had saved.

(e) Nearly all of his schooling was received from his ....

(f) His greatest invention was the ....

(g) Two other things he invented were the .... and the ....

(h) Edison's workshops are located at .... (town) .... (state).

2. Which three of these facts about Edison as a boy might have made a person think he would some day be an inventor?

(a) He did not care for books and schooling.

(b) He was always trying to find out things.

(c) He did a brave deed.

(d) He was healthy and strong.

(e) He loved machinery.

(f) He printed a newspaper of his own.

(g) He set up a laboratory in the baggage car.

3. In telling of Light's Golden Jubilee, the author is trying to make us realize how famous Edison is. Tell four things that happened at that time to show how greatly the world honored Edison.

4. How old will the electric light be on next October 21?

5. The author says that Edison was a patient man. Tell one thing to prove this.

6. What interesting fact about Edison explains why he was able to work many more hours each day than most men?

7. What two qualities of Edison's made his fellow workmen love him?

8. Explain just how a telegraph instrument spells out words. You may have to look this up. Perhaps someone in the class can get an instrument and show how it works.

You would learn some interesting things about methods of lighting by reading "The Story of Light," Husband (in *Child-Library Readers, Book Five*); and "Lamps That Light History" and "Electricity Gives Us Light," Hough (both in *The Story of Fire*).

WALTER DAMROSCH: MUSIC MASTER OF THE AIR

THELMA WILSON

Music has been called the language that everyone understands. The African savage has his simple drum made of a skin stretched over the end of a hollow log, or his flute made from a reed. We have our great orchestras of seventy or eighty players with many different kinds of instruments. The music of each speaks a language. Walter Damrosch, a great man, a great musician, and a great teacher, is spending his life helping the people of America understand the language of music.

HIS MUSICAL TRAINING

Over fifty years ago in old New York City, a group of music lovers gathered one summer evening to hear a charming program of orchestra music. Dr. Leopold Damrosch, a noted musician and leader of the orchestra, had placed his own son, Walter, in charge of the cymbals.

Under his father's direction, the fourteen-year-old lad had learned just when to strike together the thin plates of brass. But on this evening, he grew more and more nervous as the music swelled loudly into a stirring march. When Dr. Damrosch indicated that it was time for the cymbals to come in, Walter's arms felt paralyzed, and he could not lift them. So the march swept on to a close without the sharp clash of the cymbals to mark its most exciting moment. Walter's first appearance in an orchestra had been a failure!

Young Damrosch had a musical home. His father played the violin as skillfully as he conducted an orchestra; his mother was a beautiful singer. Back in Breslau, Prussia, where he had lived before coming to New York City, Walter had begun to take piano lessons before he was nine. On Sunday afternoons his entire family played and sang together. Often the leading musicians and composers of Europe visited the simple Damrosch home and filled it with their glorious music. Franz Liszt, the great Hungarian pianist, Wagner from Germany, who wrote the beautiful opera, *Lohengrin,* and Rubinstein, Russia's most celebrated pianist, were some of the famous music masters whom Walter Damrosch met while he was still a child.

Walter continued his piano lessons in New York City. During his leisure moments he rambled with his brother and sisters through Central Park or made toys with the tools which his father had provided to give extra training to his busy fingers. Indeed, the boy forgot the disgrace of his first orchestra appearance in the building of a doll's theater. This he furnished completely with a wonderful stage, brilliantly lighted, and a marvelous curtain that went easily up or down. The young musician then presented in his little theater a new opera by Wagner, his audience being all the members of his family and a few of their friends. A chum helped to pull the strings that moved the toy actors; but Walter himself played the music which told the story that was being acted out upon the tiny stage. Dr. Damrosch was quite proud of Walter's production of the opera, which had recently been heard in Germany for the first time.

Now Walter's father began to train his son to be an orchestra conductor. He gave him a place back among the violins, for he felt that Walter should have training as a member of the orchestra. As time went on, young Damrosch learned more and more about music. For the great Musical Festival of 1881, which his father spent nearly a year in preparing, Walter was allowed to drill groups of singers, and to accompany the huge chorus and orchestra upon the organ. The Festival was a success, and when it was over, Damrosch was elected by a musical society to conduct its orchestra. Though he was only eighteen years old, the young man had already won a place for himself in the musical world.

LEADER OF A MUSICAL FAMILY

To this young conductor, all music had a message; and he tried to draw out this message from his players and their instruments as he faced them with his baton. He began to think of his orchestra as a musical family. Its members spoke alone, in groups, or all together; they could express the feeling or tell the story which the composer had in mind when he wrote the music that was being played.

During his early manhood, Damrosch lost the father who had been his constant teacher and guide. Dr. Leopold Damrosch had been directing a company of opera singers, and was planning to take them on a tour of several large cities at the close of the opera season in New York City. Suddenly he was taken ill, and died. Young Damrosch stepped bravely into his father's place. Taking full charge of the opera tour, he set out for Chicago six days after his father's death. Unfortunately a severe blizzard delayed the arrival of the opera company in Chicago until the very moment when the program was scheduled to begin. In the theater, a large audience waited patiently several hours for the curtain to go up and to cheer the young leader, who was trying so earnestly to carry on his father's work.

From that time on, Damrosch led a busy and successful life. But all the time there was growing in his mind a plan which he was determined to try out. More than anything else, he wanted to make the people of America love fine music; so he planned to begin with the children themselves. In a concert arranged especially for them, Damrosch invited the children of New York City to follow him into the magic Land of Music. Young eyes glowed with interest as the leader introduced the different members of his orchestra family, explaining in a simple way just what kind of language each instrument could speak and just what work it had to do. How eagerly the children listened to the bits of melody which Damrosch then played upon the piano! He told the children that these were a sort of musical theme or topic to the composition which the orchestra was about to play.

And then the tall, genial conductor waved his baton! To the children's delight, that slender wand called forth from the orchestra pleasing sounds, through which ran, like a golden thread, the tuneful melodies which had first been heard from the piano. The violins, never silent for long, laughed in rollicking glee or sobbed as if in pain; a flute began its merry piping, and was closely followed by the delicate tinkle of the triangle and the bells. As the music went on, it seemed to make little pictures for the children to see. A party of guests arrived noisily at a castle, or a victorious general returned to his people, announced by a sounding of trumpets. These pictures, Damrosch explained, were the ones which had been

in the composer's mind when he wrote the music that had just been played.

The years passed, and Damrosch continued with his special concerts for children. In 1903 he had organized the New York Symphony Orchestra. For a number of years afterwards, he traveled with his orchestra all over the United States. Many communities he visited had never heard a symphony orchestra play. To them, as to the children of New York City, Damrosch introduced the members of his large musical family.

His audience could see that a symphony orchestra is composed of four kinds of instruments. First, there are the "strings," made up almost entirely of violins and violin-like instruments in different sizes. These out-number all the other instruments of the orchestra, for they can express more different kinds of tones and feelings as well. The strings usually carry the melody or "tune" of any selection played, and their voices are heard longer and more often than any other class of instruments while the orchestra is playing.

Then there are the "wood-winds," the flute, oboe, clarinet, etc.— only two or three of a kind. These are said to be descended from the little Panpipes of hollow reeds upon which shepherds used to play while watching their flocks. At any rate, the wood-winds have peculiar reedy voices which enable them to be heard when speaking separately, as they generally do, or even when all of the strings are playing.

The third class of instruments in a symphony orchestra includes those made of brass tubes like the trumpet, the horn, and the trombone. These can speak in mighty voices more loudly than all the other instruments put together, but not so softly as the wood-winds and the strings. Finally, there is the percussion group, generally regarded as the "noise-makers" of the orchestra. These are the cymbals, the triangle, the drums of various kinds, and other instruments thrown in to produce all kinds of thrilling and exciting effects.

BY RADIO TO MUSIC LAND

Walter Damrosch regarded radio, when it came into use, as perhaps the greatest invention of our times, and he was one of the first musicians in our country to see that radio could be used to educate the people of America in a musical way. In 1927, he resigned as conductor of the New York Symphony Orchestra, a position he had held for many, many years. Shortly afterwards he became, by means of radio, the nation's music master, so to speak. Since 1928, his audience has numbered millions at a single concert instead of a few thousand in a music hall!

No small part of this large radio audience is the increasing number of school children who listen in to the Damrosch programs on Friday mornings. These programs have been arranged in groups to include pupils from the third grade on up to students of college age; a "Musical University of the Air" Damrosch calls these broadcasts. Through them he hopes to bring about a greater love of music among the youth of the country. Perhaps, he thinks, boys and girls will become more interested in playing the different instruments and in forming orchestras within their own schools.

Radio experts have worked with Damrosch to make his orchestra programs sound just as they do in a concert hall. This skillful conductor has an excellent radio voice and in front of the microphone he gives the same kind of program that has delighted the children of New York City for many years. He has learned just how to arrange his players about him so that their instruments give, in the clearest possible way, the musical message which they have to speak.

Walter Damrosch will soon be seventy, but he stands proudly erect as he introduces his musical family over the microphone in an easy, natural voice. How his blue eyes flash beneath their shaggy brows as his hand moves the baton! Then for all his listeners upon the air, the doors of Music Land swing wide, and beautiful melodies come forth.

NOTES AND QUESTIONS

1. In the first two pages of this story find a single sentence that tells a very important reason why Walter Damrosch made music his life work.

2. Often we like to know the main facts about a person's life, such facts as you had to give in Question 1 on page 303. Make a list of five or six main facts about Walter Damrosch's life. You can begin this way: *(1) Walter Damrosch was born in* _____. Complete this sentence and go on with the others. Be sure you give important facts.

3. Name three instruments which Damrosch can play. Which one did he study particularly?

4. In what way have inventors like Edison helped Damrosch to become the nation's music teacher?

5. Below is a list of most of the instruments that make up a great symphony orchestra. Write across your paper the names of the four main divisions of an orchestra. Under each division write the instruments that belong there. You may need to use the dictionary to find what some of these are.

trumpets	trombones	flutes	cymbals	bass viols	tubas
violins	clarinets	cellos	bassoons	cornets	French horns
drums	triangles	oboes	violas	piccolos	English horns

6. Be ready to tell in your own words—

    (a) Walter Damrosch's first experience in an orchestra.

    (b) How Damrosch, while still a boy, gave a performance of an opera.

7. Find and be ready to read lines that tell just how music carries its message.

8. In this story three great musicians are mentioned—Liszt, Wagner, and Rubinstein. It would be interesting to look up something about their lives and the music they have written.

"The Head of a Large Musical Family," Large (in *Little Stories of Well-Known Americans*); and *Alice in Orchestralia*, La Prade, will tell you more about Walter Damrosch and orchestras.

THE VILLAGE BLACKSMITH

Henry W. Longfellow

The village blacksmith was the iron-worker in the days when there were no machines to stamp, cut, and hammer metal. Today there are, of course, thousands of metal-workers in factories and shops, but the blacksmith shop is seldom seen. Henry W. Longfellow's famous poem pictures for us the village blacksmith.

Under a spreading chestnut tree
The village smithy stands;
The smith, a mighty man is he,
With large and sinewy hands;
And the muscles of his brawny arms
Are strong as iron bands.

His hair is crisp and black and long;
His face is like the tan;
His brow is wet with honest sweat;
He earns whate'er he can,
And looks the whole world in the face,
For he owes not any man.

Week in, week out, from morn till night
You can hear his bellows blow;
You can hear him swing his heavy sledge
With measured beat and slow,
Like a sexton ringing the village bell
When the evening sun is low.

And children coming home from school
   Look in at the open door;
They love to see the flaming forge
   And hear the bellows roar,
And catch the burning sparks that fly
   Like chaff from a threshing floor.

He goes on Sunday to the church,
   And sits among his boys;
He hears the parson pray and preach;
   He hears his daughter's voice
Singing in the village choir,
   And it makes his heart rejoice.

Toiling—rejoicing—sorrowing,
   Onward through life he goes;
Each morning sees some task begun;
   Each evening sees it close;
Something attempted, something done,
   Has earned a night's repose.

TIM CROGAN, THE STAR APPRENTICE

David O. Woodbury

We live in a world of machines; they even make our bread and our clothing. But we must never forget the skilled and faithful men whose work makes these machines possible for us. These men are wonder-workers in metal, glass, and wood.

Here is the story of a boy who had proved that he had in him the making of a master workman. Then came his final test—the test of faithfulness.

THE YOUNG HELPER

Tim Crogan, youngest helper in the shops, leaned against the hot shell of his Big Blower, and smiled proudly. The huge machine had been built for a company in India. There they were waiting for it to blow its thirty thousand cubic feet of air per minute through their blast-furnaces. And with every foot of it, thought Tim, would go something of himself; their roaring fires would roar the harder because of him. For had he not worked eight months on her as an apprentice in the great machine-works? Had he not known her when she was no more than a shapeless pile of bolts and ribs and plates? He could remember how the overhead-crane man had shouted "He-e-eads up!" as he had sailed down the length of the building with the first load of the parts dangling from his hook. Yes, and the long weeks with wrench and other tools, so that every part in the whole machine was stamped upon his mind forever.

The foreman had said, "You're too young, kid. You'll never last on this job!" Had he? Well, Tim would say that he had. That bunch of steel and iron had grown under his own hand into this beautiful great cylinder that reached nearly to the roof of the shop, and Tim had at least a dozen finger-prints on every piece of her. Too much for him, was it? The foreman had had to eat his words. For around the boy's neck, in plain sight at that very moment, hung one of the Efficiency Medals which the company awarded to show its appreciation of a mighty task well done. To Tim, that medal was the first stepping-stone to a great career as a machinist among the giants of steel and steam. He would have parted with it, he felt, almost as unwillingly as with his own life.

The steam sang and groaned in the valve of the Blower's engine, for they were shutting her down. Instantly workmen swarmed over the scaffolding around her, putting on the final touches. For tomorrow came the first of the tests, when an agent for the firm in India must see her run and do her work before he accepted the machine.

There was a loose bolt to be tightened up from the inside, and men were at work removing the manhole plate at the side of the casing. Tim, grasping his large oily wrench, stood ready, for to him fell the job of entering the machine to do the work of tightening. A final act of devotion was this last small task for his beloved Blower. He almost wished that he might hide away within those vast insides and take care of this giant machine forever in its coming years of toil.

He had clambered inside with his extension-lamp and had settled to the work of tightening. But the job was all too short, and when it was done, Tim could not fight down the desire to see once more the insides of the great machine. It

was quitting time, anyway. Nobody would care if he did delay for a bit. He wouldn't see her again—not inside, at least. The boss machinist's voice came faintly through the manhole:

"Hey, boy, it's four-thirty—I'm going home—you close her up when you get done!"

But Tim was far away in India, listening to the roar of furnaces and watching the half-naked Hindus with their clumsy hands on his beloved Blower. As he caressed the huge fan blades and felt the smooth steel of the foot-thick shaft which turned them, he dreamed of the work they would do and thrilled with pride. He, Tim Crogan, had helped to build this thing!

SHUT INSIDE THE BLOWER

Lingering thus within the huge machine, he forgot the passage of time—failed to notice the dead silence which had closed around him. Suddenly he became aware that he was alone, shut away from the world of men. He turned back to the manhole opening. It was nowhere to be seen. The extension-lamp, which he had abandoned in his ramblings in favor of the pocket flash-light, was gone!

Instantly Tim, wide awake and trembling, was running cold fingers over the inside of the huge machine. Yes, there it was, the manhole, with the cover closed and bolted tight in place! The boss's words seemed to echo through the dark space within the machine: "Close her up when you're done!"

"Gee, I was going to," moaned the boy. "Some other fellow must have done it and have taken the lamp away. They thought I had gone home!"

Tim's first impulse was to shout. Then he remembered that no human sound could possibly be heard through that inch of steel. In his distress his mind was perfectly clear. Let's see, what had the imprisoned men on the submarine *S-4* done when the divers were outside trying to help them? They had banged on the metal walls of their prison, of course, with something heavy. . . . That wrench, where was it? Right here by the bolt that he had tightened, surely, just as he had left it to go exploring.

With fingers that trembled so hard that precious minutes were wasted, Tim fumbled with his flash-light and began to search for the wrench. It wasn't there! It had slipped down somewhere—there was no telling what had become of it. And then Tim remembered that it was long past quitting time. The shop would be deserted except for the night watchman in his far-away little office. Even if he had the wrench, no amount of banging would ever raise *him!*

For a moment the boy's mind went blank, and then he saw in a flash all the horror of the situation he was in. The acceptance tests were to begin at seven sharp in the morning! There would be only a scant five minutes after the whistle blew to get someone's attention, even if he could find that wrench in the night and judge the right time to begin his signals for help; for he had no watch. And unless he banged all night, he couldn't be sure of being heard in the morning.

Tim's flash-light, fortunately, was a new one, and undoubtedly he would be able to locate the wrench with it before long. But as he set about doing it, his mind raced on, picturing what might happen within the next few hours. Suppose he found the wrench and used it. Even suppose the men heard the noise he made before they started the Blower. Would they recognize it as a call for help, or would they think the great machine was merely stretching itself for its morning run? He was desperately afraid that they would do the latter.

TIM MAKES HIS ESCAPE

And now Tim's nerve was weakening. He slumped down in his tracks and wept—wept because, as it suddenly flashed upon him, he would not be there to see his beloved Blower pass her tests. Then came the slight bump of something touching his neck—it was the medal. With his flash-light he examined its greasy inscription, as if he did not know every word of it by heart already.

"For Faithful Service in the Company's Interest," it read around the edge. The well-remembered words steadied him. Would it be faithful service, he asked himself, until all service was complete, and the Blower was on her way to India? No, it would not, decided the boy.

"It's up to me to come out of this hole alive," he said. "I believe it can be done, and I'll do it!"

Somewhat encouraged, the boy began to look about. Two methods of escape were left: the large hole in the bottom of the Blower where the air was sucked in, and the long steel exhaust pipe which ran outdoors. Scrambling down in the uncertain glimmer of his torch, Tim tried to squeeze his slender body past the fan blades to the intake opening. For nearly an hour he tried to wriggle past the blades, but the openings were too small. He turned back again into the black depths of the machine. Only the exhaust pipe was left.

A huge outlet valve at the beginning of the pipe had been

left open. Into this he squeezed, scarcely daring to breathe for fear the hole would stop him with its sharp edges. But no; with one mighty tug he finally wriggled through. Down the long pipe came a gust of night wind. Tim almost screamed for joy. In a few minutes more he was at the end of the tube, and had tumbled in a heap into the factory yard.

Drenched with perspiration from his fright, Tim hurried home. It was late, and as he crawled into bed, a new feeling of pride came over him. For now he had suffered as well as labored for his beloved Blower!

ONE LAST SEARCH FOR THE WRENCH

There was gray dawn in the window when Tim awoke. A great day was ahead—the day of the final tests. Hooray! He couldn't sleep any more anyway. He would go down to the factory and take one more look at his Blower before she started.

At a quarter of six Tim was in the street, swinging along the half mile to the factory at a good stride. As he went, something in the back of his mind troubled him. What was it? What could be the matter on this great day? Then he stopped suddenly in his tracks. He remembered. The wrench!

Somewhere inside the Blower he had left his wrench, perhaps caught among the fan blades themselves. What would happen if they should start her up with that big tool inside? Why, it would tear the insides out of her. Weeks, perhaps months of work would have to be done over again! His *wrench!* He—Tim Crogan—the only apprentice in Shop Eighteen to have an efficiency medal just like the older workers!

The boy had been walking along in a daze, but now he began to think clearly again. Either they must not start the Blower, or he must get the wrench out of the machine before seven o'clock. Of course, he could explain to the foreman how he had been shut up inside by mistake—how he had finally escaped and forgotten his wrench. But it had all been caused by his own carelessness! The test would be delayed while they opened up the machine and got out the wrench. The foreign agent would be angry; the office would phone down to know what was the matter. That would be the end of his chance to become a machinist. No, he couldn't tell them. *He would have to go back and find that wrench!*

Tim was running now. He passed a clock in front of a restaurant—six, exactly. One hour to go back again into the machine to find the thing that he hadn't been able to find the night before. Into the yard he ran; the gateman yelled at him, but he paid no heed. Around to the back of Shop Eighteen he went, praying that nobody would see him. There was no one in sight. He grabbed a box and boosted himself up to the mouth of the exhaust pipe where it came through the wall of the building. In another minute his feet disappeared down the long tunnel leading to the inside of the machine.

It seemed to Tim that the pipe had shrunk to half its size. He was scarcely able to get through the outlet-valve at all. Finally inside, he grabbed his flash-light and began a thorough search. He was cool now—working against time for the safety of his Blower.

The minutes went by, and the hours with them, it seemed. No wrench! Every nook and corner of the giant's insides Tim searched. Nothing was there but what he knew belonged there. And yet, somewhere that wrench was lying, ready to wreck the giant machine. Faintly through the pipe Tim heard the factory whistle. One blast. Five minutes to seven! He would look five minutes more, then he would quit. No one could say that he had not done his duty.

Once more he went over the ground; once more nothing rewarded his search. Again, and fainter still, came the whistle. Two blasts! Seven o'clock. Quickly Tim scrambled back up the rough insides of the great Blower. He needed no light now, for he knew his way by heart. He boosted himself into the outlet opening, and in that second a cold chill ran through him. Daylight at the other end of the pipe was disappearing. They were closing the valve, and he was caught inside the machine! Tim slumped unconscious in the opening.

TIM AND THE WRENCH ARE FOUND

A little group of engineers stood on the shop floor beside the great Blower. Two men were swinging the big wheel which closed the outlet-valve. Others were testing and examining the various parts. The foreign agent walked up and down; he didn't seem to want to be kept waiting. The foreman stood on the scaffolding, one hand on the throttle-wheel.

"All right," the chief engineer sang out, waving his hand. "Let her have it!"

The foreman's arm tightened on the wheel, then stopped. He turned to the other men on the scaffolding.

"Where's Crogan?" he shouted. Nobody said anything. Someone on the floor bellowed "Cro-o-ogan!" through cupped hands. Men at near-by machines looked around, but the boy did not answer to his name. The chief engineer stepped forward.

"Who's Crogan, anyway?" he demanded. "Can't you start without him?"

The foreman stared down at him through sweaty glasses.

"Crogan? Oh, he's our star apprentice. He just about built this machine, he did. He wouldn't miss the tests for all the money in the world." Then he called out to one of the floor men:

"Go see if Crogan punched in this morning!"

The chief engineer controlled his impatience as best he could; the others waited in silence. A foreman is a foreman, particularly when he's standing on the scaffolding of a new machine that has not yet been accepted.

The floor man came running back.

"His clock card is there," he shouted, "but he didn't punch out last night."

The foreman then summoned Tim's gang boss. When had he seen the boy last? Where?

"Why, the kid was inside the machine when I left. I told him to put back the manhole cover when he came out!"

One of the workmen now came forward.

"Say, I put back that manhole cover myself about ten minutes after five o'clock. I thought somebody had forgotten it!"

The foreman turned to the group on the floor. His voice was sharp and firm.

"This test is off till afternoon," he said. "We have a rescue job on our hands right now!"

An hour later a white-faced boy lay on the shop floor on a blanket. The company doctor was applying smelling-salts to his nose.

"Shock," said the physician. "He will come around all right. Get the stretcher."

Tim stirred and mumbled. The foreman leaned over him to listen.

"Wrench," murmured the boy. "Don't start her; there's a wrench in her insides."

"Is this it, Tim?" the boss asked, holding up a big wrench. The boy's eyes lighted for a minute, and then he again became unconscious.

"I found it under the Blower an hour ago. It must have dropped down last night," explained the foreman. But the boy did not know that till later.

Notes and Questions

Sentences 1 to 5 have to do with certain facts about the blower. Which word or group of words correctly completes each sentence?

1. The blower was to be used in the   *iron and steel   textile   wood-working*   industry.

2. The purpose of the blower was to   *provide fresh air   make the fires burn hotter   move things by blowing them through pipes.*

3. The power that operated the blower was   *electricity   steam water.*

4. The air was forced through the blower by   *pumps   shafts fans.*

5. The flow of air through the blower could be opened or cut off by *wheels   valves   fan blades.*

6. The author tells us that the blower was a gigantic thing, and that the fan blades were huge. Find on page 318 something that gives us the idea that the fans must have been very large.

7. For the purpose of testing the blower, the air was allowed to blow out through an exhaust pipe. When the blower was actually doing its work, where would this air go?

Which words correctly complete sentences 8 and 9?

8. Tim's search for the wrench showed that he was   *a quick thinker   a skillful workman   faithful to his job.*

9. If the wrench had been left in the blower, it would have *stopped the machinery   broken a hole in the blower   smashed the fans.*

10. Are there any valves in your home or in your father's automobile? What are they for?

11. Is there anything in your home that works like a blower? What is it?

12. Find and be ready to read lines that tell—

    (a) How devoted Tim was to the blower.

    (b) That he had "made good" on the job.

Another good story by David Woodbury is "The Crane," in *St. Nicholas,* Feb., 1931.

FOREST PRODUCTS: FROM WOODLAND TO FACTORY

CHARLES LATHROP PACK AND TOM GILL

Perhaps you think of lumber as being the main use that is made of trees. This article will tell you of the many other gifts that the forests make to us. Charles Lathrop Pack, one of the authors, is the president of the American Tree Association. In addition to a busy life as a banker, he has spent many years educating people to the great value of forests. Tom Gill is a forester and a writer on outdoor life.

Lumber is only one of the many gifts the forests have to offer. Long before boards had ever been thought of, the early peoples of the world had learned to make use of many other products of the forest. In the tropics they built their homes of palm leaves and made spears and arrows of the hard, heavy woods. Throughout the world they had learned to hollow logs for canoes. It may be that with dry sticks man first made fire his servant.

From the leaves and bark and fruit of forest trees come many of the well known medicines that man through the long ages has used to cure his ills. Even today witch doctors and medicine men of the primitive tribes obtain most of their medical stores directly from the trees. Rubber, a highly important substance, was first secured from "tapping" trees discovered in the tropical forests of the Amazon, and the greater amount of "chicle," used for making chewing gum, is

From "Other Gifts of the Forest" in *Forests and Mankind* by Charles Lathrop Pack and Tom Gill. Permission of The Macmillan Company, publishers.

bled from tall evergreen trees that grow in the dark jungles of Central America and southern Mexico.

Two products of the forest—rosin and turpentine—were of service to man long before the making of paper from wood pulp and even before the lumber industry was started. These forest products are called "naval stores." In the United States their main source is the sap of the long-leaf pine and slash pines of the South. The name "naval stores" dates back to the time when this gummy sap was used to build and repair ships in the old days of wooden vessels. Today the use of rosin and turpentine covers a much wider field than shipbuilding, but the name "naval stores" still remains.

The business of manufacturing rosin and turpentine has become a most important industry, employing about forty thousand persons and each year turning out products to the value of forty million dollars.

The first step in the manufacture of turpentine and rosin is collecting the gum from the trees. The early, wasteful method was to cut a deep notch in the base of the tree, known as the box. This box held the turpentine that flowed down the tree trunk from a narrow, shallow wound made by "chipping." Once a week a chip was cut through the bark above the box, each chip being cut directly above the other. These caused the tree to "bleed" or give off sap; all during the summer the trees were chipped regularly, the sap flowing down into the box, where it was collected.

This method of "boxing" the tree has always been unsatisfactory, since it is wasteful of wood that might later be made into lumber; the box, if cut deep, weakens the tree so that it is easily destroyed by high winds. During later years this

box has been replaced by small cups hung over the base of
the tree. Into the cups lead small tin drains through which
the sap runs. Except for the cost of cups and drains, this
method is in every way better. Whatever method is used,
the sap is collected from the boxes or cups and taken to stills,
where it is made into turpentine and rosin. The tapping
season lasts for about seven months.

In America, collecting rosin from pine trees to make tar
and pitch began as far back as 1600. Today three-fourths
of the world's naval stores are produced in our Southern
States, and they find their way into every important market
of the globe. The rosin is used for gum, varnish, soap, and
the manufacture of sealing wax. Turpentine finds its uses
in paints, varnishes, coloring, and in the manufacture of a
large number of medicines.

As in lumbering, the manufacturing of naval stores can be very wasteful. Fortunately, however, manufacturers are giving up the old "box" method and are learning to make smaller chips in the tree. Usually, trees are cupped for three or four years, then cut for lumber. With the use of better methods, a tree may be cupped much longer and still produce valuable wood for boards.

The Indians taught us to make and enjoy maple sugar. In northern Minnesota one tribe still continues this industry, selling pure maple sugar in birch-bark containers, much the same as their forefathers made before the coming of the white man. Today the chief maple-sugar center is in the northeastern states.

Both the sugar and the syrup are products of the hard maple or sugar maple. The method of getting the sap and making it into sugar is simple. About the middle of March the tapping of the tree begins, and the sap flows for the following month or six weeks. Two holes, less than a half inch in diameter, are bored about two inches deep in the trunk of the tree, and a wooden spigot is inserted in these holes to conduct the sap to a bucket directly beneath. This sap is then collected, poured into great iron kettles, and boiled to a syrup. Cooking longer, until the syrup is like wax, produces maple sugar. An average tree provides over twenty gallons of sap each season, and this can be boiled down to about four pounds of sugar or two quarts of syrup. Proper tapping is not injurious to the trees.

As certain woods increased in value, wood veneers have become another important forest product. Some kinds of woods are so valuable and are becoming so scarce that it pays to cut them into very thin sheets, or slices, and glue them to a backing of some more common and cheaper wood. For furniture these thin pieces of veneer give the same appearance as if they were of solid wood, but this piecing together has other advantages. Drawers, for example, made up of several layers of veneer are stronger and less likely to warp and crack than if they were all of one piece.

Most veneers are made by first boiling a log for some hours to soften it and then revolving the log, by machinery, against a sharp knife. As it turns, the knife bites into the wood, and a long thin sheet of veneer is peeled away. Woods chiefly used for this purpose are the high-priced kinds, such as mahogany, Spanish cedar, and Circassian walnut. As our valuable hardwood trees become increasingly scarce, more and more kinds of woods are used for veneers.

In making leather from raw hides, the tannin used is obtained from the wood and bark of hemlock and oak. It is this tannin which makes leather durable and soft. During the summer the bark is peeled from the trees and taken to factories where the tannin is taken out. At one time the tanbark industry was so important that in the eastern United States hemlock trees were cut and stripped for the bark alone, the wood being left to rot. Now the scarcity of hemlock trees and the use of other tannin materials have made the industry much less important.

A great deal of wood is used for the manufacture of barrels, casks, tubs, and kegs. For these purposes, red oak, white oak, cypress, and gum are most frequently used. Excelsior is still another valuable forest product; it is used for shipping fragile material and even for making mattresses and rugs. Basswood makes the best excelsior, but cotton-wood, poplar, and white pine are also used.

The uses of wood are far from ended: paper pulp, spools, box boards, willow ware, toys, implements, tool handles, shuttles—a list would take up many pages. Indeed, over four thousand separate uses for wood have been listed.

One other product of the forest is important enough to mention here—the Christmas tree. For the Christmas tree is the great winter crop of the forest, and it is one of the forest's oldest gifts. Its history extends so far back that its origin is hard to trace. Some say the custom arose with the Egyptians, who each year in December decorated their doors with branches of the date palm. Or, it may be connected with the great tree of Norse mythology, the Tree of Time within whose roots and branches Heaven and Earth are bound.

To us, in America, the term Christmas tree means a number of different trees. The kind of Christmas tree you think of depends upon where you live, for we use firs, spruces, cedars, even magnolia. On the Pacific Coast white fir is used; in Ohio, Norway spruce; in Maryland and Virginia, the scrub pine; and farther south, cedar and holly. Hemlock, too, is a beautiful Christmas tree, but drops its needles very soon. Perhaps most widely loved of all for Christmas trees is the balsam fir, with its long horizontal branches, its deep green foliage, and spicy fragrance. Nikko fir, a beautiful native tree of Japan, has recently found favor in this country.

The question is often asked if this Christmas-tree custom does not waste the forests. Foresters reply that the Christmas trees used by every person in the land could be grown on a few thousand acres, and that their use has practically no effect on the present drain on our forests. Growing trees for the holidays is becoming an important industry. The Government in recent years has been selling Christmas trees thinned out from crowded forests of timber, thus leaving the remaining trees with more room and light. After all, so far as our wood supply is concerned, it would be more important to stop using toothpicks than Christmas trees, for each year six times as much area is cut over by the toothpick industry as for Christmas trees.

NOTES AND QUESTIONS

1. In this selection many "gifts of the forests" are named. Without rereading the article, try to make a list of at least six things we get from trees. In your list do not include wood or articles made of wood. Perhaps you can name more than six things.

2. Two things that we get from trees are secured in much the same way. What are they?

3. *Tell what words belong in the blanks.* A veneer is a .... Veneers are being used more and more because certain woods have become ....

4. The authors say that lumber was probably not the first use made of wood. Why would primitive peoples like the Indians not be able to use trees for lumber?

5. When you go home today, find what different woods were used in building your home and in making the furniture. Make a list of them.

6. In Question 1 you listed certain gifts of the forests. If you did not understand what each of these is, look them up in some reference book and be ready to report to the class.

Other good stories of the forests are "The Elk River Drive," Bassett; and "Saving the Forest," Cheyney (in *Child-Library Readers, Book Five*); and "From Logging Camp to Living Room," Baker (in *The Wonderful Story of Industry*).

A BACKWARD LOOK

Now that you have read these stories, perhaps you understand a little better why we speak of the workers of the world as the true conquerors of the earth. You have seen how Thomas Edison harnessed electricity. He made it give us light, move our loads, and do many other wonderful things for us. You have read of the gifts of the forest that waited long centuries for conquering workers to find them and make use of them for the comfort and happiness of men and women.

Stop for a moment and think of what you owe to the men and women who do the work of the world. It is a long journey from the wool on the sheep to the clothing you wear. Many people had to work in order that you might have your clothing. Your food, your home, and the other things that make you comfortable and happy come to you because men have studied and worked to conquer the earth for themselves and their fellow men.

Who are the different workmen needed to build a house? Make a list of them. What different people help to provide you with clothing? You might start with the planting of the cotton or the herding of the sheep and make a list of the workers.

There are many fascinating stories of how the work of the world is done. For example, what do you know about rubber, glass, silk, coal, and iron? Do you know the true story of the long struggle man has made to conquer these things for his use? You would be surprised at how interesting many of these stories are. Some of them you can find in the books that are named on page 452.

Part Seven
Famous Heroes of Adventure

HERE PASS MOST WONDROUS SIGHTS

T. A. JANVIER

Who'd hear great marvels told—
   Come listen now!
Who longs for hidden gold—
   Come listen now!
Who joys in well-fought fights,
Who yearns for wondrous sights,
Who pants for strange delights—
   Come listen now!

For here are marvels told
   To listen to!
Here tales of hidden gold
   To listen to!
Here gallant men wage fights,
Here pass most wondrous sights,
Here's that which ear delights
   To listen to!

GREAT HEROES LIVE FOREVER

IN THE pages of books great heroes live forever. Men who were famous centuries ago are known today to millions of people. Many of these heroes lived long before men knew how to print books, but their deeds were kept alive by wandering story-tellers, called minstrels. You are probably already acquainted with some of these famous heroes. Do you remember Beowulf, Sigurd, and Roland?

Now you are going to read of three more great heroes of adventure: Robin Hood, Achilles, and Ulysses. The legend of Robin Hood goes back at least five hundred years in the history of England. Probably the tales about him were told for many, many years before that. No one knows who first told them. So famous is Robin Hood that an entire opera of beautiful music has been written about him, and a moving picture has been made of his stirring deeds.

Achilles and Ulysses were two great heroes of ancient Greece. The stories about them go back probably three thousand years, and they have come down to us in the writings of a blind, wandering, minstrel poet named Homer. His name is famous the world over because of two great poems he wrote—the *Iliad* and the *Odyssey*. Homer probably first wandered from town to town with his harp, singing these long song-stories of great heroes.

If Homer had not written these tales in verse, we should know very little about the Greeks of ancient times. It is often true that such old, old stories are almost the only means we have of knowing how the people of those times lived.

ROBIN HOOD AND HIS MERRY MEN

Many hundreds of years ago a selfish king of England destroyed villages and farms in order to make royal forests where he might enjoy his favorite sport of hunting. He also passed severe laws to keep people from killing his deer. In spite of this, many men killed the deer and then fled into the deep forest to escape punishment. There they formed into bands and, knowing the forests so well, were safe from the king's officers. Among all these outlaws, none was ever more famous than the hero of this story, Robin Hood.

I

Many hundreds of years ago, England was so covered with woods that a squirrel was said to be able to hop from tree to tree from the Severn River to the Humber River.

But still, there were roads that ran from north to south and from east to west for the use of those who wished to travel. At certain times of the year these roads were thronged with people. Pilgrims going to some holy shrine passed along; merchants taking their goods to market; abbots and bishops riding on horseback to attend the King's Council; and, more frequently still, a knight, seeking adventures.

Besides the broad roads there were little green paths, and these led to clumps of low huts where dwelt the peasants, charcoal-burners, and plowmen. Here and there some larger clearing told that the house of a yeoman was near. Now and then as you passed through the forest, you might ride by a splendid abbey. Here you might catch a glimpse of monks in long black or white gowns, fishing in the streams that abound in this part of England, or casting nets in the fish

ponds which were in the midst of the abbey gardens. Or you
might see a castle with round turrets and high battlements,
circled by strong walls and protected by a moat full of water.

This was the sort of England into which the famous Robin
Hood was born. We know very little about him, except that
the King had declared him an outlaw, so that any man might
kill him and never be punished for it. But, outlaw or not,
the poor people loved Robin Hood and looked on him as their
friend. Many a gay young fellow came to join him, and led
a merry life in Sherwood Forest, with moss and fern for bed,
and for meat the deer that belonged to the King. Peasants
of all sorts, tillers of the land, yeomen, and knights went on
their ways freely, for Robin did them no harm. But rich
men with money-bags well filled trembled as they drew near
to Sherwood Forest. Who knew whether behind every tree
there did not lurk Robin Hood or some of his men?

II

One day Robin, walking alone in the wood, reached a river
which was spanned by a bridge so narrow that only one man
could pass. In the middle stood a stranger, and Robin commanded him to go back and let him cross. "I am no man of
yours," was all the answer he got. In anger Robin drew
his bow and fitted an arrow to it.

"Would you shoot a man who has no weapon but a staff?"
asked the stranger; and with shame Robin laid down his bow
and unbuckled an oaken stick at his side. "We will fight
till one of us falls into the water," he said; and fight they
did, till the stranger planted a blow so well that Robin rolled
over into the river.

"You are a brave soul," said Robin, when he had waded
to land; and he blew a blast with his horn which brought
fifty good fellows, clothed in green, to the little bridge.

"Have you fallen into the river, that your clothes are wet?"
asked one; and Robin made answer, "No, but this stranger
got the better of me and tumbled me into the stream."

At this the foresters seized the stranger and would have
ducked him had not their leader commanded them to stop and
begged the stranger to stay and become one of their band.
"Here is my hand," replied the stranger, "and my heart with
it. My name, if you would know it, is John Little."

"That must be altered," cried Will Scarlett. "We will call
a feast, and because he is full seven feet tall and round the
waist at least an ell, he shall be called Little John."

And thus it was done. But at the feast Little John, who
always liked to know exactly what work he had to do, put
some questions to Robin Hood. "Before I join hands with
you, tell me what sort of life this is you lead. How am I to
know whose goods I shall take, and whose I shall leave?
Whom shall I beat, and whom shall I refrain from beating?"

And Robin answered: "Look that you harm not any tiller
of the ground, nor any yeoman of the greenwood—no, nor
any knight or squire, unless you have heard him ill spoken
of. But if rich men with money-bags come your way, see
that you take their belongings. But above all else, see that
you keep in your mind the High Sheriff of Nottingham."

This being settled, Robin Hood declared Little John to be
second in command to himself among the forest band. The
new outlaw never forgot to keep in mind the High Sheriff of
Nottingham, who was the bitterest enemy the foresters had.

Robin Hood, however, had no liking for a company of idle men about him; so he at once sent off Little John and Will Scarlett to the great road known as Watling Street, with orders to hide among the trees and wait till some adventure might come to them. If they took captive earl or baron, abbot or knight, he was to be brought unharmed back to Robin Hood. But all along Watling Street the road was bare; white and hard it lay in the sun, without the tiniest cloud of dust to show that a rich company might be coming.

III

At length, just where a side path turned into the broad highway, there rode a knight, and never did a more pitiful man than he ride a horse on a summer day. One foot only was in the stirrup; the other hung carelessly by his side. His head was bowed, the reins dropped loose, and his horse went on as he would. At so sad a sight, the hearts of the outlaws were filled with pity, and Little John fell on his knees and bade the knight welcome in the name of his master.

"Who is your master?" asked the Knight.

"Robin Hood," answered Little John.

"I have heard much good of him," replied the Knight, "and will go with you gladly."

Then they all set off together, tears running down the Knight's cheeks. But he said nothing; neither was anything said to him. In this manner they came to Robin Hood.

"Welcome, Sir Knight," cried he, "and thrice welcome, for I waited to eat till you or some other had come to me."

"God save you, good Robin," answered the Knight; and after they had washed themselves in the stream, they sat down to dine off bread and wine, with flesh of the King's deer, and swans and pheasants. "Such a dinner have I not had for three weeks and more," said the Knight. "And if I ever come again this way, good Robin, I will give you as fine a dinner as you have given me."

"I thank you," replied Robin. "But before you go, pay me, I pray you, for the food which you have had. It was never the custom for a yeoman to pay for a knight."

"My bag is empty," said the Knight, "except for ten shillings only."

"Go, Little John, and look in his wallet," said Robin, "and, Sir Knight, if in truth you have no more, not one penny will I take; nay, I will give you all that you shall need."

So Little John spread out the Knight's mantle and opened the bag, and therein lay ten shillings and nothing else.

"What tidings, Little John?" cried his master.

"Sir, the Knight speaks truly," said Little John.

"Then tell me, Sir Knight, whether it is your own ill doings which have brought you to this sad condition."

"For a hundred years my fathers have dwelt and prospered in the forest," answered the Knight. "But within two years misfortune has befallen me and my wife and my children."

"How did this evil come to pass?" asked Robin.

"Through my own folly," answered the Knight, "and because of the great love I bore my son, who, before he was twenty years old, slew a knight of Lancaster and his servant. For their deaths I had to pay a large sum, which I could not raise without pledging my lands to a rich man at York. If I cannot give him the money by a certain day, my lands will be lost to me forever."

"What is the sum?" asked Robin.   "Tell me truly."

"It is four hundred pounds," said the Knight.

"And what will you do if you lose your lands?" asked Robin again.

"Sail away over the sea," said the Knight, "and bid farewell to friends and country.   There is no better way for me."

As he spoke, tears fell from his eyes, and he turned to depart.   "Good day, my friend," he said to Robin; "I cannot pay you what I should—"   But Robin held him fast. "Where are your friends?" asked he.

"Sir, they have all forsaken me since I became poor, and they turn away their heads if we meet upon the road, though when I was rich they were always in my castle."

When Little John and Will Scarlett and the rest heard this, they wept in anger and sorrow, and Robin told them to fill a cup of the best wine and give it to the Knight.

"Have you no one who would be surety for you?" said he.

"None," answered the Knight.

"You speak bravely," said Robin, "and you, Little John, go to my treasure chest, and bring me four hundred pounds."

So Little John went, and Will Scarlett, and they brought back the money.

"Sir," said Little John, when Robin had counted it and found it no more and no less, "look at his clothes, how thin they are!   You have stores of clothing, green and scarlet, in your chests—no merchant in England has so much.   I will find some to his measure."   And this he did.

"Master," spoke Little John again, "there is still something else.   You must give him a horse, that he may go to York as befits a knight."

"Take the gray horse," said Robin, "and put a new saddle on it, and take also a pair of boots with gilt spurs on them. And as it would not be proper for a knight to ride by himself on this errand, I will lend you Little John as squire."

"When shall we meet again?" asked the Knight.

"On this day twelve months from now," said Robin, "under the greenwood tree."

IV

Then the Knight rode on his way, with Little John behind him. As he went, he thought of Robin Hood and his men, and blessed them for the goodness they had shown him.

"Tomorrow," he said to Little John, "I must be in the city of York, for if I am so much as a day late, my lands are lost forever; and though I were to bring the money, I should not be allowed to claim them."

Now the man who had lent the money, as well as the Knight, had been counting the days. The next day he said to his friends, "This day a year ago there came a knight who borrowed of me four hundred pounds, giving his lands as surety. If he come not to pay his debt before midnight, the lands will be mine forever."

"It is early yet," said one; "he may still be coming."

"He is far beyond the sea and suffers from hunger and cold," said the rich man. "How is he to get here?"

"He is dead or hanged," said another, "and you will have his lands."

So they went to the High Judge whose duty it would be to declare the loss of the Knight's lands if he did not pay the money.

"If he come not this day," cried the rich man, rubbing his hands, "the lands will be mine."

"He will not come," said the Judge, but he knew not that the Knight was already at the outer gate, and Little John with him.

"Welcome, Sir Knight," said the porter. "The horse that you ride is the noblest that ever I saw. Let me lead it and the steed of your companion to the stable, that they may have food and rest."

"They shall not pass these gates," answered the Knight sternly, and he entered the hall alone.

"I have come back, my lord," he said, kneeling down before the rich man, who had just returned from court.

"Have you brought my money?"

"I have come to pray you to give me more time," said the Knight.

"The day was fixed and cannot be changed," answered the Judge, who was eating with others in the hall.

The Knight begged the Judge to be his friend and help him, but he refused.

"Give me one more chance to get the money and free my lands," prayed the Knight. "I will serve you day and night till I have four hundred pounds."

But the rich man only answered that the money must be paid that day. Then the Knight stood up straight and tall.

"You are not courteous," he said, "to make a knight kneel so long. But it is well to try out one's friends in the hour of need."

Then he looked the rich man full in the face, and the man felt uneasy and hated the Knight more than ever.

"Out of my hall, false Knight," he cried, pretending to a courage he did not feel.

But the Knight answered him, "Never was I false, and that I have shown in many a contest." Then he strode up to a table and emptied out four hundred pounds. "Take your gold which you lent to me a year ago," he said. "Had you but received me kindly, I would have paid you something more."

Then he passed out of the hall singing merrily and rode back to his house, where his wife met him at the gate. Then he told her how Robin Hood had befriended him. "But for this kindness of Robin Hood," he said, "we should now be beggars."

After this the Knight dwelt at home, looking after his lands and saving his money carefully, till the four hundred pounds lay ready for Robin Hood. Then he bought a hundred bows and a hundred arrows, and every arrow had a head of silver and peacock's feathers. Clothing himself in white and red, and with a hundred men, he set off to Sherwood Forest.

There under the greenwood tree he found Robin and his merry men waiting for him, according to the promise they had made the year before.

> "God save thee, Robin Hood,
>   And all this company."
> "Welcome be thou, gentle Knight,
>   And right welcome to me.
>
> "Hast thou thy land again?" said Robin;
>   "Truth then tell thou me."
> "Yea, 'fore God," said the Knight,
>   "And for it thank I God and thee.

"Have here four hundred pounds,
    The which you lent to me;
And here are also twenty marks
    For your courtesie."

But Robin would not take the money. A miracle had happened, he said, and it had been paid to him, and shame would it be to take it twice over.

Then he noticed for the first time the bows and arrows which the Knight had brought, and asked what they were. "A poor present to you," answered the Knight; and Robin, who would not be outdone, sent Little John once more to his treasury and bade him bring forth four hundred pounds, which were given to the Knight.

After that they parted, in much love. And Robin prayed the Knight if he were ever in any trouble, to let him know at the greenwood tree, and he would help him.

V

In many ways life in the forest was dull in the winter, and often the days passed slowly; but in summer, when the leaves were green and flowers and ferns covered all the woodland, Robin Hood and his men would come out of their warm resting places, like the rabbits and the squirrels, and would play, too. Races they ran to stretch their legs, or leaping matches were arranged, or they would shoot at a mark.

"Who of you can kill a deer five hundred paces off?" So said Robin to his men one bright May morning, and they went into the wood and tried their skill. To the great joy of Robin Hood, it was Little John who brought down the hart.

"I would ride my horse a hundred miles to find one who could match with thee," he said to Little John. Will Scarlett, who was perhaps rather jealous of this mighty deed, answered, with a laugh, "There lives a friar in Fountains Abbey who would beat both him and you."

Now Robin Hood did not like to be told that any man could shoot better than himself or his foresters; so he swore lustily that he would neither eat nor drink till he had seen that friar. Leaving his men where they were, he put on a coat of mail and a steel cap, took his shield and sword, slung his bow over his shoulder, and filled his quiver with arrows. Thus armed, he set forth to Fountains Dale.

By the side of the river a friar was walking, armed like Robin, but without a bow. At this sight Robin jumped from his horse, which he tied to a bush, and called to the friar to carry him over the water, or it would cost him his life.

The friar said nothing, but hoisted Robin on his broad back and marched into the river. Not a word was spoken till they reached the other side, when Robin leaped lightly down, and was going on his way. Then the friar stopped him. "Not so fast, my fine fellow," said he. "It is my turn now, and you shall take me across the river."

So Robin carried him, and when they had reached the bank, he set down the friar, jumped for the second time on his back, and ordered the friar to take him back across the river. The friar strode into the stream with his burden, but as soon as they got to the middle, he bent his head and Robin fell into the water. "Now you can sink or swim, as you like," said the friar, as he stood and laughed.

Robin Hood pulled himself out of the water; and while the

friar was scrambling out, Robin fitted an arrow to his bow and let fly at him. But the friar quickly held up his shield, and the arrow fell harmless.

"Shoot on, my fine fellow. Shoot on all day if you like," shouted the friar; and Robin shot till his arrows were gone, but always missed his mark. Then they took their swords, and at four in the afternoon they were still fighting.

By this time Robin's strength was wearing, and he felt he could not fight much more. "A boon, a boon!" cried he. "Let me but blow three blasts on my horn, and I will thank you on my bended knees for it."

The friar told him to blow as many blasts as he liked. In an instant the forest echoed with his horn, and it was but a few minutes before half a hundred yeomen were racing over the grass. The friar stared when he saw them; then, turning to Robin, he begged of him a boon also. This being granted, he gave three whistles, which were followed by the noise of a great crashing through the trees as fifty great dogs bounded toward him.

"Here's a dog for each of your men," said the friar, "and I myself for you." But the dogs did not listen to his words, for two of them rushed at Robin and tore his mantle of Lincoln green from off his back. His men were kept busy defending themselves, for every arrow shot at a dog was caught and held in the creature's mouth.

Robin's men were not used to fighting dogs, and they were being badly beaten. At last Little John bade the friar call off his dogs. As he did not do so, Little John let fly some arrows, which this time left dead on the ground a half dozen of the savage dogs.

"Hold, hold, my good fellow," said the friar, "till your master and I can come to a bargain"; and when the bargain was made, this was how it ran: that the friar was to leave Fountains Abbey and join Robin Hood, and that he should be paid a gold coin every Sunday throughout the year, and be given plenty of good clothes. Under the name of Friar Tuck, he became one of the most famous of Robin Hood's band.

VI

One Sunday morning, when the sun was shining and the birds singing, Robin Hood called to Little John to come with him to church in Nottingham. As was their custom, they took their bows, and on the way Little John proposed that they should have a shooting contest. Robin, who believed that he shot better than any other man living, laughed in scorn and told Little John that he should have three tries to his master's one, to which John agreed.

But Robin soon repented of his offer, for Little John speedily won the contest. At this Robin became angry and struck Little John with his hand. Little John was not the man to bear being treated so, and he told Robin that he would never more own him for master, and turned back into the wood. At this, Robin was ashamed of what he had done, but his pride would not allow him to say so; and he continued his way to Nottingham. Not without fears, he entered the church, for the Sheriff of the town was his enemy. However, there he was, and there he meant to stay. He knelt down in the sight of all the people; but only one man knew him, and that man stole out of church, ran to the Sheriff, and bade him come quickly and take his foe.

The Sheriff was not slow to do what he was bidden. He called his men to follow him, and marched to the church. The noise they made in entering caused Robin to look round. "Alas, alas," he said to himself, "now will I miss Little John." But he drew his two-handed sword and fought so savagely that twelve of the Sheriff's men lay dead before him. Then Robin found himself face to face with the Sheriff, and gave him a fierce blow; but his sword broke on the Sheriff's head, and he had shot away all his arrows. So the men closed round him and bound his arms.

Ill news travels fast, and not many hours had passed before the foresters heard that their master was in prison. They wept and moaned and wrung their hands, and seemed to have gone suddenly mad, till Little John bade them take courage and help him outwit the Sheriff.

The next morning Little John hid himself and waited with a comrade till he saw a messenger riding along the road, carrying letters from the Sheriff to the King, telling him of the capture of Robin Hood.

"Whence come you?" asked Little John, going up to the messenger, "and can you give us tidings of an outlaw named Robin Hood, who was taken prisoner yesterday?"

"You may thank me that he is taken," said the rider, "for I laid hands on him."

"I thank you so much that I and my friend will bear you company," said Little John, "for in this forest are many wild men who own Robin Hood for leader, and you ride along this road at the peril of your life."

They went on together, talking, when suddenly Little John seized the horse by the head and pulled down the rider.

"He was my master," said Little John,
"That you have brought to bale;
Never shall you come at the King
For to tell him that tale."

Then, taking the letters from the messenger, Little John carried them to the King.

When they arrived at the palace in the presence of the King, Little John and his companion fell on their knees and held out the letters. "God save you, my lord," they said, and the King unfolded the letters and read them. Then he handed his own seal to Little John and ordered him to bear it to the Sheriff and bid him without delay bring Robin Hood unhurt into his presence. "There never was yeoman in Merry England that I longed so much to see," he said. The King also ordered his treasurer to give the messengers twenty pounds each, and he made these messengers his yeomen.

Little John took the King's seal to the Sheriff, who made him and his companion welcome because they came from the King. Then the Sheriff set a feast for them, and after they had eaten, he fell asleep. Then the two outlaws stole softly to the prison. They overpowered the guard and, taking the keys, hunted through the cells until they found Robin Hood. Little John whispered to his master to follow him, and they crept along till they reached the lowest part of the city wall, from which they jumped and were safe and free.

"Now, farewell," said Little John. "I have done you a good turn for a bad one." "Not so," answered Robin Hood. "I make you master of my men and me." But Little John would not agree to this. "I only wish to be your comrade, and thus it shall be," he replied.

When the King heard of the adventure, he shouted in anger, "Little John has outwitted us both."

VII

Now the King did not intend that Robin Hood should keep on doing as he pleased; so he called his Knights to follow him to Nottingham, where they would lay plans how best to capture the outlaw. Here they heard sad tales of Robin's misdeeds, and how of the many herds of wild deer that had roamed the forest, in some places scarce one deer remained. This was the work of Robin Hood and his merry men, on whom the King swore revenge with a great oath.

All this time, and for six weeks more while he dwelt in Nottingham, the King could hear nothing of Robin. The outlaw seemed to have vanished into the earth with his merry men, though one by one the deer were vanishing, too.

At last one day a forester came to the King and told him that if he would see Robin he must come with him and take five of his best knights. The King eagerly sprang up to do his bidding, and the six men, clad in monks' clothes, mounted their horses and rode merrily along. The King wore an Abbot's broad hat over his crown, and sang as he passed through the greenwood. Suddenly at the turn of a path, Robin and his archers appeared before them.

Seizing the King's bridle, Robin said, "You will stay a while with us, Sir Abbot. We are yeomen, who live upon the King's deer, and have no other food. Now you have abbeys and churches, and gold in plenty; therefore give us some of it."

"I have only forty pounds," answered the King, "but sorry I am it is not a hundred, for you should have it all."

So Robin took the forty pounds, and gave half to his men. Then he told the King he might go on his way. "I thank you," said the King, "but I would have you know that our ruler has bid me give you his seal and pray you to come to Nottingham." At this message Robin bent his knee.

"I love no man in all the world
So well as I do my King,"

he cried. "For your tidings, Sir Abbot, which fill my heart with joy, today you shall dine with me, for love of my King."

Then Robin led the King into an open place, and took a horn and blew it loud. At its blast seven score of young men came speedily. "They are quicker to do his bidding than my men are to do mine," said the King to himself.

Speedily the foresters set out the dinner, roasts of venison and loaves of white bread; then Robin and Little John served the King. "Make good cheer," said Robin. "And then, Abbot, you shall see what sort of life we lead, so that you may tell our King."

When all had finished eating, the archers took their bows and hung rose-garlands up with a string, for every man was to shoot through the garland. If he failed, he should have a blow on the head from Robin.

Good bowmen as they were, few could stand the test. Little John and Will Scarlett shot wide of the mark. At length no one was left in but Robin himself and Gilbert of the Wide Hand. Then Robin fired his last arrow, and it fell three fingers from the garland. "Master," said Gilbert, "you have lost; stand forth and take your punishment, as was agreed."

"I will take it," answered Robin, "but, Sir Abbot, I pray you that I may receive the blow at your hands."

The King hesitated. "It is not fitting for me to smite such a stout yeoman," he said. But Robin bade him smite on and spare him not; so the King turned up his sleeve and gave Robin such a blow on the head that he lost his feet and rolled upon the ground. As the King struck this mighty blow, his hat fell back, so that Robin saw his face.

"My lord, the King of England, now I know you well," cried he; and he fell on his knees, and all the outlaws with him. "Mercy I ask, my lord the King, for all my brave foresters and me."

"Mercy I grant," then said the King; "and therefore I came hither, to bid you and your men leave the greenwood and dwell in my Court with me."

"So shall it be," answered Robin. "I and my men will come to your Court, and see how we like your service."

"Have you any green cloth," asked the King, "that you could sell to me?" Robin brought out thirty yards and more, and clad the King and his men in coats of Lincoln green. "Now we will all ride to Nottingham," said Robin.

The people of Nottingham saw them coming and trembled as they watched the dark mass of Lincoln green drawing near over the fields. "I fear lest our King be slain," whispered one to another; "and if Robin Hood gets into the town, there is not one of us whose life is safe." And every man, woman, and child made ready to flee. The King laughed aloud when he saw their fright, and called them back. Right glad were they to hear his voice, and they feasted and made merry.

A few days later the King returned to London, and Robin dwelt in his Court for twelve months.

But his men, who had been born under the shadow of the forest, could not live amid streets and houses. One by one they slipped away, till only Little John and Will Scarlett were left. Then Robin himself grew homesick. At once he went to the King and begged for leave to go on a journey.

"I may not say you nay," answered the King. "Seven nights you may be gone and no more." Robin thanked him, and that evening set out for the greenwood.

It was early morning when at last he reached the forest, and he could hear all about him the notes of singing birds, great and small. "It seems long since I was here," he said to himself. "It would give me great joy if I could bring down a deer once more." So he shot a deer, blew his horn, and all the outlaws of the forest came flocking round him. "Welcome, our dear master, back to the greenwood tree," they cried; and they fell on their knees before him in delight.

Nothing that the King could say would tempt Robin Hood back again, and he dwelt in the greenwood for two and twenty years. And he was ever a faithful friend, kind to the poor, and gentle to all women.

NOTES AND QUESTIONS

1. *(a)* Make a list of all the characters you would need if you were going to make this story into a play or a "movie."

(b) Which would be the two most important characters?

2. Choose at least five incidents that you would like to see in a "movie."

3. The artist drew three pictures for this story. What three other incidents would have made good illustrations?

4. The parts of this story are numbered but not named. Write a title for each part. Your first one might be: *I. The Home of Robin in Sherwood Forest.*

5. Pirates were outlaws like Robin Hood and his men, but they were never heroes and never so beloved. Tell something about the rulers of those times and something about Robin and his men that would explain why they were heroes to most of the people.

6. What three weapons did the outlaws use? With which one were they most skillful?

7. Be ready to tell in your own words—

(a) How Friar Tuck came to join the band.

(b) The story of the Knight who had lost his lands.

(c) How Robin met the King.

(d) How Little John rescued Robin.

The story you have just read tells only a few of the many adventures of Robin Hood. You would enjoy reading "Robin Hood, Books the First and Second," in Edith Heal's *Robin Hood.* Howard Pyle, who wrote the story about Tom Chist, has also written *The Merry Adventures of Robin Hood* and drawn beautiful pictures for it.

A SONG OF SHERWOOD

Alfred Noyes

Sherwood in the twilight, is Robin Hood awake?
Grey and ghostly shadows are gliding through the brake;
Shadows of the dappled deer, dreaming of the morn,
Dreaming of a shadowy man that winds a shadowy horn.

Robin Hood is here again; all his merry thieves
Hear a ghostly bugle-note shivering through the leaves,
Calling as he used to call, faint and far away,
In Sherwood, in Sherwood, about the break of day.

Where the deer are gliding down the shadowy glen,
All across the glades of ferns he calls his merry men;
Doublets of Lincoln green, glancing through the May,
In Sherwood, in Sherwood, about the break of day.

Calls them and they answer: from aisles of oak and ash
Rings the *Follow! Follow!* and boughs begin to crash;
The ferns begin to flutter and the flowers begin to fly;
And through the crimson dawning the robber band goes by.

Robin! Robin! Robin! all his merry thieves
Answer as the bugle-note shivers through the leaves:
Calling as he used to call, faint and far away,
In Sherwood, in Sherwood, about the break of day.

Reprinted by permission from *Collected Poems Vol. I*, by Alfred Noyes, copyright 1906, Frederick A. Stokes Company.

ACHILLES, FAMOUS LEADER OF THE GREEKS

Alfred J. Church

This story of Achilles is taken from Homer's famous poem, the *Iliad*. The word "Iliad" comes from "Ilium," the Greek name for the city of Troy, about whose capture the poem tells. Ancient Troy was located in what is now the northwestern corner of Turkey, near the Aegean Sea and the Strait of Dardanelles.

HOW HELEN'S SUITORS SWORE TO DEFEND HER
AND HER HUSBAND

Helen was the most beautiful of all the women of Greece—nay, of all the women on the face of the earth. All the princes of Greece were suitors for her hand.

"You do me great honor, my lords," said the king, her father, when all the suitors had assembled at his court, "but there is something which troubles me. You are many, and my daughter can have but one husband. How then will it be when she shall have made her choice? Will it not be that I have one friend and a score of enemies? My daughter would rather die unmarried than bring trouble upon me and my people. Therefore her resolve is this: you must swear a great oath that you will defend her and her husband, whomever she may choose, and that if he or she suffers any wrong, you will avenge it."

These words pleased the suitors, and they swore a great oath that they would defend Helen and her husband against all injury that might be done to them. After much thought Helen chose for her husband Menelaus, king of Sparta and younger brother of Agamemnon, overlord of all Greece.

HOW PARIS CHOSE APHRODITE AS THE FAIREST

Now across the sea from Greece was the famous city of Troy. Here lived a brave people who had made their city great by their industry in peace and by their courage in war.

Priam was king of Troy and much beloved by everyone. The king had many children, the youngest of whom was Paris; when he was born, a strange thing happened. A priest told Priam that Paris would grow up to be a danger and a curse to his family and to his country. So King Priam had his servants take the baby to a mountain-side and leave it there to die. Some shepherds found the child and reared him carefully, so that he grew to be a beautiful youth.

At this time the king of Thessaly married Thetis, a goddess of the sea. All the gods but Discord were invited to the wedding feast. Discord, however, came unbidden and threw into the midst of the company a golden apple upon which was written, "To the Fairest." Then she swiftly departed.

Hera, queen of the gods; Athena, goddess of war and wisdom; and Aphrodite, goddess of love and beauty, each claimed the apple, and there arose a mighty quarrel so that no god was willing to be the judge. At length Zeus, father of the gods, said to Hermes, the messenger, "There is a shepherd on Mount Ida, Paris by name; he is a son of Priam, king of Troy, and he is the most beautiful of mortal men. Let him be the judge in the matter." So Hermes took the three goddesses to Mount Ida, that Paris might judge which was the fairest.

When they stood before Paris, Hera said, "Choose me the fairest, and I will give thee lordship over the whole of Asia."

Athena said, "I can give thee wisdom and skill in war above all others." Last of all Aphrodite said, "I will give thee for wife the fairest woman in all the world, if you will choose me." Paris looked at glorious Hera, and dazzling Athena, but when he looked at Aphrodite, he said, "Thou art the fairest."

This judgment of Paris was the beginning of many troubles. Aphrodite had promised him the fairest woman in all the world. The fairest of all women was Helen, who had married Menelaus and was living happily with him and her baby daughter. But Aphrodite kept her promise and made it possible for Paris to take Helen from her home, and carry her to Troy.

Menelaus, in grief and anger because of the loss of his wife, called upon all the princes of Greece who had sworn to defend him and asked them to keep their promise.

This call was not to their liking, and many tried to avoid obeying, but at last a great army was gathered together. One hundred thousand men and twelve hundred ships crossed over to Troy to punish Paris and to restore Helen to Menelaus. Even the gods took sides. Hera and Athena had never forgiven Paris; therefore they favored the Greeks. But Aphrodite used her power to help the Trojans. Apollo, god of the sun, and Ares, god of war, also were on the side of the Trojans. So the Trojan war was a war of gods as well as of men.

WHY ACHILLES REFUSED TO FIGHT

For nine years and more the Greeks besieged the city of Troy. They pressed the men of the city very hard, so that they dared not go outside the walls. They might have taken Troy without further loss, but there arose a strife between two of the Greek chieftains, Agamemnon, overlord of all the host, and Achilles, the most valiant man among them.

The Greeks had offended the priest of Apollo, because Agamemnon had taken for himself the daughter of the priest as a prize of war and refused to give her up. Apollo was angered and sent swift death among the Greeks. Achilles, learning the cause of this misfortune, roused the anger of Agamemnon by forcing him to give up the maiden.

Agamemnon said, "I will send back my prize, Achilles, but I will take the maiden whom the Greeks have given you."

The face of Achilles grew black with anger and he cried, "You are altogether shameless and greedy, an ill ruler of men. I have no quarrel with the Trojans; I have been fighting in your cause and that of your brother Menelaus. You leave me to fight while you sit in your tent at ease. But

when the spoil is divided, you take the lion's share. Small
indeed is my share, and even the prize I took, you now take
away! So I am determined to go home."

Agememnon answered, "Go and take your men with you.
I have other chieftains as brave, who pay me due respect."

Then Achilles was insane with anger. He had half drawn
his sword when the goddess Athena caught him by his long
yellow hair and said: "I have come to end thy wrath. Use
bitter words, if thou wilt, but put aside thy sword."

Achilles answered, "I shall obey thy command." Then he
thrust the heavy sword back into the scabbard and turned to
Agamemnon.

"Drunkard, with the eyes of a dog and the heart of a
deer! Never fighting in the front of the battle! The Greeks
shall one day miss Achilles, when they fall in heaps before
the Trojan warrior, Hector, and you shall be grieved that
you have wronged the bravest of your men."

And Achilles went apart from his comrades and sat down
upon the seashore, weeping bitter tears.

Then Agamemnon went forth and took counsel with the
chiefs, and soon the shrill-voiced heralds called the Greek
host to battle. Many nations and many chiefs were there,
but none that could compare with Achilles—Achilles who
sat apart and would not go to battle.

HOW HECTOR BADE FAREWELL TO ANDROMACHE

On the other side the sons of Troy and their allies came
forth from the gates of the city and set themselves in battle
array. The most famous of their chiefs were Hector, son
of Priam, bravest and best of all, and Aeneas, son of the

goddess Aphrodite. The Greeks went forward to the battle silently and in order after their chiefs. But from the Trojan army came a confused cry, for there were men of many languages gathered. On both sides the gods urged them on.

Hector with Ares, god of war, at his side dealt death and destruction through the ranks of the Greeks. Hera and Athena saw him and were angered. They passed down to earth and brought victory to the Greeks. At last after much fighting, Hector went to the city to bid the mothers of Troy assemble in the temple of Athena to see if their prayers might not stay the anger of the goddess. Andromache, the wife of Hector, saw him and hastened to meet him. With her was a nurse bearing Hector's only child, beautiful as a star. Hector smiled when he saw the child, but Andromache clasped Hector's hand and wept, saying:

"Oh, Hector, your courage will bring you to death. All the Greeks will rush upon you and slay you. It were better for me to die than to lose you, for I have no comfort but you. My father and my seven brothers all fell by the hand of the great Achilles. My dear mother, too, is dead. You are father to me, and mother, and brother, and husband also. Have pity, then, and stay there upon the wall, lest you leave me a widow, and your child an orphan."

But Hector said, "Nay, I am not willing that any son or daughter of Troy should see me keeping away from battle."

Then Hector stretched out his arms to his child. But the child drew back in the arms of his nurse with a loud cry, fearing the shining bronze armor and the horsehair plume which nodded from his helmet top. Then father and mother laughed aloud. And Hector took the helmet from his head and laid it on the ground, and caught the child in his hands and kissed him, praying aloud:

"Grant, Father Zeus and all ye gods, that this child may be great among the sons of Troy; and may they say some day, when they see him carrying home the spoils of war, 'A better man, this, than his father,' and his mother shall be glad."

Then he gave the child to its mother; she clasped him to her and smiled a tearful smile. Her husband had pity on her and stroked her with his hand and said:

"Be not troubled overmuch. No man shall slay me unless fate orders it; but no man may escape fate, be he cowardly or brave. Go, carry on your tasks at the shuttle and the loom, and give their tasks to your maidens. Let me take thought for the battle."

Then Hector took up his helmet from the ground, and white-armed Andromache went her way to her home, often turning back her eyes. She and all her maidens wailed, for she felt that she should never more see him returning from the battle. But Hector went into battle with renewed strength, and everywhere the Greeks gave way before him.

HOW PATROCLUS WENT INTO BATTLE

Achilles was standing on the stern of his ship, looking at the battle, when his friend Patroclus ran to him, weeping bitterly. "Be not angry with me, great Achilles," he said, "for the Greeks are in deep trouble. All their bravest are wounded, while you cherish your anger. If you will not go to battle, let me go and your men with me. Let me put on your armor; so shall the Trojans be frightened, thinking that Achilles is in the battle, and the Greeks shall have a breathing space."

Achilles made reply, "I said that I would not rise up till the battle should come nigh to my ships." As they talked, the men of Troy set torches to the ships, and a great flame shot up to the sky. When Achilles saw it, he cried: "Hasten, Patroclus, for I see the fire rising from the ships. Put on my armor, and I will call my people to the war."

So Patroclus put on the armor—corselet and shield and helmet—and bound upon his shoulder the silver-studded sword, and took a mighty spear in his hand. Then he mounted the chariot drawn by the mighty horses of Achilles.

Meanwhile Achilles called his men to battle. Fifty ships had he brought to Troy, and in each there were fifty men. Then he spoke to them: "Forget not the bold words that you spoke against the men of Troy, complaining that I kept you from the battle against your will. Now you have your wish."

So the warriors went to battle in close array, helmet to helmet and shield to shield, close as the stones with which a builder makes a wall. And Patroclus, in the armor of Achilles, went in front.

Then Achilles went to his tent and took from his chest a great cup which Thetis, his mother, had given him. Now no man except Achilles drank from that cup, and he poured out of it offerings to no god but Zeus, father of all the gods. First he cleansed it; then he washed his hands, and, standing before his tent, poured out wine to Zeus, saying:

"O Zeus, I send my comrade to this battle. Make him strong and bold, and give him glory, and bring him home safe to the ships, and my people with him."

When Patroclus came to the battle and the men of Troy beheld him, they thought that Achilles had forgotten his anger and come forth. Then the men of Troy turned to flee, and many chiefs fell by the spears of the Greeks. But Apollo stirred up the spirit of Hector to go against Patroclus.

Three times Patroclus rushed against the men of Troy. But the fourth time Apollo stood behind him and struck him on the head so that his eyes grew dim. The helmet fell to the ground, and the horsehair plume was soiled with dust. Never before had that headpiece, the helmet of Achilles, touched the earth. Patroclus turned to flee, but Hector thrust his spear at him so that he fell; and Hector stood over him and cried: "Did you think to spoil our city, Patroclus? Instead, you are slain, and the great Achilles cannot help you."

But Patroclus answered, "You boast too much, Hector. It was not you that slew me, but Apollo. And mark you this, death is close to you by the hand of the great Achilles."

Hector answered, though Patroclus was dead, "Why do you prophesy death for me?   It may be that the great Achilles himself will fall by my hand."

HOW THE DEATH OF PATROCLUS AROUSED ACHILLES

Fierce was the fight about the body of Patroclus, and many heroes on both sides fell.   Hector stripped off the arms of Patroclus, the arms which Achilles had given him to wear, and put them on himself. Zeus saw him doing it, and liked it not.

Then a messenger came running to Achilles, weeping as he said, "I have ill news for you.   The men of Troy have the victory today, and, moreover, Patroclus lies dead."

Achilles took some of the dust of the plain and poured it on his head.   He wept and tore his hair.   His mother, Thetis, goddess of the sea, heard his cry and came and laid her hand on his head and asked, "Why weepest thou, my son?"

Achilles answered, "Lo! my friend Patroclus is dead, and Hector has the arms which I gave him to wear. I care not to live, unless I can avenge his death."

Then Thetis said, "Thou canst not go into battle without arms.   Tomorrow I will furnish thee with new armor."

While they talked the men of Troy drove the Greeks back more and more.   Then Zeus sent a messenger to Achilles.

"Rouse thee, Achilles," said the messenger, "or the body of Patroclus will be a prey for the dogs of Troy."

Achilles answered, "How shall I go?—for arms have I none."   The messenger replied, "Go only to the trench and show thyself; then the Greeks will have a breathing space."

So he went; and Athena put her shield upon him and a golden halo above his head, making it shine as a flame. He mingled with the battle, and his voice was as the sound of a trumpet. The men of Troy were stricken with fear, the horses backed with the chariots, and the drivers were astonished when they saw above his head the flaming fire which Athena had kindled.

The men of Troy fell back, and the Greeks took the body of Patroclus and carried it to the tent, while Achilles walked, with many tears, by the side of the body.

At dawn Thetis brought the new arms and laid them before Achilles. Loud they rattled on the ground, and all the men trembled to hear, but when Achilles saw them, his eyes blazed with fire, and he rejoiced in his heart.

So Achilles gathered the Greeks for the battle, and his armor flashed like fire. Hector saw him and rushed at him, but they did not fight; for when Hector cast his spear, Athena turned it aside, and when Achilles charged, Apollo bore Hector away. Then Achilles turned to the others and slew many of them. That hour the Greeks would have taken Troy, but Apollo saved it by drawing Achilles away from the city. Apollo took the form of a Trojan chief, and Achilles pursued him far from the walls of Troy.

HOW ACHILLES AVENGED THE DEATH OF PATROCLUS

The Trojans were now safe in the city, refreshing themselves after all their toil. Hector alone remained outside the walls, standing in front of the gates of the city. But all the while Achilles was fiercely pursuing Apollo, until at last the god turned and spoke to him: "Why dost thou pursue me, swift-footed Achilles? Hast thou not yet discovered that I am a god, and all thy fury is in vain?"

In great wrath Achilles answered him, "Thou hast done me wrong in drawing me away from the city, Great Archer. Had I the power, thou wouldst pay dearly for this cheat."

Then Achilles turned and rushed toward the city. Priam spied him from the wall, and cried to his son, and urged him to come within the walls. When Achilles approached, brandishing his great spear, Hector trembled and dared not stay. Fast he fled from the gates, and fast Achilles pursued him. Past the watch-tower they ran, past the wind-blown fig tree, along the wagon-road which went about the walls. On they ran, one flying, the other pursuing. Thrice they ran around the city, and all the gods looked on from their home on Mount Olympus. But Apollo helped Hector, or he could not have held out against Achilles, who was swiftest of foot among the sons of men.

On Mount Olympus Zeus called the gods to a council, and

he held out the great balance of doom.   In one scale he put
the fate of Achilles, and in the other the fate of Hector; and
lo! the scale of Hector sank down to the realms of death.

Achilles now drew near to Hector and threw his spear, but
Hector saw it coming and avoided it, crouching on the ground,
so that it flew above his head and fixed itself in the earth.
Athena snatched it and gave it back to Achilles, but Hector
did not see it.

"You have missed your aim, great Achilles," said Hector.
"You shall not drive your steel into my back, but here into my
breast, if the gods will it so.   But now look out for my spear."

Then Hector threw his long-shafted spear.   True aim he
took, for the spear struck the very middle of Achilles's shield.
It struck, but it did not pierce it, and bounded far away, for
the shield was not made by the hand of man.   Hector stood
dismayed, for he had no other spear.   Then he knew that his
end had come, and he said to himself, "Zeus and Apollo are
with me no longer, but if I must die, let me die bravely."

He drew his mighty sword and rushed at Achilles.   But
Achilles charged to meet him, his shield before his breast, his
helmet bent forward as he ran.   The gleam of his spear-point
was as the gleam of the evening star.   Achilles well knew the
one unprotected spot in the armor which Hector had taken
from Patroclus.   Into the spot where the neck joins the
shoulder he drove his spear, and Hector fell in the dust.

Achilles drew his spear out of the body, stripped off the
bloody armor; and all the Greeks came about the dead man,
marveling at his strength and beauty.   Looking at one another
they said, "Surely this Hector is less dreadful now than in the
day when he burned our ships with fire."

HOW PRIAM RANSOMED THE BODY OF HECTOR AND HOW
ACHILLES WAS KILLED

Andromache did not know what had happened. She sat in her dwelling, weaving a purple mantle embroidered with flowers. But when the sound of wailing came to her from the town, she rose hastily in great fear and called to her maidens: "Come to me, O maidens, that I may see what has happened, for I heard the voice of the queen, and I fear that some evil has come to the Trojans."

She hastened through the city, with terror in her heart. When she came to the wall, she stood and looked; and lo! she saw Achilles taking the body of Hector to the ships. Then her eyes grew dim, and she fell fainting.

When Priam saw Achilles take Hector's body, he determined to go forth and beg Achilles to give him the body of his dear son. He took a great cup and poured out wine to Zeus, and prayed: "Hear me, Father Zeus, and grant that Achilles may pity me. Send me a sign, in order that I may go with a good heart to the Greeks."

And Zeus heard him and sent his eagle, his favorite bird, as a sure sign. Then the old man mounted his chariot in haste, and with a herald drove forth from the palace.

When Priam came to the tent of Achilles, he leaped down from the chariot and went to the tent. The king fell on the ground before Achilles, clasped his knees, kissed his hands, and spoke: "Think of your father, godlike Achilles, and pity me. Many valiant sons I had, but most of them are dead, and he that was best of all has been slain by you. I have come to ransom him. Have pity on him and on me."

These words stirred the heart of Achilles. He stood up

before King Priam, and spoke: "How did you dare to come? You cannot raise your son from the dead."

But Priam answered, "Let me ransom Hector, my son, and look upon him with my eyes. Then may the gods grant you safe return to your fatherland. If you are willing to let me bury Hector, let there be a truce between my people and the Greeks. For nine days let us mourn, and on the tenth we will bury him, on the eleventh raise a great tomb above him, and on the twelfth we will fight again, if fight we must."

And Achilles answered, "Be it so."

Wailing and weeping, Priam and the herald took the body to the city. A daughter of Priam was the first to see her father and the herald with the body on the litter, and she cried, "Sons and daughters of Troy, go to meet Hector, if ever you met him with joy as he came back in triumph from battle."

At once there was not a man or woman left in the city. Andromache led the way, and the queen and all the multitude followed. They took Hector to his home, and the minstrels mourned while the women wept aloud. Last of all came Helen, and cried, "Many a year has passed since I came to Troy— would that I had died before! Never have I heard from your lips one bitter word. Therefore, I weep for you; no one is left in Troy to be my friend. All shun and hate me now."

For nine days the people of Troy gathered wood, and on the tenth they laid Hector upon the pile and lighted a fire beneath it. When the body was burned, his comrades gathered the bones and laid them in a chest of gold. This they covered with purple robes and put in a great coffin, and upon it they laid stones many and great. Over all they raised a mighty mound. Thus they buried Hector, defender of Troy.

But for Achilles the day of doom was not far distant. When he was born, his mother, Thetis, hearing it said that his life would be short and glorious, nevertheless wished for him a long life, even if it were not heroic. So she took the babe to the river Styx and dipped him in its waters. Now the water of this river made the body of him who bathed in it proof against all wounds. However, when Thetis dipped Achilles in the river, she held him by the heel, which alone remained untouched by the magic water. Therefore, his heel was not proof against wounds.

When the war was renewed, and Achilles strove to break through the gates of Troy, Paris, whose act had caused the war, aimed an arrow which struck Achilles in the heel, for Apollo guided the hand of Paris. So the greatest of the Greeks was slain on the very spot where he had killed Hector.

For seventeen days the Greeks mourned over his body, and on the eighteenth day they gave it burial by the side of his friend Patroclus. Over them both the Greeks raised a great mound that was the wonder of men in after times.

HOW TROY WAS TAKEN

Besides Hector and Achilles, many other chiefs met their doom on the plains before the gates of Troy during the ten long years that the city was besieged. For the gods gave victory now to the one army and now to the other.

At last Athena, always favoring the Greeks, put a thought into the mind of the crafty Ulysses, one of the greatest of the Greek warriors. Under his direction a great horse of wood was built. The Trojans were made to believe that the horse was a peace offering to Athena in order that the Greeks might have safe return to their homes. In the body of the horse, however, were hidden the bravest of the Greek chiefs. The rest of the warriors pretended to start for their homes, but really went only as far as a neighboring island.

Great was the joy of Troy when it was reported that the men of Greece had departed. The gates were opened, and the people went forth to see the plain and the camp. They stood and marveled at the great horse of wood.

One of the elders advised that the horse be brought within the walls. But one of the priests said, "What madness is this? Do you think that the men of Greece have really departed? Surely there are armed men in this mighty horse. Touch it not, for I fear the Greeks even though they offer gifts."

Then he cast his spear against the horse, and it gave forth a hollow sound. But the people did not heed him. All cried

together that the horse of wood must be brought inside the city. At once they opened the gates of the city and pulled down the adjoining wall and put rollers under the feet of the horse. So in much joy they drew it into the city by means of ropes, youths and maidens singing about it the while, and laying their hands to the ropes with great gladness.

When night was fully come and the men of Troy lay asleep, lo! from the ship of Agamemnon there rose a flame for a signal to all the Greeks. These at once manned their ships and rowed across the sea. Within the city was a Greek spy, who had gained entrance to the city by pretending that he was fleeing from the Greeks because they were about to slay him. At the same hour he opened the secret door in the great horse. Forth came the chiefs and opened the gates of the city, slaying those who kept watch.

So at last the Greek hosts swept through the streets. They took Troy with all its rich treasures, and Menelaus won back his wife, the beautiful Helen.

HOW AENEAS ESTABLISHED THE TROJANS IN ITALY

Meanwhile there came a vision to Aeneas who, now that Hector was dead, was the chief hope of Troy. It was Hector's self that he seemed to see, and the spirit said, "Fly, son of Aphrodite, fly and save yourself. The enemy is within the walls, and Troy is about to perish. You are now the one hope of Troy. Take, then, her gods and flee, seeking a home where you shall one day build a city across the seas."

Now that the Greeks held Troy and King Priam lay dead, Aeneas said to his father, "Climb, dear father, on my shoulders. I will bear you and not grow weary with the weight."

He took his small son by the hand, and so they went out through the gates, taking their household gods with them. Here Aeneas found with much joy and wonder a great company of men and women gathered together, who were willing, all of them, to follow wherever he went. The morning star was already rising over Mount Ida, and Aeneas, seeing Troy in flames, led the way to the mountains.

It was summer when Troy was taken, and during the rest of the year, Aeneas and his followers built ships for the voyage they must make to find a new home. When it was almost summer again, the work was finished, and they set sail.

There was a land named Thrace, loved by Ares more than all other lands. Here Aeneas built a city, but it was not the will of the gods that this should be the home of the Trojans. So again they launched their ships, and they came to an island sacred to Apollo. Here an oracle spoke thus to Aeneas: "Seek your ancient mother. The land that first bore you shall receive you again, and there you and your children shall rule from one generation to another."

Then the father of Aeneas remembered that the beginning of their nation had been upon the island of Crete. But after living in Crete for a time, Aeneas was told in a vision that Italy was the land that Apollo had decreed should be their home. So the men of Troy again made ready their ships and departed once again.

After many days of wandering, they came to a city ruled over by Helenus, a son of Priam, who with a handful of Trojans had escaped death. Here Aeneas and his followers were made welcome, and a great feast was given in their honor. But soon they were again on their way toward Italy.

When Hera saw Aeneas and his followers nearing their destination, she appealed to the god of the winds to drive them from their course. All the winds rushed forth together and rolled up great waves, until, worn out by the storm, the ships made for the nearest shore, Africa. Here they found a harbor. Now only seven ships remained of the twenty with which Aeneas had set sail, and the men were weary and disheartened.

In Africa Aeneas and his companions came to a city called Carthage. It was ruled over by Queen Dido, who received them with friendliness and hospitality. Aeneas would gladly have spent the rest of his days here, but it was not the will of the gods. So they left the friendly land and sailed away. After many dangers and disappointments, they at length came to a spot where from a large grove a pleasant river tinted by yellow sand burst forth into the sea. This was the Tiber, on whose banks was to be founded, in the distant future, the city of Rome.

Here the wanderings of the Trojans came to an end, and here they built their homes. In time Aeneas became king of the country. For three hundred years kindred of Hector ruled in the land, and one of the descendants of Aeneas, Romulus, became the founder of Rome.

When Hera saw that the descendants of Aeneas were settled in Italy in spite of all her planning, she begged one favor of Zeus: "Though these people are descendants of the Trojans, let them be known as Romans. Troy has perished; let the name also perish. Hera's favor was granted, and in after years the descendants of the Trojans became a great and powerful people known as Romans.

NOTES AND QUESTIONS

1. In the list below, certain of the main points of the story have been omitted. Give the points that are needed to complete the list.

(a) The Greek chiefs swear to defend Helen and her husband.

(b)

(c) The Greeks go to war against Troy.

(d)

(e)

(f) Achilles kills Hector.

(g)

(h) Troy is captured.

(i)

2. Name in separate columns, six Greeks and six Trojans. Tell who each one was, like this: (1) *Menelaus, king of Sparta.*

3. In the first list below are the names of the gods and goddesses. The phrases in the second list tell who they were. Choose the correct phrase for each name, and write them together in a column, thus: (a) *Discord—goddess of trouble.*

List 1. Discord, Thetis, Hera, Athena, Aphrodite, Zeus, Hermes, Apollo, Ares.

List 2. Goddess of war and wisdom, god of the sun, goddess of the sea, god of war, goddess of trouble, messenger of the gods, queen of the gods, goddess of love and beauty, father of the gods.

4. A certain cord or tendon in the human body has been named "Achilles's tendon." Where do you think it is?

5. Was there any act of Achilles that you think was not very heroic? What was it?

6. Be ready to read lines that tell of the sorrow caused by war.

7. Be ready to tell in your own words what happened in any of the main parts listed in Question 1.

8. In your geography or on the wall map, be ready to point out at least three of the places mentioned in this story.

You remember that Nathaniel Hawthorne rewrote some of these old Greek stories for American boys and girls. You would enjoy reading "The Three Golden Apples," in *The Wonder Book.*

THE WANDERINGS OF ULYSSES

Alfred J. Church

In another great poem, the *Odyssey,* Homer tells of the wanderings and adventures of the Greek chief, Ulysses, during his return from the Trojan war. This poem is so famous and so widely known that the word "Odyssey" has come to mean "wanderings."

THE GIANT POLYPHEMUS

When the great city of Troy was taken, the chiefs who had fought against it set sail for their homes. But the gods were angry, for the Greeks had been haughty and cruel in the day of their victory. Therefore they did not all find a safe and happy return. Some were shipwrecked, while others found everything at home so changed that they had to seek new dwellings elsewhere.

Ulysses, one of the mightiest of the great chiefs, was among the last to sail from Troy. His home was the island, Ithaca, where he expected to find his wife, Penelope, and his young son, Telemachus, whom he had left an infant ten years before. Ulysses had twelve ships, and in each were fifty men, scarcely half of those who had set out with him from Greece, for many valiant heroes slept the last sleep on the plain and on the seashore.

Ulysses with his men first sailed northwest to a land whose people had been friendly to the Trojans. Here they captured the city and in it much plunder: slaves and oxen and jars of fragrant wine. They might have escaped unhurt, but they stayed to feast and make merry on the shore, where the people attacked them. The Greeks were driven to their ships, and lost some seventy men.

Then Ulysses and his companions journeyed safely on till they came to the southern shore of Greece; but contrary currents prevented their sailing around the point, and the north wind blew so fiercely they were driven ever southward.

On the tenth day they came to the land where grew the lotus, a honey-sweet fruit. Whoever ate of it cared not to see country, wife, or children again. Now the Lotus-eaters were a friendly folk, and because the fruit was the best they had to offer, they gave some to the sailors. When these had eaten of the magical food, they refused to return to the ships; but Ulysses bade their comrades bind them and drag them back.

Then they took their oars and rowed many days till they came to the country where the Cyclops, a race of giants, dwelt. A mile or more from shore was an island with a harbor. Into this the ships passed safely, and were hauled up on the beach. The men hunted wild goats and feasted merrily on goat's meat and red wine.

The next morning Ulysses gathered his men together and said, "Stay here, all the rest of you, while I go with my ship and my company to the mainland to see what kind of people dwell upon it."

There was a great hill sloping to the shore, and here and there smoke rose from caves. One of these caves was very close to the shore. Ulysses chose twelve of his bravest men, bade the rest guard the ship, and went to see what kind of dwelling this was and who lived there. He had his sword by his side, and on his shoulders a mighty skin of wine, sweet-smelling and strong, with which he hoped to win the heart of some fierce savage.

The cave looked like the dwelling of some rich and skillful shepherd, for within there were pens for the young of the sheep and goats, all divided according to age. There were also baskets full of cheeses, and full milk pails along the walls. The companions of Ulysses begged him to depart, but he would not, for he wished to see what kind of host this strange shepherd might be.

It was evening when the shepherd came home, a mighty giant, twenty feet or more in height. On his shoulder he bore a bundle of pine logs for his fire. These he threw down outside; then he drove the flocks within and closed the entrance with a huge rock. After he had milked his goats, he kindled a fire, and the flame lighted up all the cave, showing him Ulysses and his companions.

"Who are you?" cried Polyphemus, for that was the giant's name. "Are you traders or pirates?"

Ulysses shuddered, but he answered bravely, "We are no pirates, mighty sir, but Greeks, sailing back from Troy. We have come to beg hospitality of you in the name of Zeus."

"It is but idle talk to tell me of Zeus," said the giant. "We Cyclops pay no attention to gods. Where did you leave your ship?" Ulysses knew that he planned to take the ship and break it. Therefore he answered craftily, "We have no ship, for Poseidon, god of the seas, drove it on a rock, and we are all who escaped the waves."

Polyphemus made no answer, but caught up two of the men, killed and ate them, taking huge drinks of milk between. The others could only pray to Zeus for help. When the giant had ended his dreadful meal, he lay down among his sheep and slept. Ulysses would have killed the monster, but being wise he knew that he and his comrades could not move the rock that lay against the door. So they waited till morning. When the monster awoke, he killed and ate two more of the men. Then he went to his pastures, but first he put the great rock at the mouth of the cave.

All that day Ulysses wondered what he could do to save himself and his companions, and he formed a plan. There was a mighty pole in the cave, green wood of the olive tree. Of this Ulysses cut off a piece, sharpened it, hardened it in the fire, and hid it away. At evening the giant came back, and, having done his work, feasted as before. Then Ulysses came forward with the wine-skin, and said, "Drink, Polyphemus, and see what precious things we had on our ship."

The giant drank and was pleased; he said, "Give me again to drink, and tell me your name. I will give you a gift such as a host should give his guest."

Ulysses gave him the cup and he drank. Thrice he gave it to him, and the giant drank, not knowing how it would work upon him. Then Ulysses said, "You asked my name, Polyphemus. My name is No Man. Now I ask you for the gift."

The giant answered, "My gift shall be that I will eat you last of all." Then he fell into a drunken sleep, and Ulysses bade his comrades be of good cheer. Quickly they thrust the stake of wood into the fire until it was ready to burst into flame. With it they put out the monster's eye, for he had but one eye, which was in the middle of his forehead.

The giant leaped and cried aloud with pain, so that other Cyclops heard him and came about the cave asking him,

"What ails you, Polyphemus? Is anyone robbing you or seeking to slay you?"

And the giant answered, "No Man slays me by craft."

"If no man hurts you, we cannot help you," said the others, and went away.

When morning came, the giant rolled away the stone from the door, but he sat in the opening and stretched out his hands to feel whether the men would try to go out with the sheep.

Ulysses thanked Zeus that the giant had driven the rams into the cave with the sheep, for they were great and shaggy. During the night, Ulysses had taken a ram and fastened a man beneath it, and placed two sheep, one on either side. So he did with the six men who remained of his company. There was one ram greater than all the others, and under this Ulysses clung, grasping the heavy fleece with both hands.

As the rams rushed forth to pasture, the giant sat in the door and felt the back of each, but did not think to feel what might be underneath. Last of all went the great ram. The giant knew him as he passed, and said, "How is this that you are last, you who are the leader of the flock? I wish that you could speak and tell me where this wretch, No Man, is hidden." So saying he let the ram pass out of the cave.

When they were out of reach of the giant, Ulysses loosed his hold on the ram and unbound his comrades. They hastened to their ship and to their anxious companions, who were glad indeed to see them. Quickly they put out to sea, and when they were a hundred yards or so from shore, Ulysses stood up in the ship and shouted: "Hear, Polyphemus, if any ask who blinded you, say that it was the warrior Ulysses."

The giant hurled a mighty rock where he heard the voice,

almost crushing the ship; then he lifted up his hand and prayed: "Hear me, Poseidon, King of the Sea, if I am indeed thy son. May this Ulysses never reach his home! Or if it is so ordered that he shall reach it, may he come alone and find great trouble in his house."

Ulysses and his men, bending to their oars with all their might, soon came again to the island and found their comrades. Here Ulysses divided among his company the sheep which they had taken from the giant. All with one consent gave him for his share the ram that had carried him out of the cave. This Ulysses sacrificed to Zeus. All that day they feasted, and at night they slept upon the shore.

CIRCE, THE ENCHANTRESS

After sailing many days, Ulysses and his companions came to the island of Aeolus, king of the winds, who dwelt there with his children, six sons and six daughters. Aeolus welcomed them and feasted them for a month, while he heard from Ulysses the story of all that had been done at Troy. When Ulysses begged him to help them on their way to Ithaca, Aeolus gave him the skin of an ox. In this he had bound all the contrary winds, so that they could not hinder the Greeks. But he let a gentle west wind blow to help them on their way.

For nine days the wind blew, and Ulysses held the helm. Then they came so near to Ithaca that they saw the lights of their homes, and Ulysses, being worn out, fell asleep. While he slept, one of his comrades said, "Strange how men love this Ulysses. He comes back from Troy with much spoil, but we with empty hands. Let us see what Aeolus has given him in this ox-hide."

So the men loosed the great bag, and lo! all the winds rushed out, and carried them far from their country. Ulysses, waking with the tumult of winds and waves, was in despair. He covered his face and sat thus, while the ships were driven by the winds once more to the island of Aeolus. The king of the winds was much surprised to see Ulysses again, and refused further help, saying: "Begone. We may not help him whom the gods hate, and hated of them you surely are."

So they set forth again, toiling wearily at the oars, sad at heart. As they passed a land where a race of giants lived, the giants cast great stones upon the ships, destroying all of them save that of Ulysses himself. He had started from Troy with twelve ships, and now but one remained. On they sailed, mourning for their lost comrades.

After many days they came to an island. Ulysses took a spear and sword and climbed a hill, for he wished to see what kind of land they had found. On his return he said, "I know not where we are. But I know that someone dwells in this island, for I saw smoke from the hills."

It troubled the men much to hear this, for they thought of the Cyclops. Then Ulysses divided the men into two groups, placing Eurylochus over one and himself over the other. He shook lots in a helmet to see who should go to examine the island, and the lot fell to Eurylochus. So he went with twenty-two men and found the palace of Circe, daughter of the Sun. It stood in an open space in the wood. All about were wolves and lions, yet these harmed not the men, but fawned upon them like dogs, and the men were afraid.

They heard the voice of Circe as she sang and worked her loom. So they called to her, and she came out and beckoned

them to come in. She bade them sit, and mixed for them a bowl of red wine and barley-meal, and cheese, and honey, and mighty drugs. When the men had drunk of it, she smote them with her wand. And lo! they had the heads, bristles, and voices of swine, but the heart and mind of a man were still in each. Then Circe shut them in pens and fed them acorns.

But Eurylochus, who alone had remained outside because he mistrusted the goddess, fled back to the ship and told Ulysses what had happened. Ulysses took his sword and bow, and bade Eurylochus guide him the way he had come.

When he came near the palace, he met Hermes, in the shape of a fair youth. Hermes said, "Think not to enter Circe's house to rescue thy companions lest she work her charm on thee as well. Yet, stay. Here is a plant that shall give thee power to resist her charms."

Taking the plant Ulysses went into the palace. Circe tried to change him as she had changed his comrades. But when he drank the wine, the charm did not work, for he was protected by the herb. He rushed at her with his sword, and made her swear that she would not harm him.

Meanwhile the handmaids were busy preparing food, but Ulysses did not eat. "Why dost thou sit, Ulysses, as though thou wert dumb?" asked Circe.

Ulysses answered, "Who could think of meat and drink when such things have befallen his companions?"

Then Circe led the way, holding her wand in her hand, and opened the doors of the pens, and drove out the swine that had been men. Then she rubbed on each of them another mighty drug, and lo! they became men again, only younger and fairer than before.

Then she said, "Go, Ulysses, to thy ship and bring thy comrades back with thee."

Ulysses returned to his ship, and his men were glad to see him. Together they all went to the dwelling of Circe, who feasted them royally. They remained with her a whole year.

SCYLLA AND CHARYBDIS

But when the year was passed, Ulysses begged Circe to send him home to Ithaca, as she had promised. She answered:

"I would not have thee remain in my house unwillingly, but thy return shall be difficult, because thou hast angered Poseidon, king of the sea, by blinding his son, Polyphemus." And Circe told Ulysses all that should happen to him, saying:

"First thou wilt come to the island of the Sirens, who sing so sweetly that whoever hears them at once forgets wife and child and home. Do thou, then, close with wax the ears of thy companions, and make them bind thee to the mast, so that thou mayest hear the song and yet take no hurt. And bid them, when thou shalt pray to be loosed, not to yield, but rather to bind thee the more.

"Another peril lies in thy path. Thou must go through a strait where there is a rock on either side. In one rock dwells Scylla, a horrible monster with twelve unshapely feet and six long necks, a head on each. Think not to escape her, Ulysses, for with each head she will take one of thy companions.

"But the rock on the other side is lower, and there Charybdis thrice a day draws in the water, and thrice a day sends it forth again. Choose to pass near Scylla, for it is better to lose six of thy companions than that all should perish.

"Then thou wilt come to the island where feed the oxen of the Sun. Beware that thy companions harm them not. Yet when thou comest to this island, if thou leavest the oxen unhurt, thou shalt return with thy comrades to Ithaca. But otherwise thy comrades shall perish, and thou shalt return after a long time, in a ship not thine own. Thou shalt find in thy palace, devouring thy goods, men of violence, suitors of thy wife. These shalt thou slay."

The next day they departed, and all happened exactly as Circe had foretold. At length they came to the island where fed the oxen of the Sun. Ulysses said, "Let us pass by this island, for here we shall find the greatest evil that we have yet suffered." But the men were weary of the sea and begged him to land even if only for a day.

"You force me to land," said Ulysses. "Yet promise me that you will not take any of the oxen, for if you do, great trouble will come to us." So they promised. But for a whole month the south wind blew, and they could not depart. When their meat and drink were gone, they caught fishes and birds, for they were pinched with hunger. At last Ulysses, being weary, fell asleep, and while he slept, his companions took some of the oxen and slew them. The Sun god was angry and called upon Zeus for vengeance.

Six days they feasted on the oxen, and on the seventh they set sail. But when they were out of sight of land, Zeus brought up a great storm and the mast was broken. Then a thunder-bolt struck the ship, and all the men fell overboard and perished. But Ulysses lashed the keel to the mast, and on this he sat, borne by the winds across the sea.

CALYPSO

For nine days Ulysses floated upon his raft, until he came to the island where dwelt the goddess Calypso. On this island Ulysses stayed seven years, much against his will, thinking always of his home, his wife Penelope, and his young son Telemachus. Then Athena complained to Zeus that one so just had been so long kept from his home. Zeus said that it should be so no longer, and he sent Hermes to Calypso to tell her to let Ulysses depart. Athena, meanwhile, went to Ithaca to bid Telemachus to go in search of his father.

Hermes drew on his golden sandals, took his wand in his hand, and came to the island where Calypso dwelt. A fair place it was. In the cave a fire of sweet-smelling wood was burning, and Calypso sat at her loom and sang with a lovely voice. Round about the cave was a grove of alders and cypresses, wherein many birds nested. All about the mouth of the cave was a vine with purple clusters of grapes. Four fountains streamed four ways through the meadows of green and violet. But Ulysses was not there, for he sat, as was his custom, on the seashore, weeping and groaning because he was kept from his wife and home and country.

When Calypso saw Hermes, she bade him come within, and gave him meat and drink. When he had ended his meal, she asked him about his errand. He told her that he had come at the bidding of Zeus, and that it was the pleasure of the gods that Ulysses should return to his native country. This message vexed Calypso, and she said:

"You gods are always jealous when a goddess loves a mortal man. But let him go, if it pleases Zeus. Only I cannot send him, for I have neither ship nor rowers. Yet will I willingly help him."

Hermes said, "Do this thing speedily, lest Zeus be angry with thee."

So he departed. Calypso sought Ulysses and said, "Long no more for thy native country. If thou wilt go, I will speed thee on thy way. I will help thee make a raft and will give thee bread, water, and wine, and clothe thee also, so that thou mayest return safe, for the gods will have it so."

The next day as soon as rosy-fingered Dawn shone forth, Calypso gave Ulysses tools, showed him where he might find great trees, and helped him build a raft. Calypso wove the sails, and Ulysses fitted them to the mast. On the fourth day all was finished, and on the fifth day Ulysses departed. He proceeded joyfully on his way for seventeen days. But Poseidon spied him and was angry to see him so near the end of his troubles; so he sent all the winds of heaven down upon

him. The raft was wrecked, and Ulysses was thrown into the sea. For two days and nights he swam, Athena helping him, and on the third day a great wave bore him to the shore. He dropped down on the rushes by the bank of a river and kissed the earth. Close to the river there was a wood. Here he found two olive bushes so closely grown together that neither sun nor rain could pierce through. Under these he crept, and covered himself with leaves. Athena sent down sleep upon his eyelids, and he rested after his toil.

THE PHAEACIANS

Now Ulysses had chanced upon the land of the Phaeacians. The king of this country, Alcinous by name, had five sons and one daughter, Nausicaa. One morning Nausicaa and her maidens took some clothes to the river to wash them. After they had washed the clothes and bathed themselves, they sat down to eat and drink by the river side.

After the meal they played at ball, singing as they played, and Nausicaa, fair and full of grace, led the song. But when they had nearly ended their play, the princess, throwing the ball to one of her maidens, threw it so far that it fell into the river. Then they all cried aloud, and Ulysses awoke. He thought he heard the voices of nymphs.

He came out from the place where he had slept and looked about him, bewildered. The maidens saw him, and, frightened at his wild appearance, fled hither and thither, all but Nausicaa. She called to her maidens, "Why do you flee when you see a stranger? No enemy comes here to harm us. But if any man comes here sorrowing or in trouble, it is well to befriend him." So they gave Ulysses food and clothing, and took him to the city, to the palace of King Alcinous.

A splendid palace it was, with walls of brass, and doors of gold hanging on posts of silver. On either side of the door were dogs of gold and silver. These things Ulysses gazed upon in wonder, as he crossed the threshold entering the hall. When he beheld the mighty king, Ulysses said, "I come to you and to your guests, asking a favor. May the gods bless you and them, and grant that you live in peace. But I pray you send me safe home to my native country."

The next day the king called the chiefs to an assembly and told them his purpose to send this stranger to his home, for it was their custom to show kindness to such as needed it. He bade fifty-two of the younger men make ready a ship. The elders he bade come to his house and bring the minstrel with them, for he wished to make a great feast for this stranger.

So the youths made ready the ship. Afterwards there was gathered together a great multitude, so that the palace was filled from one end to the other. Alcinous slew for them twelve sheep, eight swine, and two oxen. When they had feasted to the full, the minstrel sang to them of Achilles and Ulysses. But when Ulysses heard the song, he wept, holding his mantle before his face.

This Alcinous alone noted, and said to the chiefs, "Now that we have feasted and delighted ourselves with song, let us go forth, so that this stranger may see our games of skill and strength." So they went to the market place. A herald led the minstrel, who was blind. Then stood up many Phaea-cian youths. These strove with one another in feats of racing, wrestling, boxing, throwing the quoit, and leaping over the bar. Ulysses, too, took part in the games, though he had suffered much in battle and in shipwreck. Then the king bade the minstrel sing again.

When they were again seated at the feast, Ulysses sent a portion of his meat to the minstrel, and asked him to sing to them how, through the invention of the wooden horse, the city of Troy was at last taken. As the minstrel sang, Ulysses wept to hear the tale. Now none of all the company noted his weeping except Alcinous, who said to the Phaeacians: "Let the minstrel cease his song, for it is not pleasing to all. Tell us, stranger, your name, your people, and your home. Declare, too, why this tale of Troy moves you to tears. Did you have a relative or a loving friend who fell before the gates of Troy?"

Ulysses answered him, saying: "Now first will I tell my name. Lo! I am Ulysses, son of Laertes, and I dwell in sunny Ithaca, a rugged isle. For myself, I know of nothing sweeter than a man's own country."

Then Ulysses told all that he had done and all that he had suffered. Dead silence fell on all, as they sat spellbound within the shadowy hall. Then Alcinous commanded that rich gifts be brought so that when Ulysses set sail the next evening, he might go forth as befitted so illustrious a guest.

As soon as early Dawn shone forth, the gifts were brought to the ship. The mighty king sacrificed an ox to Zeus, ruler over all, and the minstrel played the harp. But Ulysses would ever turn his head to the splendor of the sun, as one anxious to hasten its setting, so welcome was the sinking of the sunlight to Ulysses. Then he spoke to the Phaeacians, masters of the oar, and to Alcinous the chief, saying:

"My lord Alcinous, send me in peace upon my way; and fare you well. For now have I all that my heart could wish— an escort and loving gifts. May the gods of heaven give me good fortune, and may I find my noble wife in my house and my friends unharmed. May the gods grant all manner of good to you; and may no evil come nigh your people."

Then Ulysses stepped over the threshold and departed.

THE FAITHFUL SWINEHERD

Ulysses slept while the ship was sailing to Ithaca, and when it came to the shore, he still slept. The men lifted him out and put him on the shore with all the goods the Phaeacians had given him, and so they left him. After a while he awoke, and knew not the land, for there was a great mist about him.

As he walked by the sea, lamenting his fate, Athena met him, in the shape of a young shepherd, fair to look upon.

Ulysses, when he saw him, was glad, and asked him what men called this country. The shepherd said, "You are foolish, or it may be you have come from so far that you know not this country. Men call it Ithaca."

Happy indeed was Ulysses to hear this. Yet he did not wish to say who he was. This pleased Athena, and she changed her shape, becoming like a woman, tall and fair, and said to Ulysses: "I am Athena, daughter of Zeus, and I am ever ready to stand by thee and help thee. Thou must tell no one who thou art. Thou must endure many things before thou mayest regain thy home." Then the goddess scattered the mist that was about him, and Ulysses knew the land and kissed the ground. Then the two laid plans together.

Athena said, "There are gathered in thy house many princes from Ithaca and from the neighboring islands, suitors of Queen Penelope. They say, 'Ulysses is dead; choose therefore a husband from our number.' They spend their days at games and feasting, lording it over the servants of the house. Telemachus, now grown to manhood, is vexed at heart, for they waste his wealth, and he is not master even in his own house. Penelope delays making a choice among the suitors by saying, 'Hasten not my marriage until I finish weaving this cloth, to be a burial robe for Laertes, my husband's aged father.' But for three years and more she unraveled each night what she wove in the daytime. Now, however, they have discovered her trick, and insolently they demand that she make a choice. Think, Ulysses, how thou wilt lay hands on these men, suitors of thy wife, who for years have sat in thy house eating thy food and wasting thy goods."

Ulysses answered, "Do thou help me now as of old in Troy!

Truly I had perished but for thee, yet with thee at my side I would fight three hundred men."

"Lo!" said Athena, "I will see that no man shall know thee for I will take the bright hair from thy head, and make thine eyes dull. The suitors shall pay no attention to thee, neither will thy wife nor thy son. But go to the swineherd, where he dwells by the fountain; he is faithful to thee and to thy wife and son. Meanwhile I will hasten to Sparta, to the house of Menelaus, to bring back thy son Telemachus, for he went thither seeking news of thee."

Then Athena changed Ulysses into the shape of an old beggar, and he went to the house of the swineherd.

When Ulysses came near the house, four watch dogs, big as wild beasts, rushed at him. He dropped his staff and sat down, and would have suffered harm, even on his own threshold, but the swineherd ran forth and drove the dogs away. He brought the old man in and gave him a seat of brushwood with a great goatskin over it.

"May Zeus and all the other gods repay you for this kindness," said Ulysses.

Then the two talked of matters in Ithaca, and the swineherd told how the suitors of the queen were wasting the wealth of Ulysses, saying: "Ulysses I know is dead, and either the fowls of the air or the fishes of the sea devour him."

Ulysses tried to comfort the swineherd by saying that he knew his master would return, but he would not be comforted. Then the swineherd asked the stranger, "Who are you and whence do you come?" But Ulysses answered him craftily, and told a strange tale so that he might test the loyalty of the swineherd to his master.

Meanwhile Telemachus returned to Ithaca, having been warned by Athena, who pointed out a different route so that he might avoid the suitors and have a safe return. He went first to the swineherd, as Athena had advised him. Here Ulysses made himself known to his son, and together they planned the destruction of the suitors. Lest their plans should fail, he urged Telemachus to tell no one of his return, not even Penelope herself.

THE DOG ARGUS

The next day Telemachus went to the city, but before he went, he asked the swineherd to bring the beggar to the city, for it was better to beg there than in the country.

When Telemachus arrived at the palace, he told Penelope of his visit to Sparta and how Menelaus had told him that

Ulysses was still living. But he said nothing to his mother of his father's return to Ithaca.

The swineherd and the beggar went on to the palace. At the door of the court in the dust lay the dog, Argus, whom in the old days Ulysses had reared. But before the dog had grown his full size, Ulysses sailed to Troy. While he was strong, men used him in the chase, hunting wild goats and deer. But now he lay neglected, and no man spoke kindly to him.

Well the dog knew his master, and even though he could not rise and come to him, he wagged his tail and drooped his ears. Ulysses, when he saw him, wiped away a tear, and said, "Surely this is strange that such a dog, one of so fine a breed, should lie here in neglect." The swineherd answered, "He belongs to a master who died far away. When the master is away, the slaves are unmindful of their duty." As he spoke the dog looked up at Ulysses, dropped his head upon the ground, and died. Twenty years had he waited for his master; now at last he saw him.

The swineherd and the beggar entered the hall. When Telemachus saw them, he took from the basket bread and meat and bade the servant carry them to the beggar, and also tell him that he might go around among the suitors, asking alms. So Ulysses went, stretching out his hand and noting what kind of men these suitors were. Some gave, having pity on him, but of all Antinous was the most shameless, saying, "Get yourself away from my table."

Then Ulysses said, "Surely your soul is evil, though your body is fair; for though you yourself sit at another man's feast, yet you will give me nothing." Antinous, in great wrath, took the stool on which he sat and threw it at Ulysses, striking his right shoulder. Ulysses stirred not, but stood as a rock. In his heart he thought of revenge. But he went back, and standing in the door he said: "Hear me, suitors of the queen! Antinous has struck me because I am poor. May the curse of the hungry light on him, ere he come to his marriage day!"

THE TRIAL OF THE BOW

That evening after the suitors had departed, each to his own quarters, Ulysses and Telemachus took down all the arms from the walls where they hung in the hall—spears, shields, and helmets—and put them in an upper chamber.

When the queen and her maidens came into the hall, Penelope addressed the stranger and asked him of his family and of his country. At first he did not answer, fearing, he said, to trouble her with the story of his sufferings. But after she had told him what she herself had suffered, he told her a strange tale of how he, a man of Crete, had befriended Ulysses, when he was sailing to Troy. He described the purple cloak Ulysses wore, and Penelope knew it was the very one she herself had given him. Then Penelope told him of a dream she had had. She had seen a flock of geese in her palace, and an eagle had swooped down and killed them. When she mourned for the geese, lo! a voice said, "These are your suitors, and the eagle your husband."

"Even now," she said, "the morn draws near when I must make my choice. For I have promised to bring forth the great bow of Ulysses, and whoever shall draw it most easily and shoot an arrow best at a mark, he shall be my husband."

Ulysses made answer, "It is well, O wife of Ulysses. Put not off the trial of the bow, for before one of them shall draw the string, the great Ulysses shall come and shall shoot at the mark that has been set."

Penelope marveled much to hear these words, and with her maidens went to her royal chamber; but Ulysses made plans for the morrow. The next day he was cheered, because Athena told him that she would stand at his side. It happened, too, that a woman who sat grinding grain, being very weary and hating the suitors, cried, "Grant, Father Zeus, that this be the last meal these men shall eat in the house of Ulysses!" Then, in a clear sky he heard the thunder of Zeus.

The suitors, as was their custom, came to the hall and sat down to feast. The servants carried Ulysses, as Telemachus had bidden, a full share with the others. At this the suitors laughed, and one, more insolent than the others, said, "I also will bestow on him a gift." With that he threw at him an ox's foot, but Ulysses dodged it lightly with his head.

Meanwhile Penelope went to the treasure chamber where there was great store of bronze and gold, and coffers filled with costly clothes. From the wall she took down the great bow of Ulysses, and wept as she thought of her husband. Taking the bow and also the quiver full of arrows, she went to the hall where the suitors sat feasting. She, fair and tall, stood beside a pillar, a faithful maiden on each side of her. Holding a glistening veil before her face, she said:

"You suitors who pretend that you wish to wed me, lo! here is a test of skill. This is the bow of the great Ulysses. Whoever shall bend it most easily, and shoot an arrow through the holes of the twelve axes that Telemachus shall set up, him will I follow, leaving this house, which I shall remember only as a pleasant dream."

Then she bade the swineherd bear the bow and the arrows to the suitors. Telemachus arose, and throwing from his shoulders the scarlet cloak, placed the axes, with holes in them, in a straight row with a skill that all admired.

Now the swineherd had gone forth out of the yard, and Ulysses came up behind him and said, "Look at me, for I am Ulysses who have come back in the twentieth year, and you, I know, are glad at heart that I have come."

The swineherd wept for joy and kissed Ulysses. Then Ulysses bade him to ask the women to keep within doors, nor stir out if they should hear the noise of battle. He also told the swineherd to lock the doors and fasten them securely with a rope. After this Ulysses came back to the hall. All the suitors tried in vain to bend the great bow. One groaned aloud and said, "Woe is me! not for the loss of this marriage only, for there are other women to be wooed in Greece, but that we are weaker than the great Ulysses. This is indeed a shame to tell."

But Ulysses said, "Let me try this bow, for I should like to know whether I have such strength as I had in former days." In great wrath the suitors all protested, but Penelope said, "Let the stranger try the bow!"

Then Telemachus said, "It is for me to refuse or to give the bow. No man shall hinder me if I wish that this stranger make trial of it. Go, Mother, to your chamber with your maidens and leave this matter of the bow with me."

She marveled to hear him speak with such authority, and departed. Then Telemachus ordered the swineherd to take the bow to Ulysses. Ulysses handled the great bow, trying it to see whether it had been damaged, but the suitors mocked

him. When he found it to be without flaw, he strung the bow, and, holding the string in his right hand, he tried its tone, and the tone was sweet to him as the voice of a bird. Then he took an arrow from the quiver and laid the notch upon the string and drew it, sitting as he was, and the arrow passed straight through every one of the twelve holes and stood in the wall behind.

Then Ulysses stripped off his rags and leaped upon the high platform near the door with his bow and quiver full of arrows. Throwing the arrows at his feet, he cried aloud to the suitors, "Lo, now that the trial is ended at last, let me try at yet another mark."

He aimed his arrow straight at Antinous. And all the suitors, when they saw Antinous fall, leaped from their seats; but when they looked for arms, there was neither spear nor shield upon the wall. Ulysses then declared himself, saying: "Dogs, you thought that I should never come back. Therefore have you wasted my wealth, and made suit to my wife while I yet lived, and feared not the gods. Therefore sudden destruction is come upon you. My hands shall not cease from slaying till I have taken vengeance on you all."

The suitors fell as birds are scattered and torn by eagles, and all the while Athena waved her flaming shield from above. But Ulysses spared the minstrel, for he had sung among the suitors in the hall by force and not of his free will. He spared also the herald who had cared for Telemachus throughout his childhood.

ULYSSES AT HOME

When all lay dead, Ulysses ordered the servants to cleanse the hall. When this was done, he bade the nurse go to Penelope and tell her that her husband had returned. The nurse went in haste, but Penelope made answer, "Dear nurse, the gods have taken away your reason." The nurse told her all that had happened, but still the queen doubted, and said, "Let me go down and see with my own eyes."

So she went down from her chamber and sat by the wall in the light of the fire. Ulysses sat by a pillar, with eyes cast down, waiting to see whether his wife would speak to him when she beheld him. But she was greatly perplexed; for now she seemed to know him, and now she knew him not, since he was still clad as a beggar.

"Mother," said Telemachus, "why do you sit apart from my father, and why do you not speak to him? Surely your heart is harder than stone."

Penelope answered, "Son, my mind is dazed. I have no strength to speak, nay, nor to look at him face to face."

But Ulysses said, "Stop, Telemachus. Your mother will know that which is true in good time."

When Ulysses had bathed himself and clothed himself in fair garments, he came back, and Athena shed great beauty upon him. Then he sat down as before, and said: "Surely the gods have made you harder of heart than all other women. Would any other wife have kept away from her husband, when he came back after twenty years?"

Then Penelope knew that he was her husband and ran to him. She threw her arms about him and kissed him, saying, "Forgive me if I was slow to know you; for I have ever feared that someone would deceive me by saying that he was Ulysses. Now I know that you are indeed my husband."

On the morrow Ulysses went forth to see his father, the old Laertes. Quickly he came to the well-ordered farm. There was the house, and all about it were the huts of the servants. He found his father alone, digging in the garden. Ulysses questioned him and saw that his father knew him not. As Laertes spoke of his son, now gone these twenty years, he broke down with grief. Then the heart of Ulysses was moved, and he sprang toward him, saying, "Behold, Father, I am the man of whom you speak. In the twentieth year have I come to my own country."

So he spoke, and the heart of Laertes melted within him. About his dear son he cast his arms and said, "Father Zeus, truly ye gods yet rule on high Olympus, for now my son has returned, and the suitors have paid for their insolent pride."

So did Ulysses come back after twenty years.

NOTES AND QUESTIONS

1. If you found in the library a book named *John Cameron's Odyssey* or one with the title *The Odyssey of a Sailing Vessel*, what kind of story would you expect to find in the book? (The note at the beginning of this story will help you.)

2. Make a list of about ten main events in the wanderings of Ulysses that you could use as an outline in telling the story. Begin this way: *(1) The Greeks plunder a city and are driven away.*

3. Which event in this story do you think you will remember longest?

4. Write a title for each of the pictures. Give the page number of the picture and then your title.

5. Make a list of facts this story tells us about the life of these people who lived three thousand years ago. Such things as foods, animals, games, and building materials should make up your list. You should be able to name at least fifteen items.

6. Mention three or four things Ulysses did that show he was wise and quick-witted. You may find one such incident in the last part of the story of Achilles.

7. On page 383 find a statement that tells us something about the size of the ships.

8. First read again what is said about Homer on page 336. Then find lines where Homer seems to have put himself into this story of Ulysses.

9. Choose and be ready to tell in your own words a part of this story that particularly interested you.

Two other stories of long ago are "Pegasus, the Winged Horse," Hawthorne (in *Child-Library Readers, Book Six*); and "The Song of Odysseus," Hallock (in *The Boy Who Was*).

A BACKWARD LOOK

Now you have become acquainted with some very famous people—Robin Hood, Little John, Achilles, Hector, Ulysses, and others. They are known the world over. The stories of their adventures have been written in many different languages, and boys and girls of other lands have read them just as you have.

If you keep your eyes open, you will many times find references to these heroes and their deeds in books, magazines, and even in newspapers. Have you ever seen any references to these stories or to the heroes in them? For example, a company might make bows and arrows and name them after Robin Hood. Be ready to tell about any such references you may have come upon.

Which of these stories did you like best? Can you give some good reasons why you liked it? Perhaps you can name some other great heroes of adventure about whom you know and enjoy reading. Do you know of any heroes of adventure today? What kind of person do you think may rightly be called a hero? What qualities should he have?

What did you learn about the life of the Greeks from these stories? From the story of Robin Hood, what did you learn about the England of long ago?

Nearly everyone likes adventure stories, and there are many good ones to read. In the back of your book, on page 452, are the names of some books you would enjoy. They will tell you more about the famous people to whom you have been introduced in this part of your Reader.

Part Eight
Holidays and Festivals

CHRISTMAS EVE

CHRISTOPHER MORLEY

Our hearts to-night are open wide,
The grudge, the grief, are laid aside;
    The path and porch are swept of snow,
    The doors unlatched; the hearthstones glow—
No visitor can be denied.

HOLIDAYS ARE REMEMBERING DAYS

O F COURSE you look forward to holidays with great
pleasure. You probably can hardly wait for
Christmas, your birthday, and Fourth of July. Such days
mean good times—presents, picnics, parades, and often
visits with friends or relatives.

But these days have a meaning that is deeper than
that of merely having a good time. Why is it that
throughout our land factories, stores, schools, and offices
are closed, and everyone takes part in some kind of
celebration?

The reason is that great events have happened in the
history of our nation and of the world—events which people want ever to remember. Fourth of July is set aside so
that we shall not forget the long, hard struggle through
which our nation went in order to win its freedom.
Armistice Day and Memorial Day remind us of the
brave men who have given their lives in defense of our
country. On Washington's Birthday and Lincoln's
Birthday we honor those great leaders of our people.

So, every holiday has its own special meaning. Holidays are happy days for us all, and they should be; but
we should not forget the deeper meaning that each has.
If we are happy and comfortable today, it is because
others have worked, braved dangers, and perhaps even
suffered for us. We want to honor them every year.

In this last part of your book you will read stories and
poems which tell of some holidays that we so much
enjoy. As you read, try to see how each story and
poem expresses the true meaning of the holiday.

THANKSGIVING AT TODD'S ASYLUM

Winthrop Packard

On this particular Thanksgiving, everything seemed to go wrong at Eph Todd's place. The turkey that they had such a hard time catching was too tough to eat; Eph's horse ran away with him, he forgot to do his errands, and Aunt Tildy burned the food. But it all turned out happily, as you will learn.

THE INMATES OF THE ASYLUM

People said that if it had not been for that legacy Eph Todd would have been at the poor farm himself instead of setting up a rival to it; but there *was* the legacy, and that was the beginning of Todd's asylum.

No matter who or what you were, if you were in hard luck, Todd's asylum was open to you. The old schoolhouse clock was a sample. For thirty years it had smiled from the wall, until one day it ceased to tick. It was taken gently down, laid out on a desk for a day or two, and finally was being taken to the rubbish heap when Eph Todd appeared.

"You're not going to throw that good old clock away?" Eph had asked of the man who was taking it.

"Guess I'll have to," replied the other. "I've wound it up, put 'most a pint of kerosene in it, and shook it till I'm dizzy, and it won't tick. Guess the old clock's done for."

"Now see here," said Eph; "you just let me have a try at it. Let me take it home for a while."

"Oh, for that matter I'll give it to you," the man replied. "We've bought another for the schoolhouse."

A day or two after, the old clock ticked away as soberly as ever on the wall of the Todd kitchen.

"Took it home and boiled it in potash," Eph used to say; "and there it is, just as good as it was thirty years ago."

This was not quite true, for enough enamel was gone from the face to make the exact location of the hour an uncertain thing; and there were days when the hour hand needed assistance.

"It wasn't much of a job," as Eph said, "to reach up once an hour and send the hand along one space, and Aunt Tildy had to have something to look forward to."

Aunt Tildy was the first inmate at Todd's. She passed his house on her way to the poor farm on the very day that the news of the legacy arrived, and Eph had stopped the carriage and begged the overseer to leave her with him.

"Are you sure you can take care of her?" asked the overseer, doubtfully.

"Sure?" echoed Eph with delight. "Of course I'm sure. Haven't I got four hundred dollars a year for the rest of my natural born days?"

"He's a good fellow, Eph Todd," mused the overseer as he drove away, "but I never heard of his having any money."

Next day the news of the legacy was known to everybody, and Aunt Tildy had been an inmate at Todd's ever since. She was deeply grateful, and she really managed to keep the house after a fashion, her chief care being the clock.

Then there was the inventor. He had wasted everything he had in inventing an incubator that worked with wonderful success till the day the chickens were to come out, when it caught fire and burned up, taking with it chickens, barn, house, and furniture, leaving the inventor standing in the field, thinly clad, and with nothing left in the world but another incubator. With this he had shown up promptly at Todd's, and there he had made his home.

Eph had obliged the inventor to keep his incubator in a little shed behind the barn, so that when this one burned up, there was time to get the horse and cow out before the barn burned, and the village fire department managed to save the house. Rebuilding the barn made quite a hole in the legacy, and all the inventor had to show for it was Miltiades. He had put a single turkey's egg in with a previous hatch, and though he had not raised a single chicken, the turkey's egg had hatched, and the chick had grown up to be Miltiades. Miltiades was a big gobbler now. He took care of himself, was never shut up or handled, and led a wandering life.

Last of all came Fisherman Jones. He was old now and couldn't see very well, unable to go to the brook or pond to fish, but he still started out daily with the fine new rod and reel which the legacy had bought for him, and would sit out in the sun, joint his rod together, and fish in the dry pasture with perfect contentment. You would not think Fisherman Jones of much use, but it was he who caught Miltiades and made the Thanksgiving dinner possible.

FISHERMAN JONES CATCHES MILTIADES

The new barn had taken the last of the money for that year, and there would be no more income until January first. But one must have a turkey for Thanksgiving, and there was Miltiades. To catch Miltiades became the household problem, and the inventor set wonderful traps for him, which caught almost everything but Miltiades, who easily avoided them. Eph used to go out daily before breakfast and chase Miltiades. The turkey scorned him, and grew only wilder and tougher.

The day before Thanksgiving it looked as if there would be no turkey dinner at Todd's, but here Fisherman Jones came to the rescue. It was a beautiful Indian summer day, and he hobbled out into the field for an afternoon's fishing. Here he sat on a log, and began casting his line about. Near by, under a juniper bush, Miltiades lay hidden. By and by Fisherman Jones kicked up a loose bit of bark, and saw beneath it a fine, fat, white grub, of the sort which turns into June beetles with the coming of spring. He was not so blind but that he saw the grub, and with a chuckle, he baited his hook with it.

A moment after, Eph Todd, coming out of the new barn, heard the click of a reel, and was astonished to see Fisherman Jones standing almost erect, his eyes blazing, his rod bent, his reel buzzing, while at the end of a good forty feet of line was Miltiades, rushing in frantic strides for the woods.

"Good land!" said Eph, "it's the turkey! Hold him," he yelled. "Don't let him get all the line on you! He's hooked! Hold him!"

"Eph Todd!" gasped Fisherman Jones, "this is the whoppingest old fish I ever hooked on to yet. Beeswax, how he does pull!" And with the words Fisherman Jones went backward over the log, waving the pole and a pair of stiff legs in the air. The turkey had suddenly let up on the line.

"Give him the butt! Give him the butt!" roared Eph, rushing up. The fisherman blood in Fisherman Jones

responded to this stirring appeal, and the rod bent in a tense
half circle. Then began a race such as no elderly fisherman
was ever the center of before. Round and round went
Miltiades, with the white grub in his crop, and the line above
it gripped tightly in his strong beak; and round and round
went Eph Todd, his outstretched arms waving like the turkey's
wings. In the center Fisherman Jones, too near-sighted to
see what he had hooked, had risen on one knee and was turning with the bird, his mind full of one idea—to keep the butt
of his rod aimed at the whirling turkey.

"Hang to him! Reel him in! We'll get him!" shouted
Eph; and, with the word, he caught his toe and vanished into
the depths of the prickly bush, just as the inventor came over
the hill. It would be very interesting to know what scheme
the inventor would have made up for the capture of Miltiades,
but just then he stepped into one of his own traps, set for

the turkey, of course, and, with one foot held fast, began to flounder about with cries of rage and dismay.

This brought Eph's head above the fringe of bush again, and now he beheld a wonderful sight. Fisherman Jones was again on his feet, staring in wild surprise at Miltiades, whom he sighted for the first time, within ten feet of him. The line was now slack, and Miltiades was swallowing it in big gulps, evidently determined to have not only the white grub, but all that went with it.

Fisherman Jones's cry of dismay was almost as bitter as that of the inventor, who still struggled in his own trap.

"Oh, Eph! Eph!" he whimpered, "he's eating up my tackle! He's eating up my tackle!"

"Never mind!" shouted Eph. "Don't be afraid! I reckon he'll stop when he gets to the pole!"

Eph scrambled out of his bush, and, taking up the chase once more, soon brought it to an end, for Fisherman Jones, his nerve completely gone, could only stand and mumble sadly to himself, "He's eating up my tackle! He's eating up my tackle!" and the line, wrapping about his motionless body, led Eph and the turkey in a short circle which brought the three together.

It was not until the turkey was beheaded that Eph remembered the inventor and hastened to his rescue. He was still in the trap, but he was quite content, for he was figuring out a plan for his release.

The stubbornness of Miltiades was further shown by the difficulty Eph and Fisherman Jones had in separating him from his feathers that evening; and Aunt Tildy was so interested in the plan of the inventor to raise featherless turkeys that she forgot the yeast cake she had put to soak until it had been boiling merrily for some time. Everything seemed to go wrong-end-to, and they all sat up so late that Mrs. Simpkins, across the way, remarked that either someone was dead over at Todd's, or else they were having a family party; and she was partly right both ways.

THE THANKSGIVING DINNER

The greatest misfortune came next morning. Eph started for the village with his mind full of errands for Aunt Tildy, some of which he was sure to forget, and in a great hurry lest he forget them all. He threw the harness hastily upon Dobbin, hitched him to the wagon, which had stood out on the soft ground overnight, and with an eager "Get up, there!" gave him a slap with the reins.

Next moment there was a ripping sound, and the inventor came to the door just in time to see the horse going out of the yard on a run, with Eph following, clinging to the reins.

"Here, here!" called the inventor, "you forgot the wagon. Come back, Eph! You forgot the wagon!"

"Jeddediah Jodkins!" said Eph, as he swung about the gatepost; "do you — whoa! — suppose I'm such a — whoa! whoa!—fool that I don't know that I'm not riding—whoa! in a—whoa! whoa!—wagon?" And with this Eph disappeared up street behind the galloping horse, still clinging bravely to the reins.

"I believe he did forget that wagon," said the inventor. But when he reached the barn, he saw the trouble. The ground had frozen hard overnight, and the wagon wheels sunken in it were held as in a vise. Eph had started the horse suddenly, and the obedient animal had walked right out of the shafts, harness and all.

A half hour later Eph was back with Dobbin, unharmed but a trifle weary. It took an hour more and all Aunt Tildy's hot water to thaw out the wheels, and when it was done, Eph was so confused that he drove to the village and back and forgot every one of his errands. And in the midst of all this the clock stopped. That settled the matter for Aunt Tildy. She neglected the pudding, she forgot the pies, and she let the turkey bake and bake in the overheated oven while she fretted about that clock. When the clock was finally set going, after long and careful investigation by Eph, and frantic but successful attempts on the part of Aunt Tildy to keep the inventor from ruining it forever, it was the dinner hour.

Poor Aunt Tildy! That dinner was the greatest sorrow of her life. The vegetables were cooked to rags, the pies were charcoal shells, and the pudding had not been made. As for Miltiades, he was ten times tougher than in life, and Eph's carving knife slipped from his form without making a dent. Aunt Tildy wept at this, and Fisherman Jones and the inventor looked blank enough, but there was no sorrow on the face of Eph. He cheered Aunt Tildy, and he cracked jokes that made even Fisherman Jones laugh.

"Why, bless you!" he said, "ever since I was a boy I've been looking for a chance to make a Thanksgiving dinner out of bread and milk. And now I've got it. Why, I wouldn't have missed this for anything!" And there came a knock at the door.

Even Eph looked a trifle blank at this. If it should be company! "Come in!" he called.

The door was pushed aside, and a big, steaming platter
entered. It was upheld by a small boy, who stammered,
"My moth—moth—mother thaid she wanted you to try thum
of her nith turkey."

"Well, well!" said Eph; "Aunt Tildy has cooked a turkey
for us today, and she's a good cook"—Eph did not appear
to see the signs the inventor was making to him—"but I've
heard that your mother does things well, too. We're greatly
obliged." And Eph put the platter on the table.

"She thays you c-c-can thend the platter home tomorrow,"
stammered the boy, and stammering himself out, he ran into
another. The other held high a big dish of plum pudding.
Again the inventor made signs to Eph.

"Our folks wanted you to try this plum pudding," said the
newcomer. "They made an extra one, and the cousins we
expected didn't come; so we can spare it just as well as not."

It seemed as if Eph hesitated a moment. Then he took the boy by the hand, and there was an odd shake in his voice as he said: "I'm greatly obliged to you. We all are. Something happened to our plum pudding, and we didn't have any. Tell your ma we send our thanks."

There was a sound of voices in the hallway, and two young girls entered, each carrying a basket.

"Oh, Mr. Todd," they both said at once, "we couldn't wait to knock. We want you to try some of our Thanksgiving. It was mother's birthday, and we cooked extra for that, and we've got so much we can't get all ours on the table. She'll feel hurt if you don't."

Somehow Eph couldn't say a word, but there was nothing the matter with the inventor. His speech of delighted acceptance was such a good one that before he was half done the girls had loaded the table with good things, and with smiles and nods and "good-bys," slipped out as rapidly and as gayly as they had come in. It was like a gust of wind from a summer garden.

The table, a moment ago bare, fairly sagged and steamed with offerings of Thanksgiving. Somehow the steam got into Eph's eyes and made them wet, till all he could do was to say, "There goes my last chance at a bread-and-milk Thanksgiving."

But now Aunt Tildy arose, her faded face all alight.

"Eph Todd," she said, "you needn't look so flusterated. It's nothing more than you deserve and not half so much either. Aren't you the kindest man yourself that ever lived? Aren't you always doing something for everybody, and helping every one of these neighbors in all sorts of ways? I'd

like to know what the whole place would do without you!
And now, just because they remember you on Thanksgiving
Day, you look like—"

The steam had got into Aunt Tildy's eyes now, and she
sat down again just as there came another knock at the door
—a timid sort of knock this time.

The inventor's face widened in smiles at this, but Eph
looked him sternly in the eye.

"Jeddediah Jodkins!" he said; "if that is any more people
bringing things to eat to this house, they'll have to go away.
We can't have it.   We've got enough here now to feed a—
a boarding school."

The inventor sprang eagerly to his feet. "Don't you do
it, Eph," he said, "don't you do it.   I've just thought of a
way to can it."

A thinly clad man and woman stood at the door which
Eph opened.   Both looked pale and tired, and the woman
shivered.

"Can you tell me where I can get work," asked the man,
"so that I can earn something to eat?   We are not beggars"
—he flushed a little—"but I have had no work lately, and
we have eaten nothing since yesterday.   We are looking—"

The man stopped, and well he might, for Eph was dancing
wildly about the two, and hustling them into the house.

"Come in!" he shouted.   "Come in!   Come in!   You're
the folks we are waiting for!   Eat?   Why, goodness gracious!
We've got so much to eat we don't know what to do with it."

He had them in chairs in a moment and was piling steaming
roast turkey on their plates.   "There!" he said, "don't you
say another word till you have filled up on that.   Folks"—

and he turned to the others—"these two friends have come to stay a week with us and help eat turkey. Fall to! This is going to be the pleasantest Thanksgiving we've had yet."

And thus two new inmates were added to Todd's asylum.

NOTES AND QUESTIONS

1. If you were to tell this story, you would have to remember certain facts that go together; that is, certain things happened because other things happened. For example, Todd's asylum came about because Eph was left a legacy. Which facts in the columns below belong together?

(a) The legacy	The burned food
(b) The inventor	The kindly neighbors
(c) The forgotten errands	Todd's asylum
(d) The clock that stopped	The incubator that burned
(e) Eph's Thanksgiving happiness	Fisherman Jones
(f) A surprise dinner	The runaway horse
(g) The capture of Miltiades	The unexpected visitors

2. Which one of the characters in this story most appreciated what Eph Todd had done for them all?

3. What incident in the story best shows Eph's true kindness?

4. What other scene, besides the two shown, would have made a good picture?

5. Be ready to tell in your own words how the turkey was captured.

6. Be ready to read lines that—

(a) Tell about the runaway.

(b) Show how Eph tried to make Aunt Tildy feel better over the dinner.

(c) Best show what kind of man Eph was.

Two other good Thanksgiving stories are "The Pygmies Come to Thanksgiving," Bradley (in *Alice in Jungleland*); and "The Prairie Bird's Thanksgiving," Peck (in *Thanksgiving Day in Modern Story*, Van Buren and Bemis).

THE PUMPKIN

JOHN GREENLEAF WHITTIER

Ah! on Thanksgiving day, when from East and from West,
From North and from South come the pilgrim and guest,
When the gray-haired New Englander sees round his board
The old broken links of affection restored,
When the care-wearied man seeks his mother once more,
And the worn matron smiles where the girl smiled before,
What moistens the lip and what brightens the eye,
What calls back the past like the rich Pumpkin pie?

Oh—fruit loved of boyhood!—the old days recalling,
When wood-grapes were purpling and brown nuts were
       falling!
When wild, ugly faces we carved in its skin,
Glaring out through the dark with a candle within!
When we laughed round the corn-heap, with hearts all in
       tune,
Our chair a broad pumpkin—our lantern the moon,
Telling tales of the fairy who traveled like steam,
In a pumpkin-shell coach, with two rats for her team!

THE CHRISTMAS TRUANTS

Frank R. Stockton

Here is a story of some boys who were "bored to death" with the old-fashioned Christmas; so they set out to celebrate in some different way. Then they met a band of robbers who captured them. Let us see how their Christmas celebration turned out.

OUT FOR AN EXCITING HOLIDAY

Christmas was coming, a long time ago, and the boys in a certain far-away school were talking and thinking about it. Eleven of these youngsters, who were all great friends and generally kept together whether at work or play, held a secret meeting at which they resolved that they were tired of the ordinary way of spending Christmas.

"We are bored to death," said one of the older boys, "with Christmas trees, with Christmas games, with Christmas carols, and with the hanging-up of stockings on Christmas Eve. Such things may do very well for children, but we have grown out of them."

"That's true!" cried the others. "We've grown out of that kind of nonsense."

"Yes, sir!" exclaimed the smallest boy of all, who was generally known as Tomtit. "We've grown out of that."

"Of course," said the biggest boy, who was called by his companions Old Pluck, because he had never been found to be afraid of anything, "there will be this Christmas childishness at the school, just as there has been always; and I propose that, instead of staying here and submitting to it, we run away, and have a Christmas to suit ourselves."

"Hurrah!" cried the other boys. "That's what we shall do. Have a Christmas to suit ourselves."

Having made up their minds to this, these eleven boys, on the afternoon of the next day but one to Christmas, ran away from school, in order that they might find a place where they would be free to celebrate the great holiday in whatever way they pleased. They walked as fast as they could, little Tomtit keeping up bravely in the rear, although he was obliged to run almost as much as he walked, until they were at a long distance from the school. Night was now coming on, and Old Pluck called a halt.

"Boys," said he, "we will camp at the edge of that forest, and those of you who have brought bows and arrows had better see if you can't shoot some rabbits for our supper. The unarmed members must gather wood to make a camp-fire. But if you are tired, Tomtit, you needn't do anything."

"Tired!" exclaimed the little fellow, standing up very straight and throwing out his chest; "I should like to know why I should be tired. I'll go and bring some logs."

The camp-fire was burning brightly when the boys with the bows and arrows returned, stating that they had found it rather too late in the day for game, and that it would be better to postpone the shooting of rabbits till the next morning. Old Pluck then asked the members of his little company what food they had brought with them; it was found that no one except Tomtit had thought of bringing anything. He had in his coat pocket a luncheon of bread and meat. It was then ordered that Tomtit's luncheon should be divided into eleven portions, and the little fellow was given a knife with which to cut it up.

It was at this time that there came through the forest a band of robbers—five men and a chief. These men, on their way to the castle, had been talking about the approach of Christmas.

"I am getting very tired," said the chief, "of the noisy merrymaking with which on great occasions we make our castle ring. It would be a most agreeable relief, methinks, if we could celebrate the coming Christmas as ordinary people do. The trouble is we don't know how."

"You speak well," replied one of his followers. "We would be glad enough to have the ordinary Christmas festivals if we did but know how such things are managed."

IN THE HANDS OF ROBBERS

The conversation was cut short at this point by the discovery of a camp-fire at the edge of the wood. Instantly every robber crouched close to the ground, and crept silently to the spot where the boys were gathered around Tomtit, watching him as he cut up his luncheon.

In a few moments the chief gave a whistle, and then the robbers rushed out, and each of the men seized two of the larger boys, while the chief stooped down and grasped Tomtit by the collar. Some of the boys kicked and scuffled; but this was of no use, and they were all marched away to the robber's castle, little Tomtit feeling very proud that it took a whole man to hold him by the collar.

When they reached the castle, the boys were shut up in a large room, where they were soon provided with a plentiful supper. Having finished their meal, they were led to the great hall of the castle, where the robber chief sat in his

chair of state, a huge fire blazing upon the hearth, while suits of armor, glittering weapons, and trophies of many kinds were hung upon the walls.

The boys were now ordered to tell their story; and when Old Pluck had finished it, the chief addressed his captives in these words:

"I am sure that you young fellows could never have imagined the pleasure you were going to give me when you decided to run away from school at this happy season.

"My men and myself have a fancy for a Christmas like that of other people. We want a Christmas tree, Christmas carols and games, and all that sort of festivity. We know nothing about these things ourselves, and were wondering how we could manage to have the kind of Christmas we want. But now that we have you boys with us, it will all be simple and easy enough. You shall celebrate Christmas for us in the manner in which you have always been accustomed. We will provide you with everything that is necessary, and we will have a good old school-and-home Christmas. You shall even hang up your stockings, and I will see to it that Santa Claus for the first time visits this castle. And now, my fine fellows, to bed with you, and tomorrow we will all go to work to prepare for a good old-fashioned Christmas."

The boys were taken to a large upper room, where they found eleven mattresses spread out upon the floor. They threw themselves upon their beds; but not one of them could close his eyes for thinking of the sad plight which they were in. They had run away to get rid of the tiresome old Christmas doings, and now they were to go through all those very things just to please a band of robbers. The thought of it was unbearable, and for an hour or two each boy rolled and moaned upon his mattress.

At last Old Pluck spoke. "Boys," he said, "all is now quiet below, and I believe those rascally robbers have gone to bed. Let us wait a little while longer, and then slip downstairs and run away. We can surely find some door or window which we can open; and I, for one, am not willing to stay here and act the part of a Christmas slave for the pleasure of these bandits."

The boys eagerly agreed to Old Pluck's plan, and in about half an hour they quietly arose and stole toward the stairs. The full moon was shining in through the windows, so that they could see perfectly well where they were going. They had gone a short distance down the great staircase, when Old Pluck, who led the way, heard a slight noise behind him.

Turning to inquire what this was, he was told it was the cracking of Tomtit's knees.

"Pass the word to Tomtit," he whispered, "that if he can't keep his knees from cracking, he must stay where he is."

Poor little Tomtit, who brought up the rear, was dreadfully troubled when he heard this; but he bravely passed the word back that his knees should not crack any more.

It was difficult now for Tomtit to take a step, for if he bent his knees they were sure to crack. He tried going downstairs stiff-legged, like a pair of scissors; but this he found almost impossible. So he made up his mind that the only thing he could do was to slide down the broad banister. He was used to this feat, and he performed it with much skill. The banister, however, was very smooth and steep, and he went down much faster than he intended, shooting off at the bottom, and landing on the broad of his back.

STRIKING A BARGAIN

The boys were now in the great hall, and, seeing a light in the adjoining room, they looked into it. There, upon couches made of the skins of wild beasts, they saw the six robbers, fast asleep. A happy thought now came into the mind of Old Pluck. Stepping back, he looked around him, and soon saw in one corner of the hall a quantity of rich stuffs, and other booty, bound up into bundles with heavy cords. Taking out his knife he quickly cut off a number of these cords and gave them to his companions.

"Boys," he then whispered, "I have thought of a splendid plan. Let us bind these robbers hand and foot, and then, instead of doing what they want us to do, we can make them do what we want. That will be ever so much better fun than running away."

"Good!" said the boys. "But suppose they wake up while we are tying them?"

"If we are truly brave," said Old Pluck, "we must just go ahead, and not think of anything like that."

The boys now softly slipped into the room, and as the robbers slept very soundly, it was not long before they were all securely bound hand and foot, Old Pluck going around himself to see that every cord was well knotted. Then, motioning the boys to follow him, he went into the great hall, and there he ordered his companions to arm themselves.

This command was obeyed with delight by the boys. Some took swords, some spears, while others bound around their waists great belts containing daggers and knives. Old Pluck laid hold of a huge battle-ax, while Tomtit clapped on his head the chief's hat, ornamented with eagle plumes, and took into his hand a thin, sharp sword, the blade of which was quite as long as himself.

When all were ready, the boys re-entered the other room, and, with their weapons in their hands, stood over the sleeping robbers. Raising his heavy battle-ax high above the head of the chief, Old Pluck called out to him to awake. Instantly every man opened his eyes, and struggled to rise. But when they found their hands and feet were tied, and saw the boys with their swords and spears standing over them, and heard Old Pluck's loud voice ordering them not to move, every robber lay flat on his back, and remained perfectly still.

"Now, then," said Old Pluck to the chief, "if you do not

promise that you and your men will obey me for the next two days, I will split your head with this ax."

"I am willing to bargain with you," said the chief, "and will listen to all you have to say; but for mercy's sake put down that battle-ax. It is too heavy for you, and you will let it drop on me without intending it."

"No," said Old Pluck, steadying the great ax as well as he could, "I will hold it over you until we have made our bargain."

"Speak quickly, then," said the chief, his face turning pale as he looked up at the trembling ax.

"All you have to do," said Old Pluck, "is to promise that you and your men will do everything that we tell you to do tomorrow and next day. You will not find our tasks at all difficult, and it will be only for two days, you know."

"Any sort of task, if it lasted a year," said the chief,

"would be better than having you staggering over me with that battle-ax. I promise for myself and men."

"Very good," said Old Pluck, letting down his ax as carefully as he could. "And now we will set you free."

SACKING A VILLAGE

The men were untied, the boys went to bed, and the next morning all breakfasted together in the great hall. When the meal was over, the chief pushed back his chair and addressed the boys.

"Now, then, my young friends," said he, "what is it that you wish me and my men to do?"

Then up stood Old Pluck and said, "We boys, as I told you before, ran away from school because we are tired of the old humdrum Christmas; and nothing better could have happened to us than to get you fine fellows into our power. It will be the jolliest thing in the world for us to see you and your band go through all the wild feats and bold exploits which belong to robber life; and we would like you to begin now, and keep it up all day and tomorrow."

"But what would you have us do?" asked the chief, somewhat surprised.

"I should like to see you sack a village," said Old Pluck. "How would that suit you, boys?"

The boys all declared that they thought that would do very well, to begin with.

The chief turned to his lieutenant and said, "Is there any village round here that has not been recently sacked?"

The lieutenant thought a moment. "There is Buville," he said. "We haven't been there for six months."

"Very good," said the captain, rising; "we'll sack Buville."

In a short time the robber band, followed by the eleven boys, set out for Buville, a few miles distant. When they came within sight of the village, the chief ordered his company to get behind a hedge which ran on one side of the road, and thus stealthily approach the place.

As soon as they were near enough, the chief gave a loud whistle, and the whole company rushed wildly into the main street. The robbers flashed their swords in the sunlight and brandished their spears, while the boys jumped and howled like so many bandits.

"Buville is ours!" cried the chief. "Come forth, ye cowardly villagers, and pay us tribute."

"Come forth!" yelled little Tomtit. "Surrender, and pay tribute."

At this the people began to flock into the street; and presently the principal man of the village appeared, carrying a sheet of paper and pen and ink.

"Good-morning, bold sir," he said, addressing the chief. "And what is it you'll have today? Shall we begin with flour? How will two barrels do?"

The chief nodded, and the man wrote down on his paper two barrels of flour.

"Sugar, hams, and eggs, I suppose?" continued the man.

The chief again nodded, and these were written down.

"Some groceries, of course?" said he. "And would you care for any rich stuffs?"

"Well, I don't know that we need any just now," said the chief; "but you might throw in enough gold-threaded blue taffeta to make a jacket for that little codger back there."

"Three-quarters of a yard of blue taffeta," wrote the man. And then he looked up and asked, "Anything else today?"

"I believe not," said the chief. And then brandishing his sword, he shouted: "Back to your homes, villagers, and thank your stars that I let ye off so easily."

"Home with ye!" shouted Tomtit, "and keep on thanking till we come again."

"You need be in no hurry about sending those things," said the chief to the principal man, as he was about to leave, "except the taffeta. I'd like to have that today."

"Very good," said the other, "I'll send it immediately."

As the robbers and boys departed, the latter were not at all slow to say that they were very much disappointed at what they had seen. It was tamer than a game of football.

"The fact is," said the chief, "these villagers have been sacked so often that the people are used to it, and they just walk out and pay up without making any row about it. It's the easiest way, both for them and for us; but I admit that it is not very exciting."

STILL ON THE TRAIL OF EXCITEMENT

"I should say not," said Old Pluck. "What I want is 'the wild rush and dash, the clink, clank, and the jingly-jank, hi-ho!' I'm for burning a town. That must be exciting."

"Hurrah!" said the boys. "We'll burn a town!"

"That is a very serious thing," said the chief. "Can't you think of something else?"

Old Pluck looked at him sternly. "We want something serious," he said. "What we've had so far is nothing but child's play."

The chief now saw that if he kept on with his objections he would hurt the feelings of the boys; so he consented to burn a town. A few miles to the south there was a good-sized town, which the chief thought would burn very well, and thither the boys and robbers went, carrying blazing torches.

When they reached the town and had made known their purpose, the people were filled with alarm. They crowded into the streets and begged the robbers not to burn their houses, their goods, and perhaps themselves and their children.

The chief now took the boys aside and consulted with them.

"I wish you would consider this matter a little more before you order me to set the town in flames. I am told that there is a storehouse filled with gunpowder in the center of the place, and there will be a terrible explosion when the fire reaches it."

"Hurrah!" cried the boys; "that will be splendid."

"Many of these citizens will lose their lives," said the chief, "and the rest will be utterly ruined."

"Now, look here," cried Old Pluck, "there's no use of always backing down. I'm tired of it."

"Very well," said the chief, "but you yourselves must tell the people what your decision is."

"We'll do that," said Old Pluck. "Tomtit, you go tell those people that the town has got to burn, and there's no use talking any more about it."

"That's so," said Tomtit. "She has got to burn." And with his chest thrown out, and his hands in his pockets, the little fellow boldly advanced to the crowd of people.

As soon as he came near, the old men, the women, and the children fell on their knees around him, and with tears begged him to plead with the robbers to save their town. Poor little

Tomtit was very much moved by their wild grief and despair.
Tears came into his eyes, but he kept up a brave heart and
stood true to his companions.

"It's no use," he said, "for you to be blubbering and crying.
Your houses have all got to be burned up, and the powder
has got to go off with a big bang, and your furniture and
beds will all be burned, and the babies' cradles, and—and
—I'm awfully sorry for it," and here the tears rolled down
his cheeks; "but we boys have got to stick by each other,
and you won't have any homes, and I expect you will all
perish—boo-hoo! But it won't do to back down—boo-hoo-
hoo! And the little babies will die; but the old thing has
got to burn, you know."

"Now, look here, Tomtit," said Old Pluck, who, with the
rest of the boys, had drawn near, "don't you be too hard on
these people. I say let the town stand."

The boys agreed with one voice. And Tomtit, kicking one of his little legs above his head, shouted in joy: "Yes sir, let the town stand, babies and all."

At this the women rushed up to the little fellow, and seizing him in their arms, nearly kissed him to death.

BACK TO AN OLD-FASHIONED CHRISTMAS

"I'd like to know what we are to do next," sadly remarked Old Pluck.

"I'll tell you," cried Tomtit. "Let the chief steal a bride."

The whole company stopped and looked at Tomtit. "Little boy," said they, "what do you mean?"

"Why, of course," said Tomtit, "I mean for the chief to seize a fair damsel and carry her off on his horse to be his bride, the wild hoofs clattering among the rocks."

"Hoot!" cried all the boys scornfully. And the chief said to Tomtit: "Little boy, I know of no fair damsel to steal, and besides, I do not want a bride."

"It's pretty hard," said Tomtit, wiping his eyes with his little sleeve. "I've done just what you fellows told me to, and now you won't order anything I want to see."

That night the boys ordered the robbers to hold a high celebration in the great hall. Wild songs were sung with jovial glee. The boys watched the merrymaking for some time, but they did not find it very interesting, and soon went to bed.

The next morning Old Pluck called a meeting of his companions. "Boys," he said, "this robber life is a good deal stupider than anything we left behind us. Let's get back to school as fast as we can, and enjoy what is left of the Christmas fun. We will admit that we are sorry for what we have done, and will promise not to run away again; and Tomtit can go to the master and tell him so."

"I'll be the first one whipped," ruefully remarked Tomtit; "but if you boys say so, of course I'll do it."

The boys now took leave of the robbers, Tomtit having been first presented with the piece of blue taffeta to make him a jacket.   When they reached the school, Tomtit told his tale, and he was the only one who was not punished.

Notes and Questions

1. Which phrase below do you think best describes this story?
   (a) An exciting adventure story
   (b) A story teaching a serious lesson
   (c) A good story written in the spirit of fun

2. Write the titles for four or five scenes you would have if you were making this story into a play.

3. Who would be the three most important characters in your play?

4. What is there in the way this story is written that would help greatly in making a play of it?

5. Make up a title for each of the three pictures in the story.

6. Be ready to tell in your own words or to read lines that tell about the pictures on pages 433 and 438.

You would enjoy reading these Christmas stories: "Dame Quimp's Quest," Manley (in *Christmas in Storyland,* Van Buren and Bemis); "How the Freys Spent Their Christmas Money," Stuart (in *Child-Library Readers, Book Six*); and "His Christmas Turkey," Vawter (in *Book of Christmas Stories,* Walters).

THE BISHOP'S VALENTINE

ANDREA HOFER PROUDFOOT

You have probably sent and received many valentines. Have you ever wondered how this day came to be, and what its meaning is? This story will tell you why we celebrate Valentine Day, and what its true spirit is.

Once upon a time, a long while ago, there lived in a far-off country, near the land where St. Valentine had lived, a fine young Bishop. This Bishop had heard so many beautiful stories of all the brave, helpful deeds of St. Valentine, that he loved St. Valentine very dearly, and wished that he might be like him.

Now as the Bishop kept thinking about St. Valentine and really wanting to be like him, he said to himself one day, "Why don't I do some of the kind, loving acts of St. Valentine if I am really so fond of him?" Just then he went out for a walk, and as he passed the one who scrubbed the steps, he said: "It is a pleasure to walk where it is all so clean as you make it," and the worker scrubbed harder than ever as he smiled and bowed a "Thank you."

The Bishop went on, overtaking on the way a market-woman resting a moment beside the road with her basket. "Good day, my good woman," said the Bishop. "Let me help you on a bit with your basket." And the kindly way in which he said it made the basket seem only half as heavy as it had been before.

They parted at the cross-roads, but all the way home, the

woman told her neighbors, the basket never again grew so heavy after the Bishop had smiled and helped her.

The Bishop had helped many other people in different ways before the little woman reached home to tell her neighbors this, but when he reached home he had forgotten all about helping them and only remembered the people themselves, wondering what the dear St. Valentine would do for them were he still here. Suddenly he remembered that St. Valentine's birthday was coming, and he thought, "Oh, perhaps I can write some message of love like the ones that he used to send the people." So he dipped his goose-quill into the ink and began to write. One message after another he wrote; forgetting himself, and full of love for God, St. Valentine, and all the people that he longed to help.

Some of the others, on their way to bed, passed by his desk, as he worked away so busily. He did not notice them, except to nod and smile, but even that made them feel as if they truly would begin all new on the next day, to be finer than ever. The last one to pass noticed that a strange thing was happening. As fast as the ink dried on the notes, it changed to the brightest, most shining gold you ever saw! He looked at the Bishop, but the Bishop did not seem to notice it at all; so he went to his room, looking back to watch, for the golden letters in the notes seemed to match the smile on the Bishop's face and the look in his eyes.

The next morning, however, this last one to pass by the Bishop's desk was the first one up, and going to the Bishop's desk he took the quill in his hand to examine it. He thought it must be a new kind of wonderful pen that had made the letters change, but closely as he could look, there seemed to be nothing unusual about it; it was just a common goose feather, and rather worn, at that. "Ah," thought he, "I know now! It is the ink!" Quickly he dipped the pen into the ink and wrote a few words to try it, but they were his own name, and he saw that the ink was black just like the ink of his own inkwell. He simply could not understand it. Just then along came the Bishop, who had all the notes put into a great leather bag, and a messenger sent out to deliver them. So these letters were carried to the houses the Bishop had remembered as needing some comfort, or some reminder that they were always to do their best about all their work.

You can hardly imagine the surprise of the people, young and old, who received these beautiful letters, showing such wise, strong love, and written with this sparkling, glittering gold. One little boy put the letter under his pillow, and a little girl at another house hung hers on the wall where every one could see it. The father at another house had his letter framed to keep it safe from dust or wrinkling.

However, a strange thing happened to one of these beautiful letters. The man who received it thought of the wonderful words for a while, but then he began to think about the gold letters. More and more each day he admired the gold letters, until at last he took out the note and with a fine knife scraped off all the gold and poured it into a tiny bottle. "For," said he, "I can easily remember the words, and the goldsmith will give me some money for all this wonderful gold."

So off to the goldsmith he hurried, and very important he felt as he asked the smith, "Sir, would you like to buy some very fine gold?"

"That I would," said the smith, "for I have here a most rare jewel I've long been wishing to set, if only fine enough gold could be found."

"Well, what do you think of this?" said the man, as he carefully drew the bottle from his pocket.

Oh, how the goldsmith's face shone as he saw the beautiful gold! "Where did you get such fine gold with such a wonderful luster? I have been a master workman for years, and this is the kind of gold I have dreamed of, but never seen."

Now, when the smith asked the man where he got it, he remembered the Bishop's kind, loving letter and felt very bad to think he had dared to mar such a helpful message. But he answered, "A friend sent it to me."

"Ah," said the goldsmith to himself, "it must be a terrible need that forces a man to part with such a gift from a friend." But aloud he said, "Its price is greater than rubies or emeralds or sapphires, for it is in every way superior to any gold known to us goldsmiths. There must be six ounces, too, in that bottle. It would be worth—" Now I dare not tell you how much he said, for it took the man's breath away.

The goldsmith put a six-ounce weight on one side of the scale and poured the gold slowly and carefully into the other; but it did not draw up level the six-ounce weight. So he tried five ounces—no, he had to put in four. That was still too heavy; so he slipped in three, saying, "How could I have been so mistaken!" No, the gold would not even draw up the three-ounce weight, and the two men thought this the strangest thing they had ever seen.

Surely that pile of bright gold must weigh more than *two*

ounces! Still the scales would not balance, and the men were more surprised when it would not draw up one ounce.

On through the smaller weights went the goldsmith, and the gold seemed to shine brighter and brighter. Then he came to the tiniest one. By this time the men were almost frightened, but with trembling hands the smith slipped in the smallest weight.

Just then all the gold seemed to change to the most wonderful spreading sunlight, which filled the whole room before it disappeared, and as the man wept to think of the Bishop's beautiful message, a still, small voice seemed to whisper, "The letter killeth, but the Spirit giveth life."

NOTES AND QUESTIONS

1. What was it that made the Bishop's ink turn to gold?

2. What person in another of these holiday stories had the true spirit of St. Valentine in his heart?

3. On page 442 find a sentence that best tells the spirit that was in the Bishop's heart as he wrote his messages.

4. Be ready to tell in your own words how the Bishop happened to send the messages.

You would enjoy reading "The Selfish Giant," Wilde (in *The Happy Prince and Other Fairy Tales*); and "Four-Legged Saint Valentine," Bailey (in *Merry Tales for Children*).

THE WAY OLD GLORY GOES

Frank L. Stanton

In sunlight or in stormy day,
  With friendliness or foes,
The country's going just the way—
  The way "Old Glory" goes.
Today—tomorrow—still she waves
  Over earth's Freedom or our graves!

She arches earth—a rainbow's ray,
  Or, when the storm-wind blows,
A beacon-blaze, she lights the way—
  The way that freedom goes.
Today—tomorrow—still she waves
  Over our glory or our graves.

THE STAR-SPANGLED BANNER

Francis Scott Key

O say, can you see, by the dawn's early light,
  What so proudly we hailed at the twilight's last gleaming?
Whose broad stripes and bright stars, through the perilous
      fight,
  O'er the ramparts we watched were so gallantly stream-
      ing;
And the rockets' red glare, the bombs bursting in air,
Gave proof through the night that our flag was still there;
O say, does that Star-Spangled Banner yet wave
O'er the land of the free and the home of the brave?

On that shore dimly seen through the mists of the deep,
　　Where the foe's haughty host in dread silence reposes,
What is that which the breeze, o'er the towering steep,
　　As it fitfully blows, now conceals, now discloses?
Now it catches the gleam of the morning's first beam—
In full glory reflected now shines in the stream;
'Tis the Star-Spangled Banner; O long may it wave
O'er the land of the free and the home of the brave!

And where are the foes who so vauntingly swore
　　That the havoc of war and the battle's confusion
A home and a country should leave us no more?
　　Their blood has washed out their foul footsteps' pollution.
No refuge could save the hireling and slave
From the terror of flight, or the gloom of the grave;
And the Star-Spangled Banner in triumph doth wave
O'er the land of the free and the home of the brave!

O thus be it ever, when freemen shall stand
　　Between their loved homes and the war's desolation;
Blest with victory and peace, may the heav'n-rescued land
　　Praise the Power that hath made and preserved us a
　　　　nation!
Then conquer we must, for our cause it is just,
And this be our motto, "In God is our trust";
And the Star-Spangled Banner in triumph shall wave
O'er the land of the free and the home of the brave!

A BACKWARD LOOK

THE stories and poems you have just read have helped you understand better the true spirit of some of our holidays. Which of the three stories in this part was the most serious one? Which story had both a funny side and serious side to it? Which of the three did you like best? Can you give reasons for liking it best?

Perhaps you have never realized that each nation has its own particular holidays. The boys and girls of those other lands look forward to their holiday celebrations just as you do to yours. Do you remember any holidays or festivals of other lands? Certain stories in this book told you about some of them. It would be interesting to find something about celebrations in other countries. Perhaps other nations have days like our Fourth of July, set aside in memory of the time when they won their freedom. How is Christmas celebrated in other lands than ours?

On page 452 you will find a list of books that contain many interesting stories about holidays. You will enjoy reading them.

GOOD BOOKS TO READ

PART ONE. THE OUTDOOR WORLD

In Brightest Africa, by Carl Akeley. Doubleday
"J. T., Jr."; The Biography of an African Monkey, by Delia Akeley. Macmillan
Trailing the Tiger, by Mary Hastings Bradley. Appleton-Century
Poetry's Plea for Animals (poems), by Frances E. Clarke. Lothrop
Cop, Chief of Police Dogs, by Reginald Cleveland. Bradley
Wild Life of Our World, by Parrish Crossland. Collins
The Forest of Adventure, by Raymond Ditmars. Macmillan
Three Boy Scouts in Africa, by Douglas, Martin, and Oliver. Putnam
The Pointed People (poems), by Rachel Lyman Field. Macmillan
Let's Look at the Stars, by Edwin B. Frost. Houghton
Martin Johnson, Lion Hunter, by Fitzhugh Green. Putnam
Trails to Woods and Waters and *The Way of the Wild,* by Clarence Hawkes. Macrae Smith Co.
Lion, by Martin Johnson. Putnam
Jungle Babies, by Osa Johnson. Putnam
The Jungle Book, by Rudyard Kipling. Doubleday
Jungle Beasts and Men, by Dhan Gopal Mukerji. Dutton
Holiday Hill, by Edith Patch. Macmillan
Woodland Tales, by Ernest Thompson Seton. Doubleday
Beyond the Pasture Bars (Bruce Horsfall illustrations), by Dallas Lore Sharp. Appleton-Century
The Birds Began to Sing, by Anna Bird Stewart. McBride
Jungle Man and His Animals, by Carveth Wells. Duffield

PART TWO. AIRWAYS AND ROADWAYS

Little America and *Skyward,* by Richard E. Byrd. Putnam
The Pony Express Goes Through, by Howard R. Driggs. Stokes
The Big Aviation Book for Boys, by Joseph Lewis French. McLoughlin Bros., Inc.

Pioneers All!, by Joseph Lewis French. Bradley

The Picture Book of Ships, by Peter Gimmage and Helen Craig. Macmillan

The Picture Book of Travel, by Berta and Elmer Hader. Macmillan

Complete Model Aircraft Manual, by Edwin T. Hamilton. Dodd

Historic Airships and *Historic Railroads*, by Rupert S. Holland. Macrae Smith Co.

Flying and How to Do It!, by A. Jordanoff. Grossett

Skyward Ho!, by Franklin K. Mathiews. Grossett

The Pool of Stars, by Cornelia Meigs. Macmillan

All Sail Set, by Armstrong Sperry. Winston

How They Carried the Mail, by Joseph Walker. Sears

Silver Wings, by Raoul Whitfield. Knopf

Part Three. Stories That Never Grow Old

Peter Swiss, by Helen Coale Crew. Harper

Tales Worth Telling, by Charles J. Finger. Appleton-Century

I Know a Secret, by Christopher Morley. Doubleday

Book of Pirates and *Stolen Treasure*, by Howard Pyle. Harper

You Fight for Treasure!, by E. A. Stackpole. Morrow

The Home Book of Verse for Young Folks (revised), by B. E. Stevenson. Holt

Treasure Island (Wyeth illustrations), by Robert Louis Stevenson. Scribner

Query Queer, by Jay T. Stocking. Pilgrim Press

Fanciful Tales, by Frank R. Stockton. Scribner

Rainbow String, by Algernon Tassin. Macmillan

The Happy Prince and Other Fairy Tales, by Oscar Wilde. Putnam

Marauders of the Sea, by N. C. Wyeth. Putnam

Part Four. Young American Citizens

Understood Betsy, by Dorothy Canfield. Holt

Three Points of Honor, by Russell Gordon Carter. Little

Alison Blair, by Gertrude Crownfield. Dutton

A Little Freckled Person (poems), by Mary Carolyn Davies. Houghton

Girl Scout Stories, Second Book, by Helen Ferris. Doubleday

Those Plummer Children, by Christine Govan. Houghton
The Builder of the Dam, by William Heyliger. Appleton-Century
On the Trail of Washington, by Frederick Trevor Hill. Appleton-Century
The Dragon Fly of Zuni, by Alida Sims Malkus. Harcourt
The Jumping-off Place, by Marian Hurd McNeely. Longmans
Invincible Louisa, by Cornelia Meigs. Little
The Life of Abraham Lincoln for Boys and Girls, by Chas. W. Moores. Houghton
Two in Patches, by Blanche R. More. Penn
American Twins of the Revolution, by Lucy F. Perkins. Houghton
Abe Lincoln Grows Up, by Carl Sandburg. Harcourt
Boyhoods of the Presidents, by Bessie White Smith. Lothrop
Boy Scouts' Life of Lincoln, by Ida M. Tarbell. Macmillan
The Widow O'Callaghan's Boys, by Gulielma Zollinger. McClurg
Boy Scouts' Year Books. Appleton-Century

PART FIVE. BOYS AND GIRLS OF OTHER LANDS

Sidsel Longskirt and Solve Suntrap, by Hans Aanrud. Winston
Waterless Mountain, by Laura A. Armer. Longmans
Girls in Africa, by Erick Berry. Macmillan
Noah's Grandchildren, by Julier C. Chevalier. Doubleday
The Boy with the Parrot, by Elizabeth Coatsworth. Macmillan
A Boy in Eirinn, by Padraic Colum. Dutton
Alanna, by Helen Coale Crew. Harper
Saturday's Children, by Helen Coale Crew. Little
Treasure Flower, by Ruth Gaines. Dutton
Katrinka, by Helen Eggleston Haskell. Dutton
The Trumpeter of Krakow, by Eric P. Kelly. Macmillan
Where It All Comes True in Scandinavia, by Clara E. Laughlin. Houghton
Boys and Girls of Many Lands, by Inez N. McFee. Crowell
Camel Bells, by Anna Ratzesberger. A. Whitman
Dawn Boy of the Pueblos, by Lena B. Scott. Winston
Dobry, by Monica Shannon. Viking
Canute Whistlewinks, by Zacharias Topelius. Longmans
Friends in Strange Garments, by Anna Milo Upjohn. Houghton

Part Six. Workers and Their Work

Wonderful Story of Industry, by Ellen Friel Baker. Crowell
Heroes of the Shoals, by Allen Chaffee. Holt
The Story of Light, by Jeanette Eaton. Harper
Washington, D. C., The Nation's Capital, by Frances M. Fox. Rand
Story of Fire, by Walter Hough. Doubleday
Great Moments in Science, by Marion Florence Lansing. Doubleday
Alice in Orchestralia, by Ernest La Prade. Doubleday
Little Stories of Well-Known Americans, by Laura A. Large. Wilde
Grindstone Farm, by Henry B. Lent. Macmillan
The Boy's Life of Edison, by William H. Meadowcroft. Harper
Industrial Plays for Young People, by Virginia Olcott. Dodd
Anchors Aweigh!, by Oliver G. Swan. Dorrance
Overcoming Handicaps, by Archer Wallace. Doubleday

Part Seven. Famous Heroes of Adventure

Robin Hood, by Paul Creswick. McKay
The Boy Who Was, by Grace Taber Hallock. Dutton
Stories of Greek Gods, Heroes, and Men, by Caroline H. and Samuel
 B. Harding. Scott
Tanglewood Tales for Girls and Boys and *A Wonder Book for Girls
 and Boys,* by Nathaniel Hawthorne. Houghton
Siegfried, by Edith Heal. Rockwell
The Knights of the Golden Spur, by Rupert Sargent Holland. Apple-
 ton-Century
The Merry Adventures of Robin Hood, by Howard Pyle. Scribner

Part Eight. Holidays and Festivals

Feast of Noel, by Gertrude Crownfield. Dutton
Children's Book of Thanksgiving Stories, by Asa Don Dickinson.
 Doubleday
Christ Legends, by Selma Lagerlöf. Holt
Days and Deeds (poems), by B. E. Stevenson. Doubleday
Christmas in Storyland and *Thanksgiving Day in Modern Story,* by
 Maud van Buren and Katharine Isabel Bemis. Appleton-Century
Happy Holidays, by Frances G. Wickes. Rand
For Days and Days (poems), by Annette Wynne. Stokes

GLOSSARY

PRONUNCIATION KEY

The pronunciation of each word is shown just after the word, in this way:
ab bey (ab′i). The letters and signs have sounds as in the words shown below. The accented syllable has ′ after it. ′ shows a secondary accent.

a at, can	e end, bend	o on, not	u up, but
ā came, face	ē equal, be	ō more, open	ū use, pure
ä far, father	ė her, certain	ö move, to	u̇ full, put
â all, ball	ę prudent, towel	ô off, song	ụ nature, picture
à ask	i it, pin	ǫ actor, second	ṅ as in French
ã care, dare	ī line, mine		bon
ạ alone, company		ṭ picture	o is half-way be-
ä̧ beggar, opera			tween ō and ô

A single dot under ā, ē, ō, ö, or ū means that the sound is a little shorter, as in cottạge, rẹduce, demọcrat, intö, ụnited.

A

ab bey (ab′i), the home of monks
ab bot (ab′ǫt), head of an abbey
A bou Ben Ad hem (ä′bö ben ä′dem)
a bound (ạ-bound′), are found in great numbers
ac cord, made of all sweet accord (ạ-kôrd′), like beautiful, soft music
ac cu rate (ak′ụ-rạt), exactly right; true to life
A chil les (ạ-kil′ēz)
ad mi ra tion (ad-mi-rā′shǫn), liking; approval
Ae ne as (ẹ-nē′ạs)
Ae o lus (ē′ǫ-lus)
Ag a mem non (ag-ạ-mem′non)
air a-growin', is growing
air-pres sure in di ca tor (ãr′presh′ụr in′di-kā-tǫr), dial showing pressure of air
Al cin o us (al-sin′ǫ-us)

al der (âl′dėr), a kind of small tree that grows in moist ground
Al giers (al-jērz′)
Al ham bra (al-ham′brạ)
al lies (ạ-līz′), those banded together to help one another
An dres (än-drās′)
An drom a che (an-drom′ạ-kē)
a noint ed (ạ-noin′ted), had oil poured upon himself
An tin o us (an-tin′ǫ-us)
ant lers (ant′lėrz), horns of deer
Aph ro di te (af-rǫ-dī′tē)
A pol lo (ạ-pol′ō)
ap pli ca tion (ap-li-kā′shǫn), a request for a position
ap pren tice (ạ-pren′tis), one who is learning a trade
ar bu tus (är-bū′tus or är′bū-tus), a trailing plant having fragrant pink or white flowers

453

ar cade (är-kād′),   walk or street with an arched roof

arches earth, flies above the land

A res (ā′rēz)

ar ray (a̧-rā′),   order of battle

ar ti fi cial (är-ti-fish′a̧l),   made by man, not by nature

ar tis tic sense (är-tis′tik),   good taste and skill

as tron o mer (as-tron′ō̧-mėr),   one who studies the heavenly bodies, such as the stars

A the na (a̧-thē′nä)

at ten tive, lend attentive ear (a̧-ten′tiv),   listen carefully

au thor i ty (â-thor′i-ti),   power

au to mat i cal ly (â-tō̧-mat′i-ka̧l-i), mechanically, without the aid of human hands

B

bagged, killed or captured in hunting

bail (bāl),   dip water from

bal ance of doom (bal′a̧ns),   scales in which the gods weighed the fortunes of men

bale, brought to bale, made trouble for

Bal holm (bäl′hōm)

Bar ba ry States (bär′ba̧-ri),   certain countries on the north coast of Africa

bar be cue (bär′bȩ-kū),   feast where an ox, hog, or other animal is roasted whole

bar ren (bar′ȩn),   bare, with nothing growing

bat on (bat′on or bä-tôṅ),   stick or wand used by an orchestra leader for beating time

battlements, irregular top of the high walls of a castle

beacon-blaze, signal fire

beam, large plank or timber; the timber that braces the sides of a ship

be calmed (bȩ̄-kämd′),   kept from sailing because of lack of wind

bel fry (bel′fri),   tower for bells

bel lows (bel′ōz),   instrument for blowing fires

bending of the new sails, fastening of the sails in place for use

be sieged (bȩ̄-sējd′),   surrounded by an army

bev y (bev′i),   flock; company

be witch ing ly (bȩ̄-wich′ing-li),   in a very charming manner

bier (bēr),   framework for holding a dead body

Bi ri (bi′ri)

blast-fur nace (blàst′fėr′na̧s),   furnace used in the process of making iron

blind, screen used by hunters

block, pulley

Boc u ly (bok′ū-li)

bolted, ran away

bom bard ed (bom-bär′ded),   shot at many times

boon, favor

Bo tan i cal Gardens (bō̧-tan′i-ka̧l), place where many kinds of plants are raised

bow (bou),   front end of a ship

bow sprit (bō′sprit or bou′sprit), large pole reaching forward from the front end of a ship

brake, thick growth of bushes

bram ble (bram′bl),   rough, thorny shrub

bran dish ing (bran′dish-ing),   shaking in a threatening way

Bres lau (bres′lou)

brim ful (brim′fúl′),   full to the very top

broken links of affection restored, the meeting again of relatives or friends who have been separated

bulk, quantity

bunting, colored cloth used for decoration

Bu rum (bū′rum)

C

ca ble, ocean cable (kā′bl), a bundle of wires wrapped in a waterproof covering and laid under water to carry telegraph messages

ca boose (ka̩-bös′), last car on a freight train

cal lus (kal′us), hard, thickened skin; **took on callus**, became hard and tough

Ca lyp so (ka̩-lip′sō)

cap size (kap-siz′), upset or overturn

car di nal flower (kär′di-na̩l), kind of bright red flower

ca reer (ka̩-rēr′), the way a person spends his life

carried away, broke away

Car thage (kär′tha̩j)

cat a ract (kat′a̩-rakt), waterfall

cer tif i cate (sėr-tif′i-ka̩t), written statement

Cey lon (sē-lon′)

chains of silver rhymes (rīmz), verses that sound very musical

chant ing (chȧn′ting), saying in a singing voice

Cha ryb dis (ka̩-rib′dis)

chasm (kazm), very large, deep crack

che bec (che̩-bek′), a very small bird of the flycatcher family

cher ish (cher′ish), keep or hold with loving care

chip munk (chip′mungk), a small striped animal

Cir cas sian (sėr-kash′ia̩n), a kind of walnut tree

Cir ce (sėr′sē)

cir cuit (sėr′kit), journey from beginning to end

cit a del (sit′a̩-de̩l), a fort or castle within or near a city

clears the harbor, leaves the harbor

cleat (klēt), small piece of wood used as a fastening

cleav ing (klē′ving), cutting

cleft (kleft), an opening or crack

clipper, the fastest kind of sailing ship

clois ter (klois′tėr), a covered passage open on one side

coastwise, that keep close to land

codg er (koj′ėr), fellow

cof fers (kof′ėrz), chests

col li sion (ko̩-lizh′o̩n), a striking together with force

combed (kōmd), looked over very carefully

com mend ing (ko̩-men′ding), praising

com mis sion (ko̩-mish′o̩n), a number of persons appointed to do a certain work

com mo dore (kom′o̩-dōr), commander

com pan ion a ble (ko̩m-pan′yo̩n-a̩-bl), pleasant as a comrade

com pos ing new lyr ics (ko̩m-pō′-zing; lir′iks), making up new songs

con fer ence (kon′fe̩-re̩ns), meeting to talk about something

con fi dence (kon′fi-de̩ns), a feeling of trust in someone or something

con ser va tion ist (kon-sėr-vā′sho̩n-ist), one who helps to protect and preserve wild life

con sol ing (ko̩n-sō′ling), cheering; comforting

con sta ble (kun′sta̩-bl), officer who makes arrests

Co per ni cus (kō̩-pėr′ni-kus)

cop per head (kop′ėr-hed), a large, poisonous snake

---

at, cāme, fär, âll, ȧsk, cãre, a̩lone, beggȧr; end, bē, hėr, towe̩l; it, līne; on, mōre, tö, ôff, actȯr; up, ūse, pu̇t, natu̇re; na̩ture. A single dot under ā, ē, ō, ö, or ū means that the sound is a little shorter, as in cottȧge.

corn crib, small building with sides made of slats, for storing ears of corn

corn dodgers, cakes made of corn meal, baked hard

Co ro na do (kō-rō̯-nä′dō)

corse let (kôrs′let), armor for the body

coun sel or (koun′sel-o̯r), adviser

coup ling (kup′ling), connection; link used to join two railway cars

cou ri er (kö′ri-ėr), messenger

cradle, long wooden fingers on the handle of a scythe, just above the blade, for catching the grain as it is cut

craft (kråft), trickery, deceit; boats

Crete (krēt)

crev ice (krev′is), crack

crop ping (krop′ing), eating grass

cross sea, ocean having waves running in different directions

cross-timbers, beams going across the ship from side to side

crow bar (krō′bär), bar of iron used for raising heavy objects

cru ci ble (krö′si-bl), container in which metals are melted

cul ti va ted (kul′ti-vā-ted), improved by care and attention; containing plants and shrubs set out and carefully tended

Cy clops (sī′klops)

cyl in der (sil′in-dėr), a long object shaped like a roller

D

Dam rosch, Le o pold (dam′rosh, lē′-ō̯-pōld)

dam sel (dam′ze̯l), young unmarried girl

dap pled (dap′ld), spotted

deck, decorate

de cree (dē̯-krē′), law; order

deer mouse, a kind of mouse that can jump several feet

de sign (dē̯-zīn′), drawing; plan

des o la tion (des-o̯-lā′sho̯n), complete ruin

de tached (dē̯-tacht′), unconnected

de vour ing thy goods (dē̯-vour′ing), wasting what belongs to you

Di do (dī′dō)

dig ni ty (dig′ni-ti), noble manner

din gy (din′ji), soiled; dark

dirk knife (dėrk), clasp knife with a blade like a dagger

dis as ter (di-zàs′tėr), misfortune

dis may (dis-mā′), terror; fright

dis tin guish (dis-ting′gwish), see well enough to make out

dis tract ed (dis-trak′ted), very much troubled; almost insane

dock, place for ships to be loaded

doom, destruction

doub let (dub′let), close-fitting garment for men, covering the body from the neck to below the waist

dread, dreadful; causing fear

dusk y (dus′ki), dark-skinned

E

ef fi cien cy (e-fish′e̯n-si), ability to do a thing well

e lapsed (ē̯-lapst′), passed

ell, forty-five inches

em barked (em-bärkt′), set out

em e rald (em′e̯-ra̯ld), a bright green gem

e merged (ē̯-mėrjd′), came out

e mer gen cy (ē̯-mėr′je̯n-si), sudden need for quick action

en coun ter (en-koun′tėr), unexpected meeting; battle

en dur ance (en-dūr′a̯ns), ability to hold out under difficulties

Ep i me theus (ep-i-mē′thūs)

es cort (es′kôrt), person or group of people that accompany someone to show him honor or to protect him

Es quire (es-kwĭr′), a title used instead of Mr.

es sen tial (e-sen′shạl), necessary

es tab lish ment (es-tab′lish-mẹnt), place of business

Eu ryl o chus (ū-ril′ọ-kus)

e vap o ra ted (ē-vap′ọ-rā-ted), passed off; disappeared

e ven tide (ē′vn-tĭd), evening

ex alt ed (eg-zâl′ted), important and dignified

ex ceed ing (ek-sē′ding), very great

ex cel si or (ek-sel′si-ọr), fine, curled shreds of wood

ex er tion (eg-zėr′shọn), unusual effort

ex haust pipe (eg-zâst′), pipe through which steam or air escapes

ex per i ments (eks-per′i-mẹntz), tests or trials

ex ploits (eks′ploits or eks-ploits′), deeds

F

fal ter (fâl′tėr), fail; grow less

fas ci na ted (fas′i-nā-ted), charmed; greatly interested

fa tal (fā′tạl), deadly; destructive

fa tigue (fạ-tēg′), weariness

fawned, acted in a humble and friendly way

feat (fēt), great deed

fe ro cious (fẹ-rō′shus), fierce; savage; cruel

fer til i ty (fėr-til′i-ti), richness in producing crops

fil a ment (fil′ạ-mẹnt), thread or threadlike object

fitful, irregular; by fits and starts

fixed, motionless

fjord (fyôrd), narrow inlet of the sea, between high cliffs

flat, level stretch of land, usually along the banks of a river

floats (flōts), flat-topped vehicles without sides for carrying something in a procession

floun der (floun′dėr), plunge about; struggle without making much progress

flour ish ing (flur′ish-ing), growing well

flus ter a ted (flus′tėr-ā-ted), excited and bothered

Foch (fọsh)

font, basin holding water used in baptizing

forded, crossed the streams at shallow places without bridges

fray, fight

fruit less (frōt′les), unsuccessful

G

gait, manner of moving on foot

gales, strong winds; storms

gallantly, bravely and gaily

gal leys (gal′iz), large, low vessels moved chiefly by oars

gar land (gär′lạnd), wreath of flowers or leaves

gates of the Med i ter ra ne an (med′i-tẹ-rā′nẹ-ạn), points of land in southern Spain and northwestern Africa, lying on either side of the Strait of Gibraltar (which connects the Atlantic with the Mediterranean Sea)

ge nial (jē′niạl), kindly; cheerful

ge nius (jē′nius), one having great natural ability

gen tians (jen′shạnz), plants with beautiful flowers, usually blue

gen u ine ness (jen′ū-in-nes), being what one seems to be

Gi bral tar (ji-brâl′tạr), a high rock and town in southern Spain

at, cāme, fär, âll, ạsk, cāre, ạlone, beggạr; end, bē, hėr, towẹl; it, lῑne; on, mōre, tö, ôff, actọr; up, ūse, pút, natụre; nạture. A single dot under ā, ē, ō, ö, or ū means that the sound is a little shorter, as in cottạge.

give him the butt, turn the rod so that the big end points toward the fish, in order to take the strain when he is struggling to get away

gla cier (glā′shiĕr), slowly moving body of ice

glade, open space among trees

glancing through the May, moving quickly through flowering shrubs

gleam ing (glē′ming), bit of light

gnashed (nasht), struck together

goad ing (gō′ding), driving or pushing forward

goose-quill (gōs′kwil), writing-pen made from a goose feather

goose-stepped, walked forward, raising first one foot, then another very high

gored, pierced with horns

go ril la (gō-ril′ạ), a kind of large ape

Gra na da (grạ-nä′dạ)

greenwood, forest

griev ous ly (grē′vus-li), painfully

grist mill, mill for grinding grain into flour

grouse, a kind of game bird

Gua dal quiv ir (gwä-dạl-kwiv′ĕr)

guid ance (gī′dạns), direction; assistance

Guit er man (git′ĕr-mạn)

gust y (gus′ti), windy

H

hag gard (hag′ạrd), having a care-worn appearance

hailed, saluted

ha lo (hā′lō), circle of light

hal yard (hal′yạrd), rope used for raising and lowering sails

handmaids, servant girls

hardtack, a kind of hard bread used by sailors and soldiers

hart, male red deer

hav oc (hav′ọk), complete destruction

haze, slight cloudiness in the air

Hel e nus (hel′ę-nus)

He ra (hē′rạ)

herb (ĕrb), plant used for medicines

Her mes (hĕr′mēz)

hil locks (hil′ọks), small hills

hireling, soldier who is fighting for pay only

horny hands of toil, the hard, rough hands of workers

hos pi tal i ty (hos-pi-tal′i-ti), welcome into a home; food and shelter given in kindness to another

host, whole army; great numbers

household gods, gods of the home; images of the gods

hulks, forms

hull, body of a ship

Humber, a river in England. See **Severn**

Hun ga ri an (hung-gā′ri-ạn)

Hunt, Leigh (lē)

I

i de al ly (ī-dē′ạl-i), perfectly

il lus tri ous (i-lus′tri-us), famous

im pend ing (im-pen′ding), hanging over; ready to happen

im ple ment (im′plę-mẹnt), tool

in cu ba tor (in′kụ-bā-tọr), box that can be kept warm for hatching eggs

in fan cy (in′fạn-si), earliest days; babyhood

in flam ma ble (in-flam′ạ-bl), easily set on fire

in mates (in′māts), occupants; persons in an asylum

in so lent ly (in′sọ-lẹnt-li), insultingly; rudely

in struc tion (in-struk′shọn), lessons given by a teacher

in vad ed (in-vā′ded), entered by force

in vain, without success

in vis i ble (in-viz′i-bl), unseen

Ith a ca (ith′a̤-ka̤)

J

jags, sharp, ragged peaks

jaun ty (jân′ti or jän′ti), lively; stylish; showy

Jo se (hō-zā′)

K

Kar sten (kär′sten)

ka ty did (kā′ti-did), a large green insect which makes a shrill noise

keel, long timber running the whole length of the bottom of a ship

keel son (kel′sǫn), heavy timbers above the keel of a ship

knee, piece of timber used to fasten the beams of a ship to its sides

knuck le (nuk′l), small end of a leg of mutton; joint

Kra kow (krä′kō)

L

la bo ri ous (la̤-bō′ri-us), very difficult; requiring much work

La er tes (la̤-ėr′tēz)

la ment ing (la̤-men′ting), mourning over the things that had happened to him

lashings, fastenings

lath, thin strip of wood, nailed on a wall to hold the plaster

ledge (lej), shelf

leg a cy (leg′a̤-si), gift left to a person by the will of someone who has died

leg end (lej′ẹnd or lē′jẹnd), a story that has come down from the past

lev ers (lev′ėrz or lē′vėrz), bars of wood or metal for raising, moving, or prying up heavy objects

li chen (lī′kẹn), small plant that grows on rocks and walls

lines parted, ropes broke

Liszt, Franz (list, fränts)

lit ter (lit′ėr), stretcher for carrying a helpless person

live li hood, gaining a livelihood (līv′li-hu̇d), earning a living

liv er y (liv′ėr-i), uniform

lo cust (lō′kust), a kind of grasshopper which destroys crops

log book, the full record of a ship's voyage

Lo hen grin (lō′ẹn-grin)

loi tered (loi′tėrd), walked slowly; lingered idly

lope, an easy, swinging gallop

Lo thar (lō′tär)

lu rid (lū′rid), glaring; terrible

lurk (lėrk), hide

lus ti ly (lus′ti-li), strongly

M

maiden voyage, the first trip made by a ship

ma jor i ty (ma̤-jor′i-ti), more than half of a number of persons or things

make port, arrive at the place to which the ship is sailing

manhole plate, cover of metal which can be removed to allow a man to enter

manned the brakes, applied the brakes by hand

man tle (man′tl), cloak

Mar ti nel li (mär-tē-nel′lē)

mar vel ing (mär′vẹ-ling), wondering greatly

Ma ry a (mä-rē′a̤)

Ma rye (mä′ri)

at, cāme, fär, âll, a̤sk, câre, a̤lone, beggär; end, bē, hér, towel̤; it, līne; on, mōre, tö, ôff, actǫr; up, ūse, pu̇t, natūre; natṳre. A single dot under ā, ē, ō, ö, or ū means that the sound is a little shorter, as in cottạge.

ma tron (mā′trŏn),   woman who
manages a household; wife

med i cal stores (med′i-kạl),   supplies of medicine

me mo ri al (mē-mō′ri-ạl),   something (such as a building or statue)
put up to remind people of a man
who is dead

Men e la us (men-e-lā′us)

Middle Ages, period of time between
the years 476 and 1453

Mi ke no (mǐ-kē′nō)

Mil ti a des (mil-tǐ′ạ-dēz)

Mi na (mi′nạ)

min is ter of state (min′is-tėr), person of high rank acting as an agent
for the ruler of a country

mis chie vous (mis′chi-vus), naughty

moat, deep ditch around a castle,
usually filled with water

mo not o nous (mō-not′ō-nus),   con-
tinuing in the same tone

Moor ish kings (mŏr′ish),   rulers of
a people who came to Spain from
northern Africa

more o ver (mōr-ō′vėr),   besides

mor tal (mŏr′tạl),   a person who is
not a god; that must die

mor tal ly (mŏr′tạl-i),   severely
enough to cause death

mur mur ous (mėr′mėr-us),   low and
not clear

musk rat (musk′rat),   a small fur-
bearing animal that lives in the
water

mystery, be friendly with their
mystery, understand all of their
secrets

my thol o gy (mi-thol′ō-ji),   a group
of old tales telling about the gods
of a people

N

naph tha (naf′thạ),   a liquid used
for fuel and for cleaning. It is very
easily set on fire.

na tive cus toms (nā′tiv kus′tọmz),
ways the natives have of living,
dressing, hunting, etc.

nat u ral ist (naṭ′ụ-rạl-ist), one who
studies Nature

Nau si ca a (nâ-sik′ạ-ạ)

nay, not only that, but also

nigh (nī),   near

Nor dahl (nôr′däl)

norther, strong, cold north wind

nymphs (nimfs),   beautiful maidens,
related to the gods and having some
magic power

O

ob sti nate ly (ob′sti-nạt-li),   stub-
bornly

of fi cial-look ing (ọ-fish′ạl-lúk′ing),
important-looking

O lym pus (ọ-lim′pus)

op po nent (ọ-pō′nẹnt),   player on
the opposite team

or a cle (or′ạ-kl),   the voice of a god

o rang-u tan (ọ-rang′ọ-tan′),   a kind
of large ape

or chid (ôr′kid),   a plant with beautiful flowers of a queer shape

O slo (ō′slö or ôs′lō)

outlet valve, valve that regulates
flow of air, steam, or water

out-towers, is taller than

P

pad ding (pad′ing),   walking or running with steady, quiet footfalls

pal sy (pâl′zi),   a disease which
causes parts of the body to tremble

Pan do ra (pan-dō′rä)

pan ic-strick en   (pan′ik-strik′n),
overcome by sudden fright

pa pier-ma che (pȧ-pyä-mä-shā),   a
substance made of paper pulp mixed
with glue and other materials to
make it hard and strong when it
dries

par a chute (par′-a̯-shöt), a device in the form of a large umbrella, used in falling from a balloon or from an airplane

par a lyzed (par′-a̯-līzd), made unable to move

passing few, a very small number

Pa tro clus (pa̯-trō′klus)

pendulum, weight so hung that it swings to and fro

Pe nel o pe (pē̯-nel′ō̯-pē̯)

Pe pin (pā-pēn′)

per cus sion group (pėr-kush′ọn), instruments of an orchestra sounded by striking

per plexed (pėr-plekst′), troubled

pet tish (pet′ish), cross

Phae a cians (fē̯-ā′shạnz)

pheas ants (fez′ạntz), a kind of large wild birds

Phoe ni cian (fē̯-nish′ạn), belonging to a people who lived in ancient times along the coast of Syria, at the eastern end of the Mediterranean

phos pho rus (fos′fō̯-rus), a yellowish, wax-like substance used in making matches

pilgrims, persons who make a journey to a holy place

pin-wheeled, came down in circles

pis ton rod (pis′tọn), piece of machinery that works back and forth like a bicycle pump

pit e ous ly (pit′ē̯-us-li), very sadly; in a way that moves the heart

pledge thee our deathless faith, promise that we will always be true to you

plight (plīt), condition

plumped (plumpt), dropped heavily

point, strong point, what he knows or cares most about

poised (poizd), balanced

pol i tics (pol′i-tiks), matters that have to do with running the government

pol lu tion (pọ-lū′shọn), uncleanness

Pol y phe mus (pol-i-fē′mus)

pom pa dour (pom′pa̯-dör), hair brushed straight up

pose (pōz), position of the body

Po sei don (pō̯-sī′dọn)

pounds, a unit of English money. In ordinary times a pound is worth about $4.86.

poured out wine, made an offering before prayer

powers, abilities

preened (prēnd), smoothed with the beak

prel ate (prel′ạt), minister

pres to (pres′tō), at once

prey (prā), kill for food; an animal seized for food

Pri am (prī′am)

proph e cy (prof′e-si), something told about the future

proph e sy (prof′e-sī), tell what will happen; tell beforehand

pros pered (pros′pėrd), had good fortune; been successful

pros per ous (pros′pėr-us), successful

prov ince (prov′ins), country or region

prow (prou), the front end of a boat

pur suit (pėr-sūt′), chase

Q

quaint (kwānt), odd but attractive-looking

qua ver ing (kwā′vėr-ing), trembling; shaking

quest (kwest), search

at, cāme, fär, âll, ȧsk, cāre, a̯lone, beggạr; end, bē, hėr, towe̯l; it, līne; on, mōre, tö, ôff, actọr; up, ūse, pu̇t, natūre; na̯ture. A single dot under ā, ē, ō, ö, or ū means that the sound is a little shorter, as in cottạge.

queue (kū), braid of hair hanging down the back

quiv er (kwiv'ẽr), case for holding arrows

quoit (kwoit), iron ring

R

raf ters (ràf'tẽrz), beams that support the roof of a house

ram parts (ram'pärts), protecting walls for defense

range, extent

"rass ler" (ras'lẽr), wrestler

ra vine (rạ-vēn'), deep, narrow valley

re cur rence (rẹ-kur'ẹns), the coming again

red haw (hâ), the small red fruit of the hawthorn tree

reed, a kind of tall grass

re gat ta (rẹ-gat'ạ), a rowing or sailing race

re li a ble (rẹ-lī'ạ-bl), to be depended on

re pro duc tion (rē-prọ-duk'shọn), likeness; copy

rep tile (rep'til), snake, lizard, turtle, etc.

re tort ed (rẹ-tôr'ted), answered quickly

re vealed (rẹ-vēld'), showed

re verse lev er (rẹ-vẽrs' lev'ẽr or lē'vẽr), lever, the working of which causes the engine to back

reviewed the troops, watched the soldiers pass in parade

rhi no (rī'nō), a short name for rhinoceros

rig ging (rig'ing), ropes and chains fastened to the masts and sails of a vessel

rig or (rig'ọr), severe cold

Rim fa (rim'fạ)

ring, metal circle through which the ropes were passed

roam (rōm), wander

rocket, light sent up as a signal

rollers, long, heavy waves

Rom u lus (rom'ū-lus)

Ron da (rōn'dä), a small town in Spain, about forty miles north of Gibraltar

ros in (roz'in), a hard yellow gum, made from the pine tree. Rosin is rubbed on violin-bows.

rosy-fingered Dawn, sunrise with its red beams like a goddess's fingers

royal chamber, queen's own room

ru bi cund (rö'bi-kund), red or rose-colored

Ru bin stein (rö'bin-stīn)

rue ful ly (rö'fúl-i), sadly; gloomily

run to rhyme (rīm), make rimes; be musical

S

sack, plunder after capturing

Sac ra men to (sak-rạ-men'tō), a city in California

sa fa ri (sạ-fä'rẹ or suf'ạ-rē), a hunting journey or march

sanc tu a ry (sangk'ţū-ạ-ri), a place where all kinds of wild life are protected

sandpiper, a small shore bird

sap phire (saf'ĩr), a brilliant, blue gem

scab bard (skab'ạrd), a sheath for a sword or knife

scaf fold ing (skaf'ọl-ding), supporting framework

scheme (skēm), plan

schol ar ship (skol'ạr-ship), an allowance paying all or part of a student's expenses

scrim mage (skrim'ạj), confused struggle over the ball

scud ded (skud'ed), ran swiftly

sculp tor (skulp'tọr), person who makes statues or models in clay

Scyl la (sil′ą)

seaworthy, able to stand stormy weather on the sea

self-sac ri fice (self-sak′ri-fīs), the giving up of something to help others

sem a phore (sem′ą-fōr), an instrument used in signaling, by colored lights, extending arms, flags, etc., on a railroad

sen try boxes (sen′tri), shelters for guards

se rene (sē-rēn′), clear; calm

Sev ern (sev′ėrn), river in England; **from the Severn to the Humber,** all the way across England, from west to east

Sev ille (sev′il or sē-vil′), a city in Spain

sex ton (seks′tǫn), man who takes care of a church

shel lac (she-lak′), a quick-drying varnish

shock (shok), pile of corn stalks or of bundles of grain set up in a field

shrine, place where sacred things are kept

shrouded, covered

shun, keep away from

shut tle (shut′l), tool for weaving

siding, the boards in the outside wall of a house

sim pli ci ty (sim-plis′i-ti), desire for plain, simple things instead of show and style

sin is ter (sin′is-tėr), evil-looking

Sjo strand, O le (shō′stränd, ō′lē)

skir mish (skėr′mish), a fight

sledge (slej), heavy hammer

slough (slou), a wet or marshy place

slug gish (slug′ish), slow; dull

smite (smīt), strike

smithy, a blacksmith's shop

smote, struck

Spa do ni, Gia co mo (spä-dō′nē jä-kō′mō)

spe ci men (spes′i-men), an animal or any object selected as a good example of its class or kind

spec tac u lar (spek-tak′ū-lär), very showy

spellbound, charmed

spent, tired. **well spent,** worn out

spig ot (spig′ǫt), faucet

spin dle (spin′dl), tool used in spinning yarn

spoils, booty; plunder

sproutlands, places covered with young trees coming up from seed dropped by older trees

stalked (stâkt), walked proudly

stam pede (stam-pēd′), sudden running away of a herd of animals, usually because of fright

stan dard (stan′dȧrd), heavy timbers holding up a platform

Stan nik, I vor (stan′ik, ī′vôr)

stat u esque (staṭ-ū-esk′), resembling a statue

stay, stop; check

stealth i ly (stel′thi-li), secretly

stepping, setting the masts into the ship

sti fled murmur (stī′fld), smothered sound, not easily heard

straight for ward ness (strāt′fôr′-wȧrd-nes), being direct and truthful

strat e gy (strat′ē-ji), cunning trick

strong point, his strong point, thing he knows most about

strove (strōv), tried hard; struggled

struc ture, animal structure (struk′-ṭūr), the form or build of an animal

---

at, cāme, fär, âll, ȧsk, cāre, ą lone, beggȧr; end, bē, hėr, towel; it, līne; on, mōre, tö, ôff, actǫr; up, ūse, pút, naṭūre; naṭure. A single dot under ā, ē, ō, ö, or ū means that the sound is a little shorter, as in cǫttȧge.

stud ding (stud′ing), upright supports on which laths are nailed in making a partition

Styr i a (stir′i-ạ), a part of southeast Austria in Europe

sub tle (sut′l), delicate

su et (sū′et), beef or mutton fat

suit ors for her hand (sū′tọrz), men seeking to marry her

sul len ly (sul′ẹn-li), gloomily silent

su pe ri or (sū-pē′ri-ọr), better in quality

sure ty (shör′ti), security for the debt

Sus que han na (sus-kwẹ-han′ạ)

Swa hi li (swä-hē′lẹ)

T

tack le jammed (tak′l jamd), rigging caught, so that it would not work

tal lied (tal′id), scored; checked; counted

tap ping (tap′ing), cutting into trees to get sap

tax i der mist (tak′si-dẹr-mist), man who stuffs and mounts animals

tech nol o gy (tek-nol′ọ-ji), knowledge of machinery and inventions

te leg ra phy (tẹ-leg′rạ-fi), the work of sending and receiving telegrams

Te lem a chus (tẹ-lem′ạ-kus)

tender, coal-car behind the engine

tense (tens), strained; tight

thatch ing (thach′ing), roof made of straw, reeds, etc.

Thes sa ly (thes′ạ-li)

The tis (thē′tis)

Thrace (thrās)

thresh ing floor (thresh′ing), hard-packed ground on which grain is beaten to free the kernel from the husk

throt tle lev er (throt′l lev′ẹr or lē′-vẹr), bar that supplies and shuts off the steam

tiles (tīlz), pieces of baked clay in various forms, used for decoration, floors, and roofs

to ken (tō′kn), sign

toll, payment or tax for special service

took coun sel with (koun′sel), asked the advice of

tot tered (tot′ẹrd), walked unsteadily

tow er ing steep (tou′ẹr-ing), high slope

tow ing (tō′ing), pulling

trade winds, winds that blow toward the equator. In the northern hemisphere the trade winds blow from northeast to southwest.

train, crowd; company

trai tor (trā′tọr), one who aids the enemy against his country

treach er ous (trech′ẹr-us), not to be trusted

tre men dous (trẹ-men′dus), great or terrible

trem u lous (trem′ū-lus), shaking; trembling

trib ute (trib′ūt), a sum of money or a tax paid to the ruler of a country

Trip o li (trip′ọ-li)

Tro jans (trō′jạnz)

troop er band (trö′pẹr), company of soldiers

truce (trös), a rest agreed upon by those fighting

Tu nis (tū′nis)

tur rets (tur′ets), small towers

tu tor (tū′tọr), teach outside the schoolroom

U

U lys ses (ū-lis′ēz)

un con ven tion al (un-kọn-ven′shọn-ạl), uncommon; carefree; natural

unsheathes its blades, sends up new shoots

V

valiant (val′yȧnt), very brave

valor (val′ọr), bravery

varied (vā′rid), different

vault (vâlt), cellar with an arched ceiling

vauntingly (vân′ting-li), boastingly

veneers (vẹ-nērz′), thin sheets of fine wood used on the outside of furniture

vengeance (ven′jȧns), punishment

vespers (ves′pẽrz), evening service

vesper sparrow, name given a kind of sparrow because of its habit of singing in the evening

veteran (vet′ẹ-rȧn), old soldier

vexation (vek-sā′shọn), anger; annoyance

vibrate (vī′brāt), move to and fro rapidly; quiver

victim, person injured by another

vise (vīs), tool for holding objects firmly

Vistula (vis′t̜ū-lȧ)

vivid (viv′id), bright

Vladimir Alley (vlad′i-mēr)

W

Wagner (väg′nẽr)

wallowing (wol′ō-ing), rolling

Wanda (won′dȧ)

watercourse (wâ′tẽr-kōrs), the bed of a stream

water polo (pō′lō), game played in the water by teams of swimmers with a ball

Wawel (vä′vel)

ways, sloping platform upon which a ship is built

weasel (wē′zl), small animal with a long, slender body, that feeds on mice, chickens, etc.

weirdly (wērd′li), in a ghostly manner; wildly

wharf (hwârf), landing-place for boats

whence (hwens), from where

whipsaw, a long narrow saw which cuts curved shapes

whopping est (hwop′ing-est), very largest

wide bloom, blossoming flowers everywhere

winds (wīndz), blows (a horn)

wine-skin, large bag made from an animal skin, and used for holding wine

wiry (wīr′i), lean and strong

witchery (wich′ẽr-i), enchantment

withstand, endure

woodland (wúd′lȧnd), woods

Y

yacht (yot), boat for pleasure trips

yaller-legged (yal′ẽr-leg′ed), yellow-legged

yard, long wooden bar to which sails are fastened

yeoman (yō′mȧn), English farmer who owned his own land

Z

Zeus (zūs)

---

at, cāme, fär, âll, ȧsk, cãre, ạlone, beggạr; end, bē, hẽr, towẹl; it, līne; on, mōre, tö, ôff, actọr; up, ūse, pút, nat̜ūre; nat̜ure. A single dot under ā, ē, ō, ö, or ū means that the sound is a little shorter, as in cottȧge.